1981

TT 74–52050

MINERALOGY OF CARBONATITES

[MINERALOGIYA KARBONATITOV]

Yu.L. KAPUSTIN

Nauka Publishers
Moscow, 1971

Translated from Russian

Published for the Smithsonian Institution, and the National Science Foundation, Washington, D.C., by Amerind Publishing Co. Pvt. Ltd., New Delhi
1980

Translated and published for the Smithsonian Institution, pursuant to an agreement with the National Science Foundation, Washington, D.C., by Amerind Publishing Co. Pvt. Ltd., 66 Janpath, New Delhi 110 001

Translator: Dr. D.K. Biswas
General Editor: Dr. V.S. Kothekar

Available from the U.S. Department of Commerce,
National Technical Information Service,
Springfield, Virginia 22161

Printed at Oxonian Press Pvt. Ltd., Faridabad, India

UDC 553.2

The book examines the structure and regularities of occurrence of complex massifs of ultrabasic rocks and carbonatites, their petrologic features and sequence of formation. It describes in brief their spatial and genetic associations with the other types of rocks. Special attention has been paid to the examination of geological structure, regularities of formation, petrographic features and mineral content of carbonatites. An attempt has been made to systematize available information on all carbonatite provinces of the world and their comparative analysis is given. The book highlights regularities of development of carbonatite bodies, their zonation and formation stage. Two major types of carbonatites—early and late—have been identified and for each of them peculiarities of structure and composition have been indicated. A description of 117 minerals is given, many of which are extremely rare and are typical for the above rocks. Their composition, properties and conditions of occurrence are given.

The book presents 90 original comprehensive analyses of minerals; more than 500 determinations of individual elements have been used and results of a vast number of x-ray, thermal and other methods of analyses considered.

Editor-in-Chief

E.I. SEMENOV
Doctor of Geological and Mineralogical Sciences

PREFACE

For the first time the massifs of ultrabasic and basic rocks and carbonatites were described in the end of the 19th and beginning of the 20th century (Högbom, 1892, 1895; Brögger, 1921). In the period that followed they were reported from many parts of the world (Africa, North and South America, Siberia, Kazakhstan, India). Presently the carbonatite formation may be referred to as most widely distributed. Investigations of L.S. Borodin, A.G. Bulakh, E.L. Butakova, N.A. Volotovskaya, A.I. Ginzburg, L.S. Egorov, A.A. Kukharenko, G.G. Moor, M.P. Orlova, O.M. Rimskii-Korsakova, L.K. Pozharitskaya, A.S. Sergeev, A.A. Frolov, Yu.M. Sheinmann, E.M. Epshtein and other Soviet scientists and also of W.C. Brögger, R. Brauns, J.B. Dawson, K.A. Davies, F. Dixey, T.C. James, T. Deans, H. Von Eckermann, M.S. Garson, J. Gittins, B.C. King, E.S. Larsen, D. Guimaraes, W. Von Wimmenauer, D. Sutherland, E.W. Heinrich, S.J. Shand and other foreign scientists have contributed comprehensive material on petrology, composition and regularities of formation of massifs.

The book presents results of investigations of ultrabasic and basic rock massifs and carbonatites of Kola Peninsula and Siberia. The author participated in these investigations during the period from 1958 to 1969. It presents generalized literature data on other regions. Major attention in this book is focused on examination of geologic position, structure and mineralogy of carbonatites. Besides, the structure and regularities of formation of massifs as a whole have been treated briefly.

The author expresses his gratitude to E.I. Semenov, Doctor of Geological and Mineralogical Sciences, who took the trouble of reading the text and made many valuable remarks; to L.K. Pozharitskaya, Doctor of Geological and Mineralogical Sciences; to E.M. Es'kova and R.P. Tikhonenkova, Kandidates of Geological and Mineralogical Sciences for discussing various topics and offering valuable suggestions; to Prof. H. Von Eckermann for his kind donation of rock samples from the Alnö massifs, and finally to Prof. T. Deans for his communication on the structure of carbonatites of Africa.

CONTENTS

Chapter I

DISTRIBUTION OF ALKALINE ULTRABASIC MASSIFS AND CARBONATITES

Complex massifs of alkaline ultrabasic rocks and carbonatites are known to occur in different parts of the world. Sheinmann (cited from Gaidukova et al., 1962) described 17 occurrences in different regions. But this number has now been swollen by recent finds in Kazakhstan, Greenland, Canada and other places. Most of the smaller occurrences characterized by individual spatial and structural setting can be grouped in bigger ones.

Sheinmann (1955, 1956, 1960b, 1969; Sheinmann et al., 1961) showed that complex massifs of alkaline ultrabasic rocks are typical platform-type[1] intrusions concentrated along the outer edges of the older platforms, particularly in the shields (Baltic, Aldanian, Canadian, Brazilian, African). These are confined to four types of structures: (i) edges of platforms; (ii) marginal zones of platforms; (iii) large regional faults; and (iv) regional postfolding fractures in the geosynclines. These structures can in practice be reduced to fractures at the periphery of platforms and the zones of regional and global fractures in older formations. Occurrence of deep-seated alkaline ultrabasic magmatism toward the edge of platforms is explained by the great depth of the fractures in these zones. As a rule the central parts of platforms are devoid of magmatism (with the exception of traps).

In recent years smaller bodies of carbonatites have been discovered at the center of the Siberian Platform (Mikhenko, 1967), although Frolov doubted the affinity of these rocks to carbonatites and classified them as products of contact metamorphism of sedimentary limestone. Carbonatites were found in the Anabar Dome (Marshintsev et al., 1966; Kovalskii and Egorov, 1966), on the Timan Ridge and even at the center of the Russian Platform (Ruzhit-

[1]'Intracratonic' according to the English literature—Editor.

skii, 1963). It is possible that these massifs are more widely distributed than is currently believed and may occasionally occur in the central part of platforms. But the development of a thick sedimentary mantle on the platforms hampers discovery of these ancient intrusives, especially because of their small dimensions.

Complex massifs are not known to occur in all platforms. Even within a platform the distribution of the massifs is irregular, which may be ascribed to irregular tectonic deformations or to covering of individual parts by younger sedimentary layers. Most numerous occurrences of carbonatites are known from the bigger shields in Africa, America, Siberia and the Baltic (Table 1). A brief account of the characteristics of these principal regions is given below.

THE SIBERIAN PLATFORM AND ADJOINING REGIONS

Several important alkaline ultrabasic massifs and a few small isolated carbonatite bodies are known to occur along the border zone of the Siberian Platform. A few small groups of massifs are also found in the northern part of the platform (Maimecha-Kotui Province). This region is composed of subhorizontal sedimentary piles of Sinian and Early Paleozoic ages covered with older deposits (Atlasov, 1958; Sheinmann, 1946, 1947; Moor, 1940, 1957a, b, 1958; Butakova and Egorov, 1962). They dip northwest into the Taimbyr depression where they are associated with younger rocks (Fig. 1). Complex massifs in this region occur in a chain running northeast and northwest (Egorov et al., 1968) and intrude the Paleozoic sedimentary rocks. They are associated with basaltic and alkali basalt effusives of Permo-Triassic age, indicating that the age of the massifs is also Permo-Triassic (Moor, 1958; Shikhorina, 1959).

Most of the smaller massifs and carbonatites occur as subvertical stocks 10–15 km^2 in area, but larger massifs are also known to occur: Odikhinch (56 km^2) and Gulinskii (more than 500 km^2 at the present level of erosion and possibly more than 2,000 km^2 on the geophysical interpretation). According to Butakova (1956) and Zhabin (1965) the Gulinskii massif shows either the fractured-lamination or the laccolith form. A little distance from this massif there are well-developed alkaline basaltoids, part of which is associated with early stages of volcanism preceded by intrusions of ultrabasic and alkaline rocks. Most of the massifs of Maimecha-Kotui Province are composed of alkaline ultrabasic rocks and carbonatites showing complex structures and multiphase formation.

In the southeastern part of Maimecha-Kotui Province there is the Anabar Dome comprising schists of Precambrian age which, in places, are covered with younger layers of Paleozoic and Mesozoic continental deposits. In the southern part of this dome (Kuonapka river basin) several small (to 1 km^2)

ring dikes, stocks and pipes of kimberlites, picrites, porphyrites, carbonatites and their volcanic breccias are found concentrated in some places (Milashev et al., 1963; Kovalskii and Egorov, 1966; Marshintsev et al., 1966). These pipes cut across the metasediments and contain foreign rock fragments. These encircle the pipes. They consist of gneisses, eclogites, ultrabasites and carbonatites at depths. In some places the foreign rock fragments constitute 60% of the total. Distribution of these pipes and stocks is controlled by the system of tectonic zones that is conspicuous in the Anabar Dome in the north-northwest

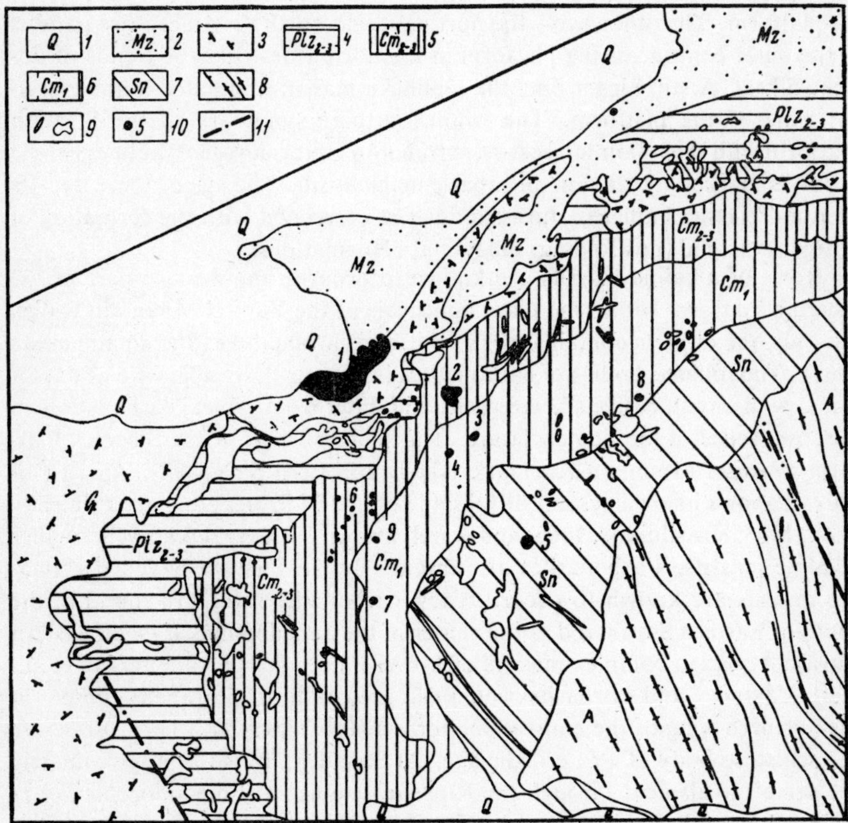

Fig. 1. Geological map of the northern parts of Siberian Platform (after Nalivkin et al., 1956; Butakova and Egorov, 1962).

1—Quaternary deposits; 2—Mesozoic deposits; 3—Effusive bodies (alkaline near to Gulinskii massif) of Permo-Triassic age; 4—Middle-upper Paleozoic deposits; 5—Middle-upper Cambrian deposits; 6—Lower Cambrian carbonate-sandy deposits; 7—Sinian carbonatic deposits; 8—Archean gneisses and migmatites; 9—Dikes and the principal rock mass; 10—Massifs of alkaline ultrabasic rocks and carbonatites (*1*—Gulinskii, *2*—Odikhinchia, *3*—Sona, *4*—Kuvda, *5*—Magan, *6*—Romanikha, *7*—Bor-Yryakh, *8*—Nemakit, *9*—Dalbikha); 11—Faults.

direction. Localization of these pipes is confined to the area of several tectonic deformations or indicates the presence of several complex massifs at depths not exposed by erosion.

The submeridional system of tectonic zone of crystalline basement of the Anabar Dome possibly extends in the north right up to Maimecha-Kotui Province. The development of alkaline ultrabasic magmatism in the northern part of the Siberian Platform was probably determined by the combination of three systems of regional tectonic trends. The slightly older one among them (the north-northwest one) is significant for the crystalline basement of the platform. The other two—the northeast and northwest ones—are parallel to the outer contour of the platform in the north (these are the trends of dolerite dikes). A still bigger one, the Gulinskii massif, is situated in the marginal zone of the platform. The whole northern boundary of the Siberian Platform with the adjoining east-west trending Hercynian geosynclines (in the north) is marked by alkaline-ultrabasic magmatism. The age of these massifs (Permo-Triassic; in places, Jurassic) may be correlated with the formation of postgeosynclinal (postfolding) tangential deformations.

Rows of alkaline massifs are known to occur in the western part of the Siberian Platform within the older upheavals of the Yenisei Mountain Ridge, but only one of them contains rocks similar to carbonatites (Sheinmann et al., 1961). The foliated bodies of carbonatites in Tungussk Syncline are not associated with any intrusive silicate rocks and differ from typical carbonatites in the strict sense of the nomenclature. The southern part of the Siberian Platform (Yenisei Mountain-Kuznetsk Ala-Tau-Eastern Sayan-Siberian part of Baikal) shows its own system of folding pattern of Proterozoic age (Smirnov et al., 1963; Krasilnikov, 1966) and is well known for several relatively smaller alkaline massifs. Carbonatites are absent. But in Eastern Sayan carbonatite massifs are known to occur. A few carbonatite veins are found in the south of Eastern Sayan and at the center of the Sangilen massif (southeastern Tuva). At Sayan complex massifs of Lower Paleozoic age (Sheinmann et al., 1961; Lavrenev and Pozharitskaya, 1958) are confined to grabens present in the northern wing of the main anticlinorium (Proterosayan). They cut across the schistose body of Proterozoic age. At Sangilen, massif of approximately the same age also cut through the Riphean sedimentary metamorphic layers confined to older tectonic zones (Proterozoic?) of interlocking characters. The carbonatite massifs of this region are close in age to the postfolding deformations developed in the adjoining region of Lower Paleozoic (Salair) folds (southern slopes of Eastern Sayan and Tuva).

On the eastern flank of the Siberian Platform (Aldan Shield), near the junction with the Mongolian-Okhotsk belt (Mesozoic age), rows of complex stocklike massifs, 3–5 km in size, are known to occur (Zdorik and Runov, 1961). The age of these massifs (determined by geological factors) varies from Precambrian to Mesozoic. The only known occurrence of an intrusive body of pyroxenite in the Sikhote-Alin Mountain Range, which stretches along the southeastern part of the Siberian Platform and belongs to the Mesozoic folded zone, is regarded by Rub and Zalishak (1964) as a well-developed formation of Mesozoic age (postfolding).

In Kazakhstan, in the Kokchetava block (medium-size massif), rows of alkaline ultrabasic rocks and carbonatite bodies (Paleozoic) occur. They cut across the Precambrian schists and are confined to the stable linear tectonic zone (Letnikov and Zagumenova, 1962). Massifs (up to 1.5 km in length) are sharply inclined toward the tectonic zones, and alkaline rocks are found in their extended parts.

In the Asian part of the Urals (eastern slope) the most important is the stretched alkaline intrusive of Ilmen'-Vishnevikh Mountain composed of miascite but containing multiple zones of carbonatization and carbonatite veins. These are regarded as carbonatites by Zhabin (1959). In mineral composition (Kapustin, 1964) and geosynclinal nomenclature these carbonatites differ from typical carbonatites (Shaneri et al., 1967) and must be classed with independent formations of hydrothermal carbonatite veins genetically related to nepheline syenites. These veins are widely distributed in most of the massifs of southern Siberia (Eastern Sayan, Tuva, North Prebaikal).

THE RUSSIAN PLATFORM AND THE ADJOINING REGIONS OF EUROPE

In the Russian Platform most areas are covered with thick sedimentary layers of Upper Paleozoic and Mesozoic ages. Typical carbonatite massifs are known to occur near the northern part (Baltic Shield), while the presence of carbonatites in the Timan Ridge, as mentioned earlier, is not confirmed. Deep drilling during the last few years has revealed the existence of thick volcanic cones (Vardanyantz, 1961; Rujitzki, 1963) at the center of the Russian Platform (Moscow syncline). The larger among them (20–30 km in diameter) are confined to Vorotilovsk Mountain of the crystalline basement (north of Gorki Mountain) and show their typical funnel-shaped forms filled with zeolitic breccias as the principal rock, mixed with carbonatized effusive material intersected by carbonatite dikes. Similar volcanic cones are also known in the free zone, i.e. from Kaluga Uplands which is covered by alkaline ultrabasic lava and effusives in Ukraine (Pokrovo-Kireevskii region), and in the Voronezsk Upland.

Several complex alkaline ultrabasic intrusive rocks and carbonatites occur in the northwestern part of the Russian Platform, i.e. in the Baltic Shield. At the northeastern tip there is Kola-Karelia Province (14 massifs) and to the west (in Scandinavia) massifs only of this type (Fen, Alnö, Ivaara). Some parts of Kolo Peninsula are confined within the older Baltic Shield, whose structure dominated the structure in the northwestern direction. As evidenced by geophysical studies (Tzirulnikova et al., 1967), these structures have the form of blocks. Alkaline ultrabasic magmatism is here confined to the linear system principally along the east-west tectonic zone (Fig. 2) of branching character and intersects the blocks (Volotovskaya, 1958, 1960; Kukharenko, 1958, 1967).

To the west of the Kola Peninsula, amid the Precambrian gneissic metasediments, there is the Ivaara massif and still farther west the Fen and Alnö massifs. In the northwest at the border of Grampiansk geosynclinal zone lies the Stjernöy massif (Heier, 1964). Most of the massifs of this region are of hypabyssal facies and show the forms either of vertical or of steeply dipping asymmetric stocks. The age of these massifs in the Kola Peninsula varies between 400 and 350 million years (Kukharenko et al., 1965; Kukharenko, 1967; Shaneri et al., 1967). Intrusions of these massifs are possibly related to the rejuvenated older tectonic zone of the adjoining north Grampian geosyncline (Caledonian age). The age of the other Fenno-Scandinavian massifs is also Caledonian (Kukharenko, 1967; Brögger, 1921; Eckermann, 1948a; Heier, 1964).

Somewhat unique occurrences of some alkaline ultrabasic magmatism are reported from Western Europe (Branco, 1894). From Oslo (Belyavskii, 1963) and Rhine region (Brauns, 1919, 1926; Brauns and Brauns, 1925) Tertiary grabens and volcanic necks are well known and these are full of alkaline effusive materials (Laacher Sea region). In the Upper Rhine region there is the famous Tertiary Kaiserstühl volcano with alkaline effusive materials and carbonatites (Knop, 1892; Wimmenauer, 1959, 1963). Numerous small volcanic cones and pipes full of alkaline materials are also known to occur in the Rhone region (Velde, 1967). From the Appenine Peninsula (Albanian Mountain and nearby Bracciano Lake) Tertiary volcanic pipes surrounded by alkaline ultrabasic effusive upheavals (Strüver, 1887) are well known. Their contemporaries, Vesuvius (Somma) and Etna, still erupt alkaline materials. Within the eruptive materials of Somma and in the volcanic pipes of the Albanian Mountains and in Bracciano Lake large (up to 10 m) blocks of calciphyres containing magnetite, apatite and silicates—all minerals characteristic of carbonatites (forsterite, diopside, phlogopite and others)—occur. Probably these blocks do not contain xenoliths mixed with Tertiary sediments as shown by Strüver (1887) and Zambonini (1935). The blocks of deep-seated carbonatites do not reach the top level, as is evidenced by the presence of alkaline glasses in calcites (Strüver, 1887). The compositions of lavas of Somma and volcanic necks of Bracciano Lake are similar to those of the lava of Kaiserstühl (phonolite, tephrite and feldspathic rocks).

The structural setup and the nature of associations of alkaline and alkaline ultrabasic massifs of eastern and Southern Europe have not been properly studied. But Kukharenko (1967) traced the zones of higher tectonic activities that started from the Kola Peninsula through Fenno-Scandinavia, joining them with the distorted north-south zones of the Oslo region—the grabens of

Prerhine—and, still farther south, with the structure of the Eastern Mediterranean Sea and the grabens of the Red Sea. This structure coincides with the great African dislocation. Possibly the development of Tertiary-Quaternary tectonic dislocations and associated volcanism belongs to a single global tectonism passing through Eastern Europe and then merging with the great African dislocation.

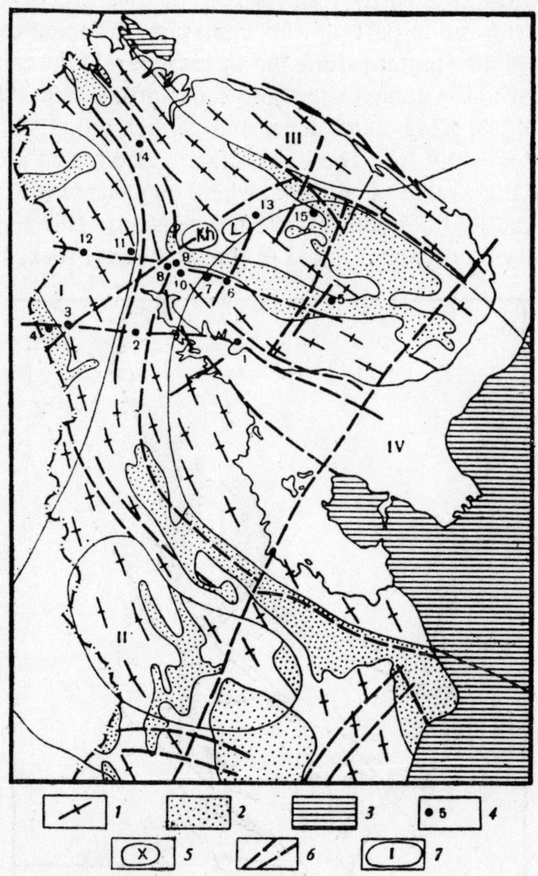

Fig. 2. Tectonic map of Kola Peninsula and Karelia (after Kukharenko, 1967).

1—Archean gneisses, granites and migmatites; 2—Karelian formation; 3—Postkarelian formation; 4—Massifs of alkaline ultrabasic rocks and carbonatites (*1*—Turii Peninsula, *2*—Kovdozero, *3*—Vuoriyarvi, *4*—Sallanlatva, *5*—Pesochnyi, *6*—Ingozer, *7*—Salmagorsk, *8*—Afrikanda, *9*—Ozernaya Varaka, *10*—Lesnaya Varaka, *11*—Mavrgubinsk, *12*—Kovdor, *13*—Kurginsk, *14*—Sebl-Yavr, *15*—Kontozersk); 5—Hercynian nepheline-syenite massifs (Kh—Khibinsk, L—Lovizersk); 6—Tectonic zones; 7—Foundation blocks (I–V).

THE AFRICAN SHIELD

Most of the carbonatite massifs (over 60%) of the world are concentrated in Africa. The number of intrusives, volcanoes, and independent carbonatite bodies here exceeds 150. More than 50 of these are large massifs. Most of them occur within the territory of the African Shield, especially along the eastern flank of the continent. A small number occur to the south and southwest. Carbonatites affected by younger geosynclinal processes occur in the north and northwestern part of the continent. Independent massifs are oriented in a chainlike pattern along the western part of the continent (Fig. 3) and are confined to the complex tectonic zones of the great African dislocations (Bowen, 1938; King, 1965; King and Sutherland, 1960; Bailey, 1961; Kun, 1961; Borodin, 1963b). These massifs are also traced along the southwestern edge of the Arabian Peninsula, where they merge with the deep-seated grabens of the Red Sea (northwestern extension). This zone (at least its southern branches) probably formed in the Archean (Brock, 1959; Du Toit,

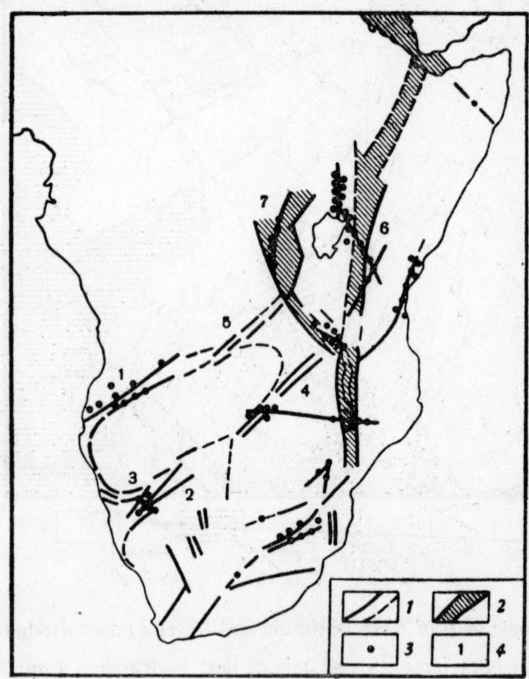

Fig. 3. Tectonic map of southeastern Africa (after Du Toit, 1957; Brock, 1959; Kun, 1961; Borodin, 1963b; Kilotukhin et al., 1964).

1—Fractured zones; 2—Rifts; 3—Massifs of regional tectonic systems; 4—Main regional tectonic systems (*1*—Lusaka-Lomagundi, *2*—Ganzi Ridge, *3*—Damara, *4*—Luangwa and Muwa, *5*—Upemwa, *6*—Eastern rift, *7*—Western rift).

1957; Dixey, 1959) and developed with time from south to north. The age of these intrusives with their associated interruptions varies from Precambrian (in the south) to Paleozoic and Mesozoic (at the center) to Quaternary (in the north). To the north of this zone there is a larger development of younger rifts (Nyasa, Tanganyika). Carbonatite volcanoes (Lengai, Kerimasi, Kaliyango and others) and rows of young alkaline basalts (Bufumbiru, Kim Lake region) occur in this zone. The close association between these volcanoes and the rifts signify spontaneous disposition of volcanoes in the rift valleys as well as in their walls, and common orientation of the rift valleys and the volcanic chains (Davies, 1952, 1956; Kun, 1961; Searle, 1952; Borodin, 1963b). A few groups of massifs and volcanoes that occur along the large rift zone of Lake Tanganyika-Nyasa continue farther to the south and north.

The numerous, complex branches of the great African Rift Valley can be divided into a series of small tectonic zones. Besides the dislocations of African territory subparallel to the north-south direction, regional tectonic zones are well known along the northeast and east-west directions, comprising independent large blocks of massifs and shields formed during either the Archean or the Proterozoic period (Brock, 1959, Fig. 3). Complex massifs of alkaline and carbonatite rocks that occur in the west and southwest of Africa are oriented along the mid-platform tectonic system of Ganzi Ridge (Etaneno, Okoruzu and others), Lusaka-Lomagundi (Kaluve and others) and Zambia. About 10–20 independent massifs are known to cluster in the southwest and western part of the continent, confining themselves to the intersection of the north-south (rift) and the east-west system of dislocation. (In the area from the south of Lake Tanganyika-Nyasa to the north of Lake Kivu about 30 small volcanoes are situated in a stretch of 40 km south of Hanang volcano to Bazutu in Tanganyika.)

In Africa the wide development of intrusives of different periods, the varied nature of erosional surfaces and the dissimilar structural patterns are chiefly responsible for the different compositions and structural configurations of the massifs. Most of the massifs are oval (in plan) and form conical stocks, pipes and a volcanic crater that cut across the Precambrian metasediments. In the south ancient, deep-seated and eroded massifs (Spitzkop, Palabora, Pilansberg and others) (Shand, 1928, 1931, 1947) and sub-volcanoes are known to occur (Hudini, Kruidfontein) (Fockema, 1949) while in the north subvolcanic stocks and pipes (Tertiary and Recent) are found. These are often accompanied by alkaline (sometimes carbonatites) effusives and lavas (Holmes, 1952; Holmes and Harwood, 1932, 1937) and filled-up volcanic cones (Napak, Kuzingiri, Elgon, Lengan, Kaliyango and others). Their sizes vary from about 50 km (Elgon volcano) to about 10 km in diameter (Spitzkop intrusive) to smaller volcanic craters and necks a few meters across (for example, Hananga near Mbulu, Tanganyika (Downie and Wilkinson, 1962; Freitaz, 1959). Intrusive bodies of sizes between 2 and 8 km also occur

(Lueshe, Mbeya, Chilwa, Muambe, Toror, Napak, Bukusu, Shawa, Dorowa and others).

THE BRAZILIAN AND CANADIAN SHIELDS AND THE ADJOINING REGIONS OF NORTH AMERICA

The occurrence of carbonatites is well known in North and South America. Here they are confined mainly to the edge of older platforms. In Brazil these massifs occur in the form of a chain running about 1,000 km down the Atlantic coast, from the city of Florianopolis in the south to the city of Sao Paulo in the north and extending up to Pavanaibi in the northeast (Alves, 1960; Guimaraes, 1957, 1960). These massifs are mostly concentrated on the edge of the Brazilian Shield and comprise Precambrian metasediments along the upper margin of the Parana Trough (Fig. 4). This trough formed reefs on the crystalline basement and rejuvenated during the Mesozoic in association with effusives covered by basaltic lava (Bischoff, 1956; Stille, 1942; Grabert, 1960). Alkaline massifs traversing the Precambrian formation are considered as Mesozoic in age (Jurassic-Cretaceous—Alves, 1960; Guimaraes, 1960; Heinrich, 1967; Tuttle et al., 1967). These massifs are confined to a large regional tectonic zone that surrounds the Parana Trough. In the east they extend north-south but in the north, to the west (Fig. 4). These massifs are either bosses or stocks with areas covering about 50 km^2 (Jacupiranga).

In North America, in the United States (Missouri, Ohio, Arkansas, Colorado, Arizona) and in Canada (the Great Lake region and around Algoma-Sudbury) large complex massifs, e.g. Magnet Cove, Iron Hill, Oka, Ice River, Nemogosenda, Nipissing and others as well as individual intrusive bodies and dikes of alkaline ultrabasic rocks are well known (Heinrich and Levinson, 1961; Heinrich and Anderson, 1965; Heinrich and Dahlem, 1965; Heinrich, 1967; Hogarth, 1957; Parker et al., 1962; Deans, 1955, 1968; Tuttle et al., 1967). Large groups of intrusive gabbro-syenites, stocks and dikes of alkaline rocks (Democrat Creek, McClure, Mayantinz, Iron Mountain, etc.) are devoid of any carbonatite and probably they do not belong to any such known type formations. Some of the alkaline massifs and carbonatite veins of Southern Canada (Halliburton-Bancroft, Nisikkatch Lake and the skarn series of Grenville) belong to the carbonatite group (Heinrich, 1967) but differ appreciably from them in composition. The alkaline rocks of Bancroft are very similar to normal miascites of postmagmatic carbonatization (Vishnevik and Ilmenski type of the Urals) while the formations of the Greenville Series and the Lake Nisikkatch area are probably analogous to the magmatic skarn and phlogopite-calcite veins (with diopside and scapolite) of Aldana and Sludiyan (Korzhinskii, 1947, 1953). For a clear idea of the origin of these formations more detailed studies are needed.

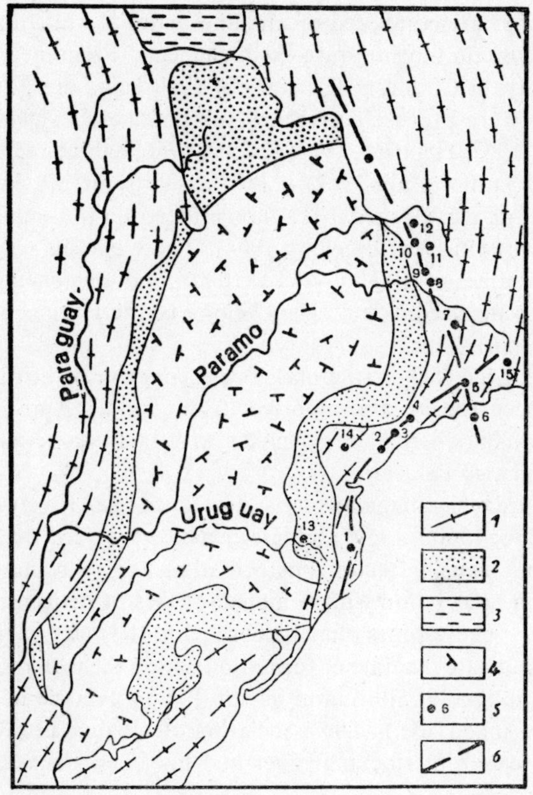

Fig. 4. Distribution of alkaline and carbonatite massifs of South America (after Bischoff, 1956; Alves, 1960; Kolotukhin et al., 1968).

1—Precambrian; 2—Gondwana subcontinental series (Carboniferous); 3—Cretaceous deposits; 4—Traps (Jurassic-Triassic age); 5—Massifs of alkaline ultrabasic rocks and carbonatites (*1*—Anitapolis, *2*—Jacupiranga, *3*—Serrote, *4*—Ipanama, *5*—San Hordo, *6*—Trinidad, *7*—Pokosdi Kaldas, *8*—Tapira, *9*—Barreiro de Arasha, *10*—Serra Negra, *11*—Bededoiro, *12*—Koromandel, *13*—Lyages, *14*—Itapirapua, *15*—Itatiaiya); 6—Tectonic zones.

The structural setup of the North American massifs has not been sufficiently studied but they are mostly confined within the platforms (the Canadian Shield) or within the zones of postfolding uplift (Magnet Cove, Iron Hill, Ravalli County and Lemhi County) or prefolding (Mountain Pass) activity. The age of the massifs of this region varies from Precambrian (Mountain Pass) through Paleozoic (Canadian massif) to Mesozoic-Tertiary (Bearpaw Mountain, Ravalli County and Lemhi County). The forms and configurations of these massifs vary widely. Here the well-known large stocklike bodies of complex structures as well as the concentric zonal structures (Magnet Cove, Oka, Nemegosenda) are composed of several rock types. The observed dikes and volcanic pipes are composed of alkaline material while the series of carbonatite veins contain thorium-rare-earth elements (Fremont County, Lemhi County and Ravalli County). The sizes of such veins are not large but in some places they are profusely present (Heinrich and Lavinson, 1961; Heinrich and Quon, 1963; Heinrich, 1967; Kaiser, 1956; Sahinen, 1957; Olson and Wallace, 1956; Tuttle et al., 1967). The massifs occurring in the northern part of this region, e.g. Grenedal-Ika, are situated on the southwestern coast of Greenland (Upton, 1961; Emeleus, 1964). These massifs occur in the form of oval-shaped stocks of alkaline rocks (10 km in diameter) and cut through the Precambrian metasediments. They belong to the Harder group of intrusives (Precambrian).

Most of the large carbonatite massifs are concentrated in the type areas. Independent occurrences are reported from India (Amba Dongar and Koratti), Sri Lanka (where placer deposits with baddeleyite and zirkelite are well known) and also Pakistan.

Alkaline ultrabasic magmatism is developed exclusively on platforms (Sheinmann, 1956, 1960b, 1969) and later extended toward the margins of the platform, thereby causing tectonic deformations, or rejuvenated the ancient tectonic uplift in association with complete phases of orogenic movement in the geosynclines. These zones often lie parallel to the margins of the platform and their ages indicate the time of formation within the geosynclines (Caledonian in the Baltic Shield; Silurian in Sayan; Permo-Triassic in north Siberia; Caledonian in Canada, etc.). The association of alkaline ultrabasic magmatism with deep-seated interlocking zones and lineaments is well illustrated in Africa.

Among the complex multiphase massifs of alkaline ultrabasic rocks that developed with time, only the age of the first intrusive and effusive phases can be compared to the mountain-building stage of the geosynclines. The dike series are younger by 50–100 million years (Kukharenko et al., 1965; Shanin et al., 1967). The volcanic effusions of this type display a short time interval of formation (preceding intrusion) but in the multiphase Gulinskii massif these effusions were formed during the Permo-Triassic period (some parts probably during the Jurassic) (Butakova and Egorov, 1962). Development of magmatism in the great African Rift Valley shows wide variation of time ranging from Precambrian to Recent. Still, the massifs of different periods show the same general characters.

Thus the essential conditions of formation of complex massifs and carbonatites indicate the presence of deep tectonic zones within the platforms (mostly long-lived older deposits). Inclination toward the rejuvenated deformations explains the multiphase character of this type of massif and establishes the formation of several open fractures and the penetration of several successive proportions of melts and solutions.

The carbonatite massifs are characteristically inclined toward the platforms, thereby indicating their close relationship with magmatic origin. In all, the platforms display three magmatic groups: alkaline and alkaline ultrabasics, kimberlites and traps, and basaltoids (Kuznetzsov, 1963). The petrological and spatial interrelationships of these groups are well characterized in many parts of the world (Sheinmann et al., 1961; Sheinmann, 1969). End members within these groups are composed of true alkaline rocks (nepheline syenites) and are mostly superficial in nature, e.g. traps and basaltoids. The compositions of alkaline ultrabasic rocks and carbonatite bodies overlap. These are sometimes spatially inclined toward the well-developed zone of alkaline and trap magmatism, on the one hand, and show association with both alkaline and other rocks on the other. In almost all the carbonatite provinces the most important is the presence of nepheline syenites. In Africa, the USA, Canada, Fenno-Scandinavia and Siberia nepheline syenites are frequently seen associated with carbonatites. Moreover, nepheline-syenite massifs are often multiphase in character, e.g. Khibinsk-Lovozersk (Eliseev and Fedrov, 1953; Vlasov et al., 1959). In south Siberian massifs not only ijolites but also alkaline rocks (pyroxenites, picrites, porphyrites, olivine-rich alkaline lamprophyre and effusives) are always found. In most of the provinces the age of these alkaline ultrabasics and that of the nepheline syenites is almost identical. But nepheline syenites are younger in age, e.g. in the Kola Peninsula the age of the carbonatite massif is 400–320 million years while that of the nepheline syenite (Khibinsk and Lovozersk) is 375–250 million years.

Similar cases are reported from the Eastern Sayan and Tuva where the age of carbonatites is between 450 and 350 million years and that of nepheline syenites between 350 and 270 million years (Butakova, 1965; Yashina, 1962; Yashina and Borisevich, 1966; Shanin et al., 1967).

Associations of carbonatites with kimberlites were reported long ago (Daly, 1925; Sheinmann, 1955; Sheinmann et al., 1961). These rocks are often inclined toward a single tectonic zone (southeast Africa, northern Siberia) and Sheinmann combines them into a single group. This combination is explained not only by the spatial relationship but also by the presence of primary calcite in kimberlites often formed by the process of secondary carbonatization (Bebrievich et al., 1959; Marshintzev et al., 1966) and sometimes by the presence of independent carbonatite veins within the kimberlite pipes (metal-bearing kimberlite pipes of South Africa—Daly, 1936). Moreover, numerous occurrences of dikes of alnöites, picrite-porphyries, kimberlites and kimberlite carbonatites, similar in composition and structure to normal kimberlites, are well known in many alkaline ultrabasic massifs of Eastern Sayan, Gulinskii, Alnö, Fen, Kovdor, Vuoriyarvi, etc. (Butakova and Egorov, 1962; Eckermann, 1964, 1966; Heinrich, 1967).

Association between alkaline ultrabasic and trap magmatism (Sheinmann, 1955) is not so conspicuous and spatially both types of magmatism persist, but not so closely as is seen in the Siberian Platform and northwestern Africa. In such associations alterations of the principal and essential alkaline effusives are generally found in the effusive body. Such alterations are well developed at the margins of the Gullnskii massif and in the Elgon and Kilimanjaro volcanoes. Similarly, alkaline lamprophyres are always present in the series of dikes of the principal massifs of the Kola Peninsula and in the lower Yenisei (Norilsk group). Normal and principal rock constituents are rarely seen in the compositions of carbonatite massifs. Thus the alkaline lamprophyres are absent from the African and Siberian massifs. But only in the Fenno-Scandinavian region of Stjernöy and near the Kaiserstühl and Magnet Cove massifs are these rocks widely distributed. Shonkinites are reported from Mountain Pass (Olson et al., 1954). Tephrite dikes, theralites, essexites and other alkaline rocks are reported from Siberia, Iron Hill, and Mountain Pass. Occurrences of carbonatites comprising normal rock constituents are negligible and regarded as practically nonexistent. A strong genetic relationship between carbonatites and the principal magma can be established neither by petrographic nor by geochemical methods. But the genetic relationship of carbonatites with alkaline and ultrabasic magmatism as well as with kimberlites is beyond doubt.

The spatial distribution of alkaline ultrabasic massifs in all the important provinces is characterized below:

1) restriction to deep tectonic deformations;
2) development mainly along the border zones of older platforms and shields and profuse occurrence in geosynclines;
3) persistent occurrences with kimberlites and alkaline rocks.

The massifs with kimberlites, nepheline syenites, traps and alkaline basaltoids indicate characteristic groups of platform-type magmatic intrusions (Sheinmann et al., 1961; Kuznetsov, 1964; Vorob'eva, 1960, 1963). Their associations with somewhat deeper deformations indicate, significantly, the depth of the magma formation and magmatic basins responsible for the source material of these intrusive masses (Sheinmann, 1969).

Chapter II

PETROLOGICAL CHARACTERISTICS OF THE CARBONATITE MASSIFS

HISTORY OF FORMATION OF THE MASSIFS

The study of important massifs has been complicated by the development of new ideas regarding their petrological characteristics and genetic relationship with particular types of magmas. Along with ultrabasic and alkaline rocks (Baltic Shield, North Siberia, southwestern Africa) alkaline gabbroids (Magnet Cove, Grönnedal-Ika, Kaiserstühl, Stjernöy), leucite rocks, nepheline syenites, alkaline syenites and trachytes (Siberian massifs, Lueshe, Toror, Chilwa and others) and even granitoids and rhyolites (Mountain Pass, Kruidfontein) occur in some of the massifs. The complex nature of the massifs is mainly due to their relationship with carbonatites derived from different magmas or perhaps to the presence of different rocks in the course of their multiphase formation (within the framework of the single magmatic formation) or again to spatial association of heterogenic intrusions of different periods within a single structure.

Differences of opinion persist regarding the relative occurrences of individual formations of carbonatite massifs. Many authors (Butakova et al., 1957, 1958, 1962; Borodin, 1957, 1960, 1965a; Ginzburg et al., 1958; Ginzburg and Epshtein, 1967; Egorov 1960a, 1964; Sheinmann et al., 1961; Kukharenko et al., 1965; Kukharenko, 1967) have shown a definite spatial relationship between ultrabasites, alkaline rocks and carbonatites (within a single massif) while their similar geological age and geochemical specifications group them within a single formation. Regarding the spatial associations of these massifs Borodin (1963b, 1965a) assumed two differently formed complexes: (i) ultrabasites associated with carbonatites, and (ii) alkaline rocks associated with carbonatites. The basis for this assumption may explain, to some extent, the spatial relation between ultrabasic and alkaline magmatism as is evidenced in the Aldan Shield. Here the dunite massifs (Inagli, Konderskii) of Proterozoic age are known along a long stretch while the alkaline rocks of Mesozoic age are developed along their periphery (Bilibin, 1940b; Elyanov and Moralev, 1961; Kravehenko and Vlasova, 1962). The Konderskii massif, however, was formerly considered otherwise (Andreev, 1958; Sheinmann et al., 1961). But Bogomolov (1964) showed the metasedimentary origin of its carbonatite rocks (calciphyres).

In order to explain the genetic and geochronological relation of different rocks of the complex massifs it is necessary to determine the absolute ages of these rocks. In cases of sharp differences in age (as in the Aldan Shield) it is not possible to group them in a single formation. Only in a few areas (Western Sayan, Maimecha-Kotui Province, Africa) may relatively close ages of all the intrusive rocks of these complex massifs be inferred. Occurrences of ultrabasic and alkaline effusive bodies composed of pyroxene, melilite and nepheline and also the intrusive alkaline ultrabasites (alkaline peridotites), ankaratrites, hatangites, olivine ijolites and melteigite-porphyry in the massifs (Gulinskii, Changel, Turi Mis, Kaiserstühl) and lavas of Africa explain the age and genetic proximity of the ultrabasites and alkaline rocks. In most of the complex carbonatite massifs postijolitic, precarbonatitic and postcarbonatitic alnöite-picrite dikes and damkjernites occur. They are similar in composition to alkaline ultrabasites containing nepheline, melilite, olivine, pyroxene and biotite.

In recent years there has been a tendency to discard the idea of a single carbonatite formation. Borodin (1963b, 1966b) divided the formations into four groups: (1) alkaline-ultrabasic massifs and nepheline syenites; (2) alkaline gabbroids and nepheline syenites; (3) nepheline and feldspathic syenites; and (4) alkali syenites and grano-syenites. Kukharenko (1966, 1967) divided the platforms and shields into two subformations: (1) kimberlitic and alkaline ultrabasic; (2) alkaline ultrabasics. He also subdivided the folded regions into two subformations: (1) nepheline syenite-peridotite-gabbro; (2) pyroxenite-shonkinite-syenite. But it is difficult to formulate subformations in areas where almost all the rocks essential for different subformations occur within a single massif. The representative of relatively rare subformations of alkaline gabbroids may be significant in massifs like Stjernöy, Kaiserstühl, and Magnet Cove. But the gabbroids among them are probably not genetically related to carbonatites, which are much older, and the composition of the rock does not tally with true gabbroid composition (for details, see below). Moreover, besides gabbroids, ijolites, melilitic rocks and syenites are also known to occur in Magnet Cove (Landes et al., 1932; Erickson and Blade, 1963). Grouping of independent subformations of nepheline syenites, alkali-syenites and grano-syenites with carbonatites is also difficult because these types of rock are widely distributed. In the majority of cases carbonatites are not found around them (Prebaikal, Kuznetsk-Ala-Tau, Tuva, Yenisei

Mountain Ridge, Kola Peninsula, Los Island, and others). Nepheline syenites are found in almost all the carbonatite massifs but in varying proportions (in Kola Peninsula, Maimecha-Kotui Province, Eastern Sayan and in many African massifs only a few nepheline syenite dikes are seen). Formulation of a kimberlitic and carbonatite subformations (Kukharenko, 1966) is controversial, as the minerals of Nb and Zr are rare in kimberlites and are not also associated with carbonatites. The process of carbonatization is local in nature and obviously cannot be advocated. Strontium and barium-bearing minerals (strontianite, celestine, barite) and also chlorite, zeolite and serpentine (Bobrievich et al., 1959) are associated with carbonatites and are characteristic of hydrothermal veins.

Restriction of complex carbonatite massifs of different compositions to a single formation can now be fully justified. Their distinct spatial associations with other types of magmatic formations, definite geotectonic positions and retention of petrological characters throughout practically the whole of geological history (Precambrian to Recent) permit us to regard this single formation as an independent one. The division into subformations on the basis of different rock associations and spatio-structural characters (alignment toward the platform and the folded region) is as difficult as dividing massifs of similar composition into different structural zones. But within a single zone it is quite appropriate (Table 1). Examples are cited from Africa, where within a single structural zone nepheline syenite massifs (with or without carbonatites), ijolites or altered complex massifs and volcanoes of magmatic origin and of different composition are found (Toror-Moroto-Napak, Elgon, Ngualla-Mbulu-Mbeya-Nkombwa, Chilwa series, Tundulu-Songwe-Kangankunde, etc.).

FORMATION OF THE MASSIFS

Carbonatite massifs of different types of formation may show some similarity, although the individual representatives of each type may differ in the structural setup and rock composition. Previously these differences were believed to be due to the association of massifs with different magmas, but they can also be explained as the outcome of vertical zonation.

Different intrusive or effusive formations, depending on the depth of emplacement and erosional surfaces, predominate in the massifs of alkaline ultrabasics as well as in other pluto-volcanic rocks. Sheinmann (Sheinmann et al., 1961) differentiated three facies based on erosional sections: hypabyssal, volcanic veins, and effusive. The Baltic Shield, Siberian, Canadian, North American and South African massifs may be classified under hypabyssal facies, which is dominated by intrusive formations. They are composed entirely of crystalline rocks and form bosses and pipes that dip steeply at depths and traverse the different rock assemblages (Figs. 5–8). Their primary intrusive

Table 1. Principal formation of carbonatite massifs in different parts of the world

Types of region		Region	Morphology of massifs	Principal rock constituents	Examples (massifs)
Ancient platforms and shields		Baltic Shield	Rounded, concentric zonal stocks	Pyroxenites, olivinites, ijolites, turjaite, carbonatites	Kovdor, Vuoriyarvi, Sallanlatva, Afrikanda, Alnö, Fen-Odikhincha, Magan, Bor-Uryakh, Gulinskii, Kugda
		North Siberian Platforms	Rounded, concentric zonal stocks, stratified bodies	Pyroxenites, olivinites, ijolites, turjaite, carbonatites	Odikhincha, Magan, Bor-Uryakh, Gulinskii, Kugda
		Canadian Shield	Rounded, concentric zonal stocks	Pyroxenites, nepheline syenites, ijolites, carbonatites	Nemegosenda, Nipissing, Oka
		Brazilian Shield	Rounded, concentric zonal stocks	Pyroxenites, nepheline, syenites, ijolites, carbonatites	Jacupiranga, Sorrets, Tapira, Barreino de Araxa, Ipanesua
		Africa	Rounded, conical, concentric zonal stocks, conical veins, volcanic crater and cones	Pyroxenites, ijolites, nepheline, syenites, olivinites, carbonatites	Palabora, Tundulu, Spitzkop, Bokusu, Toror, Mbeya, Rangwa, Kizingiri, Lengai
Folded regions	Ancient	North America	Rounded, concentric zonal stocks, dikes, vein system	Pyroxenites, ijolites, carbonatites, trachytes, syenites	Iron Hill, Magnet Cove
		Siberia and Kazakhstan	Rounded, concentric zonal stocks, linear bodies	Pyroxenites, ijolites, carbonatites, nepheline syenites	Bolshetagninskii, Kitoiski, Krasnomaiskie
	Recent	Europe and elsewhere	Rounded, stocks, linear system of body, volcanic pipes	Nepheline syenites, syenites, essexites, ijolites, carbonatites, shonkinites, pyroxenites	Kaiserstühl, Laakherskie, Lake Bracciano, Sikhote-Alin, Mountain Pass

nature is evidenced by their intrusion into folded structures and veining along the layers of different rocks. They are well preserved in Maimecha-Kotui Province (Fig. 5, *a–d*). For volcanic facies, which are widely prevalent in the African and European massifs, the most characteristic feature is the presence of a well-developed volcanic apparatus with a central stock (nucleus) and a series of ring dikes around it or more or less preserved volcanic cones or plugs with their swellings (Laacher Sea plug, Lake Bracciano region). The boundaries between these facies developed in accordance with the prevailing conditions. It is found in some cases that effusive masses and a thick intrusive body composed entirely of crystalline rocks are exposed within a single erosional surface. The Gulinskii and Kaiserstühl massifs and several other volcanic veins of Africa contain ultrabasic and other intrusive rocks along with ultrabasic and alkaline lavas. In most of the deep-seated massifs of various regions volcanic pipes or dikes of alnöites, kimberlites, agglomerates and breccias are found to occur. Moreover, within the framework of a single formation and a single region there are differences among individual massifs in regard to depth of emplacement. In Maimecha-Kotui Province the holocrystalline intrusive rocks along with deep-seated massifs (Odikhincha, Fig. 5, *b*; Bor-Uryakh, Fig. 5, *c*; Kugda, Fig. 5, *d*) are associated with the lavas of the Gulinskii massif (Fig. 5, *a*). In the Kola Peninsula, not far from the Gulinskii massif (Afrikanda, Lesnaya and Ozernaya Varaka, Kovdor, Vuoriyarvi) there is a Sallanlatva massif, whose structure and composition are similar to some of the subvolcanic stocks of Africa.

In multiphase massifs that have been studied rocks are formed in definite sequences and occupy definite positions in space. Hypabyssal massifs (Maimecha-Kotui, Kola, South Siberia, North America and South American provinces) are characterized by distinct zones of concentrically distributed rocks that surround a single or several centers (Figs. 5–8). As a result two types of rock sequence are developed: one from the center of the massif to its periphery and the other from the periphery to the center, corresponding to two essentially different types of zones. The central type (Anderson, 1936) of massifs witnesses the multiphase intrusions that develop from the periphery toward the center (with an older nucleus and younger rocks at the periphery), according to Borodin (1960, 1963b), are classified with the peripheral types of intrusions. Examples of the latter type are found in many alkaline ultrabasic massifs of Kola Peninsula (Kovdor, Fig. 6, *a*; Vuoriyarvi, Fig. 6, *c*; Pesochnyi, Fig. 6, *h*; Afrikanda, Fig. 6, *f*) in Maimecha-Kotui Province (Odikhincha, Fig. 5, *b*; Gulinskii, Fig. 5, *a*), and in Africa (Spitzkop, Fig. 7, *g*; Dorowa). The volcanic nucleus and xenoliths of ultrabasites preserved around the alkaline rocks of these massifs are often replaced by mica or rocks of mixed composition (mica-pyroxene-forsterite and others) due to intensive metasomatism. The alkaline rocks may show asymmetric or perfectly concentric zones at the peripheral region (Vuoriyarvi, Afrikanda, Lesnaya Varaka).

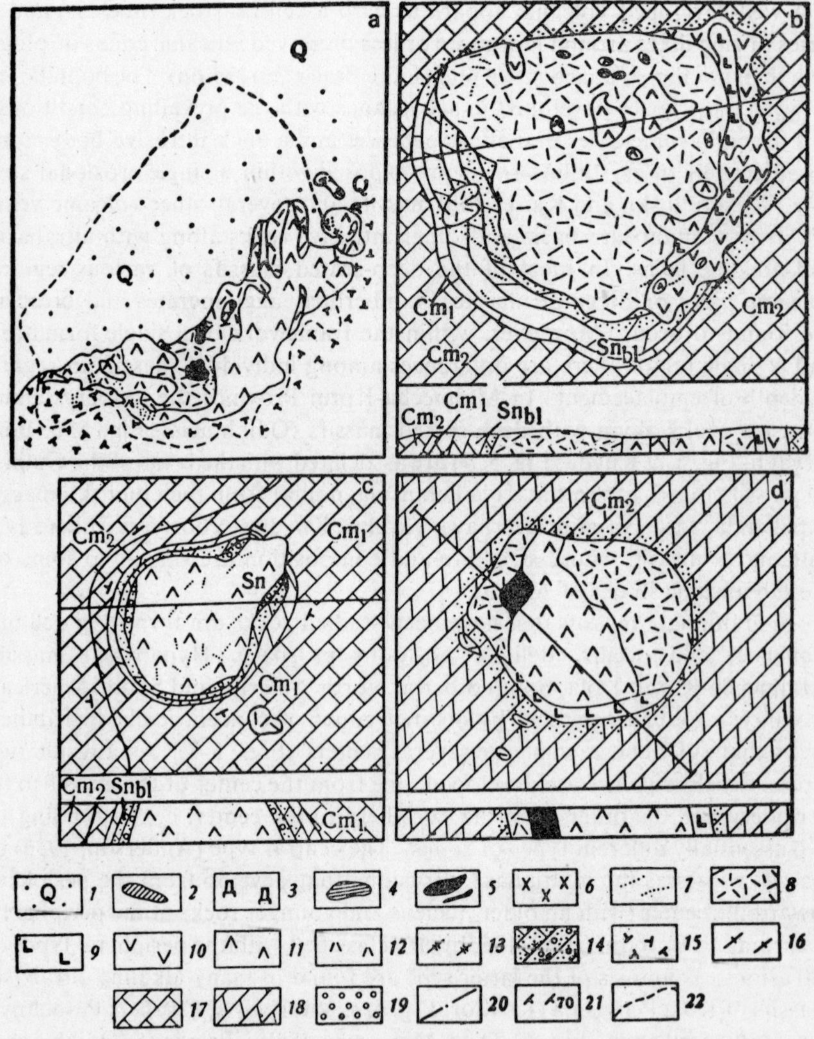

Fig. 5. Structural map of alkaline ultrabasic rocks and carbonatites of Siberia.

a—Gulinskii; b—Odikhincha; c—Bor-Yraykh; d—Kugda; e—Magan (Butakova and Egorov, 1962); f, g—Massifs of southeastern Siberia; h—Bolshetagninskii (Frolov, 1960; Frolov and Bagdasarov, 1967; Frolov et al., 1969). 1—Quaternary deposits; 2—Zones of hematization and fluoritization; 3—Late ankerite-dolomitic carbonatites; 4—Schistose early carbonatites with richterite; 5—Early (and undisturbed).

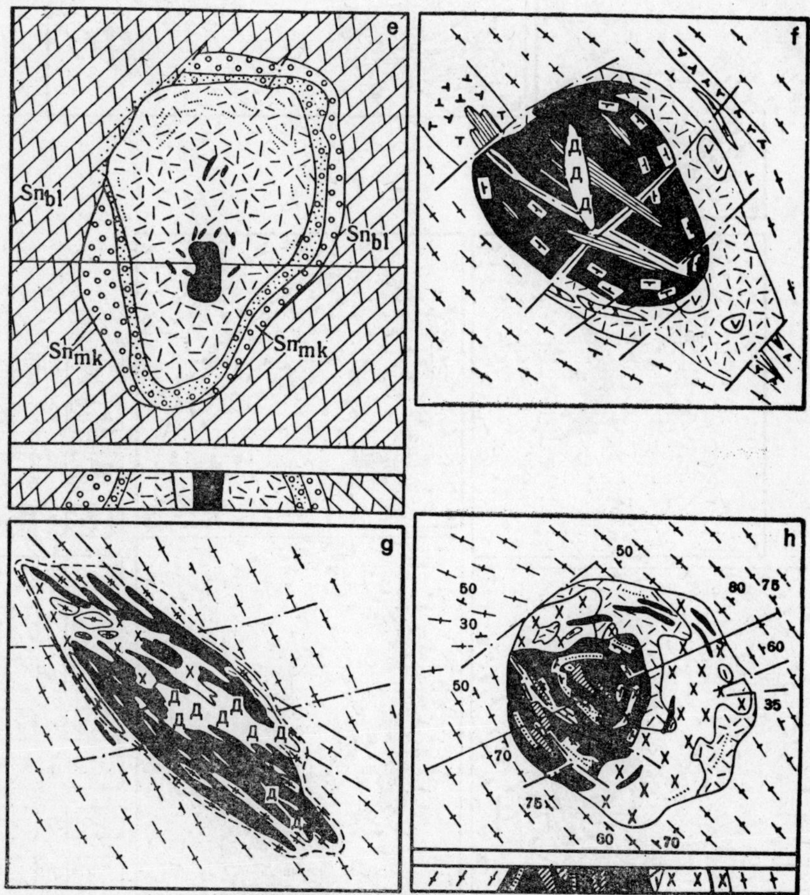

carbonatites; 6—Nepheline and alkaline syenites; 7—Dikes of alkaline rocks; 8—Ijolites, melteigites; 9—Turgites; 10—Pyroxenites; 11—Olivinites, peridotites; 12—Maimechites; 13—Fenitized rocks; 14—Metamorphosed contact facies; 15—Effusives and diabasic dikes; 16—Mixed crystalline schists; 17—Alkalies; 18—Dolomites; 19—Conglomerates; 20—Faults; 21—Bedding elements; 22—Contour of Gulinskii massif age of mixed rock; Cm_2—Middle Cambrian, Cm_1—Early Cambrian, Sn_{b1}—Sinonian (Sn_{b1}—Bilyakh Shield, Sn_{mk}—Mukunsk Shield).

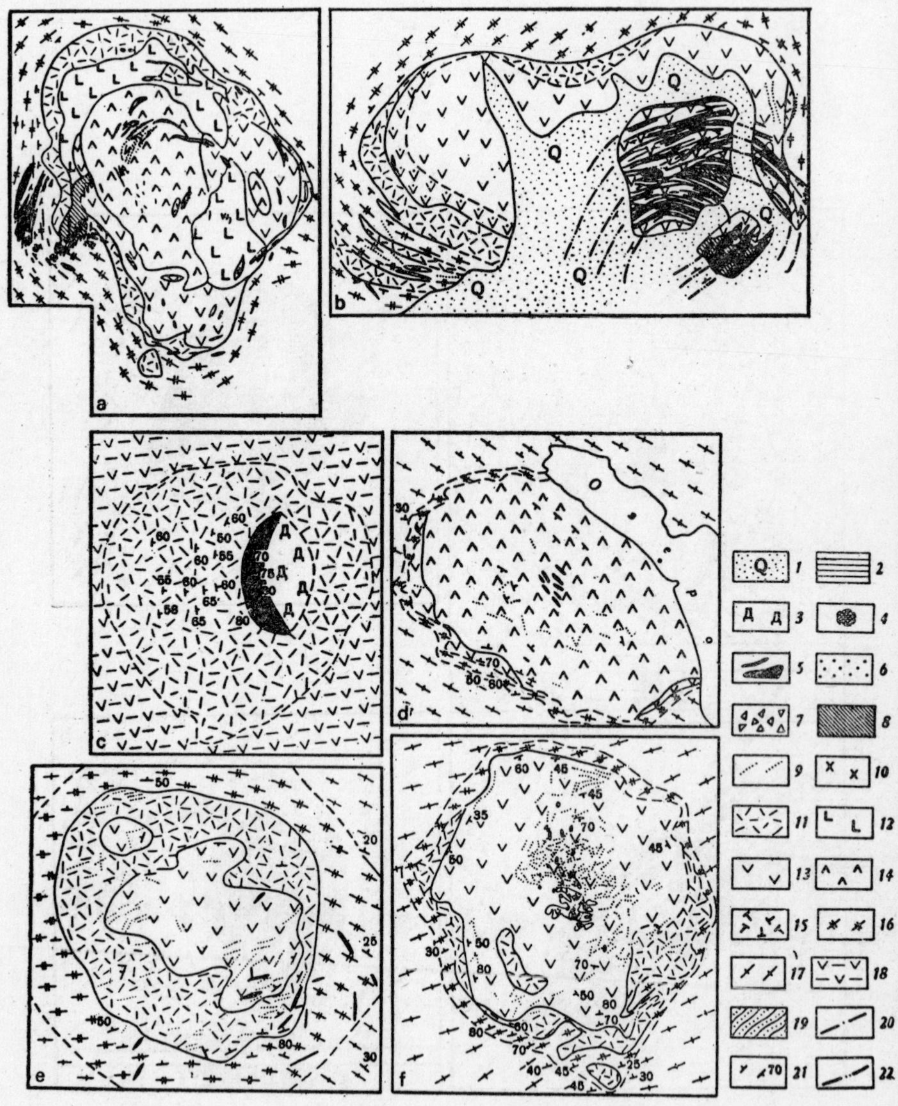

Fig. 6. Distribution of alkaline ultrabasic rocks and carbonatites in European massifs.

a—Kovdor; b—Vuoriyarvi; c—Sallanlatva; d—Lesnaya Varaka; e—Ozernaya Varaka; f—Afrikanda; g—Salmagorsky; h—Pechosnyi (Borodin, 1960; Kukharenko et al., 1965; and after present author); i—Alnö (Eckermann, 1950); j—Fen (Saether, 1948); k—Stjernöy (Heier, 1964); l—Kaiserstühl (Wimmenauer, 1963).

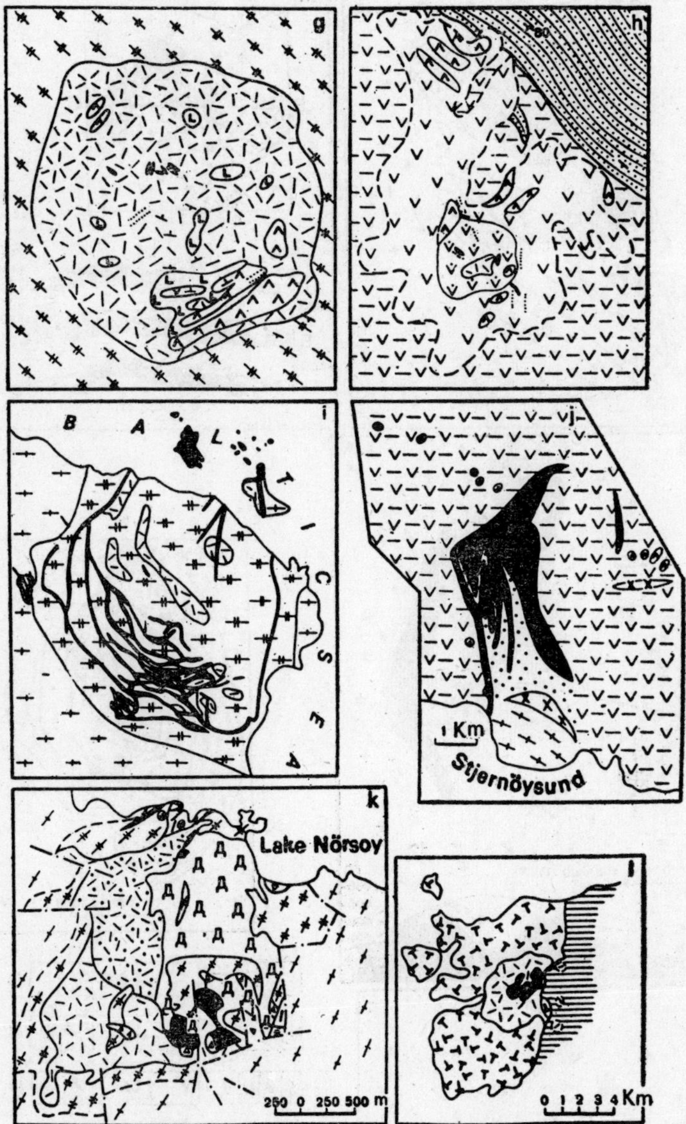

1—Quaternary deposition; 2—Tertiary deposition; 3—Late ankerite-dolomite carbonatites; 4—Shtaffelitic breccia; 5—Early (or not determined) carbonatites; 6—Carbonatized rocks; 7—Breccia; 8—Magnetite-forsterite rocks; 9—Dikes of alkaline rocks; 10—Nepheline syenites; 11—Ijolites; 12—Turgites; 13—Pyroxenites; 14—Olivinites; 15—Alkaline effusive rocks; 16—Fenitized rocks; 17—Mixed granite-gneiss and schists of Archean age; 18—Mixed gabbro, metagabbro and metadiabase of Proterozoic age; 19—Sandstones, quartz and conglomerates of Proterozoic age; 20—Faults; 21—Dip and strike; 22—Boundary of carbonatite body.

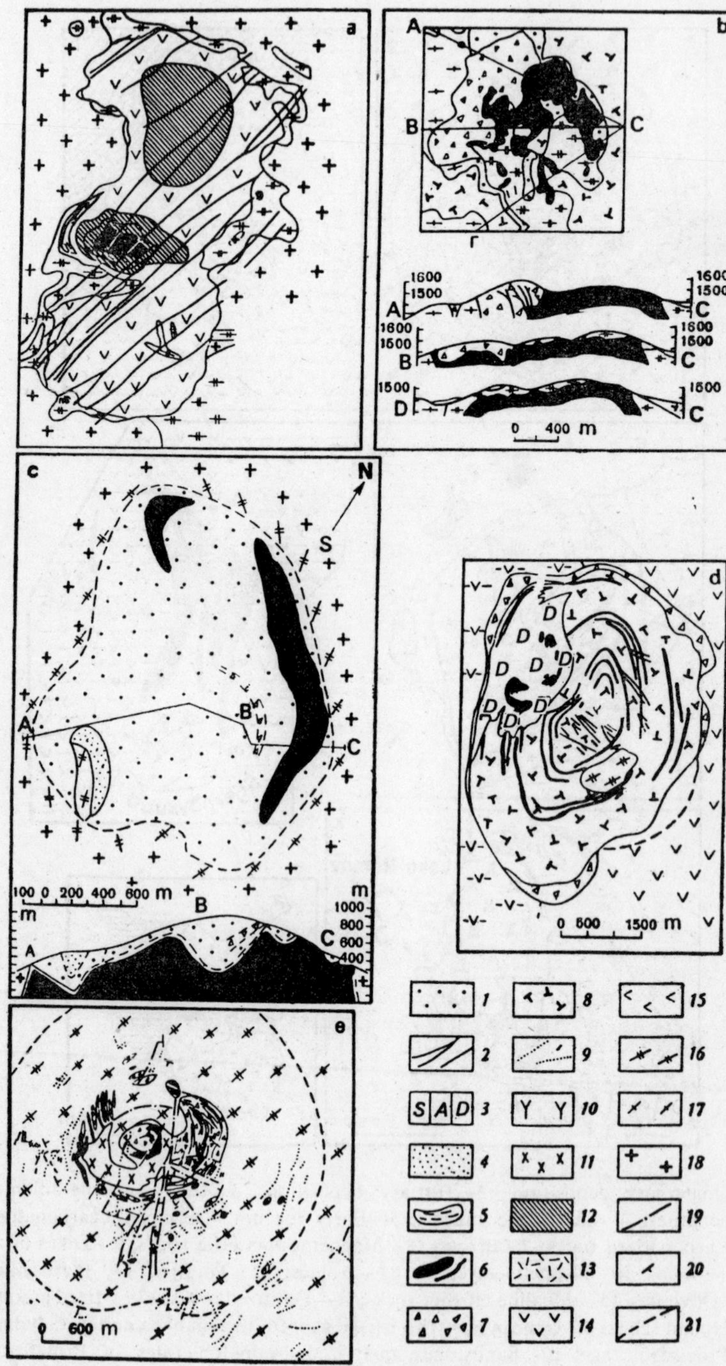
a
b
A
B
C
Г
1600
1500
D
0 400 m
c
N
S
100 0 200 400 600 m
m
1000
800
600
400
d
D
0 600 1500 m
e
0 600 m
SAD
1
2
3
4
5
6
7
8
9
10
11
12
13
14
15
16
17
18
19
20
21

Fig. 7.

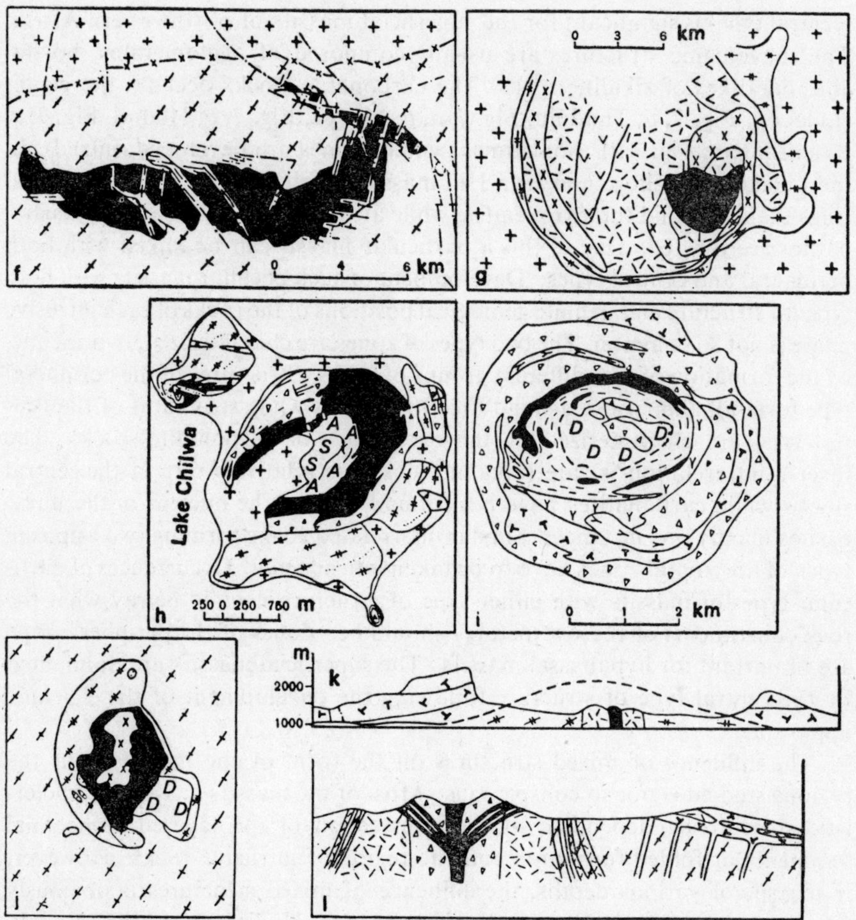

Fig. 7. Distribution of alkaline ultrabasic rocks and carbonatites in massifs of Africa.

a—Palabora (Russel et al., 1954); b—Mbeya (Fick and van der Heyde, 1959); c—Mrima (Coetzee and Edwards, 1959); d—Hudini (Tuttle, Gittins et al., 1967); e—Tundulu (Garson, 1962); f—Kaluve (Bailey, 1960); g—Spitzkop (Strauss and Truter, 1951a); h—Chilwa (Garson and Smith, 1958); i—Kruidfontein (Tuttle, Gittins et al., 1967); j—Lueshe (Meyen and Bethune 1960); k—Napak (King, 1949); l—Rangwa (McCall, 1958). 1—Quaternary and weathered rocks; 2—Dolerite dikes; 3—Late carbonatites (*S*—Sideritic; *A*—Ankeritic, *D*—Ankerite-dolomitic); 4—Carbonatized and apatitized rocks; 5—Dolomitized (?) carbonatite; 6—Early (not determined) carbonatites; 7—Breccia; 8—Effusive rocks; 9—Dikes of alkaline rocks; 10—Rhyolites; 11—Alkaline and nepheline syenites; 12—Micatized rocks; 13—Ijolites, meltigites; 14—Pyroxenites; 15—Diorite, theralite; 16—Fenites; 17—Schists and gneisses; 18—Granites; 19—Faults; 20—Dip and strike; 21—Boundary of carbonatite rocks.

Conversely, the development of massifs from the periphery to the center (central type) is significant for the superficial massifs of northwestern Africa. The subvolcanic structures are usually composed of agglomerates, bosses, and ring dikes of alkaline rocks. The carbonatite stocks occur at the center (Lulekop, Fig. 7, *a*; Tundulu, Fig. 7, *a*, *b*; Mbeya, Fig. 7, *b*; Hudini, Fig. 7, *d*; Kruidfontein, Fig. 7, *i*). Sometimes twinned zones are developed (mixed). In the Lulekop Spitzkop, and Iron Hill massifs alkaline rocks form peripheral rings that surround the pyroxenites, while at the center of the massifs carbonatites are formed. Due to this a particular massif can be linked with both peripheral and central types. Development of such peculiar massifs with both types of structure and definite geological positions of the rocks of each intrusive phase is not so common. The two types of zones are characterized, in principle, by the formation of two different groups of rocks. Structures of the peripheral type form alkaline rocks around the ultrabasites while structures of the central type are characterized by the occurrence of carbonatite stocks. The reverse interrelation is rare (alkaline rocks are relatively rare at the central stocks while carbonatites have been found around the nucleus of the ultrabasites in only one instance). Similar interrelated rocks forming two opposite types of horizontal zones have to be taken into account. Occurrences of particular types of massifs with either type of structure usually betray what the rock constituents of these structures should be. Zones of the peripheral type are important for hypabyssal massifs. The superficial massifs are dominated by the central type of structure following the development of the volcanic apparatus.

The influence of mixed structures on the form of the intrusives in the regions studied is not so conspicuous. Most of the massifs possess characteristic structures independent of the intersection of the layered monoclinal sediments or folded formation and the region of intrusive rocks. However, in massifs of various depths, the influence of mixed structures is obviously different. In volcanic stocks (Longui, Homa, Hudini, Muambe, Napak, Toror), rings and arclike bodies cut across the mixed rocks independent of the nature of their structure. The structural setup of most of the massifs has not been studied elaborately enough to justify a generalization. But from the literature, from the structure of the massifs of Siberia and America and from the present study (in the Kola Peninsula) it may be supposed that their forms under deep-seated conditions depend on the structures of the mixed region. The characteristic distribution of individual rocks within the general structure and the influence of mixed structures on their characters has not been fully investigated. It may be mentioned here that along with the oval-shaped massifs (western Africa), bodies of ultrabasic rocks and lenticular or even dikelike carbonatites are known to occur (Kazakhstan, Kovdor, Pesochnyi, Kaluwe, Zangu). In some of the massifs it was observed that the forms and distribution of rocks depend on local structures of the mixed region. Formations of independent structures around these massifs were frequent. In the Kola Peninsula massifs with their own characteristic appearance, i.e. the development of secondary dome-shaped, pseudoplicated structures in the metamorphic piles around the complex massifs are noted. Similarly, in Kovdor the massifs cut through the folded masses of biotiteplagioclase gneisses and granite-gneisses of the White Sea and run northwest. But nearer the massifs these folded masses are more resistant in nature. The northwestern extension of the gneisses ends in the northwestern part of the massif. At the western margin the gneisses run north-south and in the south they encircle the massifs. In the north and west the gneisses dip below the massifs. In the east their dip directions change from west (in the north) to southeast (in the south). In the south they form domes and dip toward the south away from the massifs (Fig. 6, *a*). The general structure of the gneisses is a dome overturned toward the west-northwest. The formation of the gneissic structure is related to the presence of numerous fractures, rough contacts, and broken gneisses around the massifs. Most of these fractures are filled in with ijolite dikes, nephelinite, alkaline and nepheline syenites, and metasomatic veinlets.

Around Vuoriyarvi, within the gneisses and migmatites of the White Sea Series (confined to the northwestern folds dipping toward the south), banding of rocks exerts resistance (Fig. 6, *b*). In the north the gneisses occupy larger areas and surround the massifs dipping below them. In the west and southwest they surround the massifs on the southern side. The gneisses are scattered and intersected by numerous linear zones of weak tectonic deformations or by dikes of alkaline rocks and metasomatic plagioclase-pyroxene veins near all the contacts. Uplift and splitting of the gneisses are observed at the contacts of the massifs of the Khabozerpski group (Afrikanda, Ozernaya Varaka), but in these places they were not studied in detail due to lack of information.

The most convincing example of the formation of an individual massif with localized structures is observed in Maimecha-Kotui Province. Here the whole series of intrusives cut through the ferruginous carbonate bodies of Cambrian-Riphean age and appear at the center of the anticlinal dome (Fig. 5). Fractures around the massifs were not observed (Sheinmann et al., 1961; Butakova and Egorov, 1962; Egorov and Surina, 1961). This accounts for the plasticity of the sediments in the region. Formation of the dome may be related only to the inner massifs as the relatively younger folds to the north of the Silurina Platform are of Proterozoic age (Doriterian), while the Cambrian Riphean sediments are horizontal in nature. Resistance associated with the banding of the metamorphic rocks is observed in the individual massifs of Africa (Toror, Mbeya, Rangwa, Napak, Fig. 7), Jacupiranga (Fig. 8, *d*), and possibly Oka. The foliation plane in the upper part of the kyanite gneisses (relatively deep) of the western border of the Lueshe stock has been replaced by migmatite (Fig. 7, *k*). It is less probable that the formation of kyanite is related to the process of fenitization (Meyer and Bethune, 1958, 1960) as the

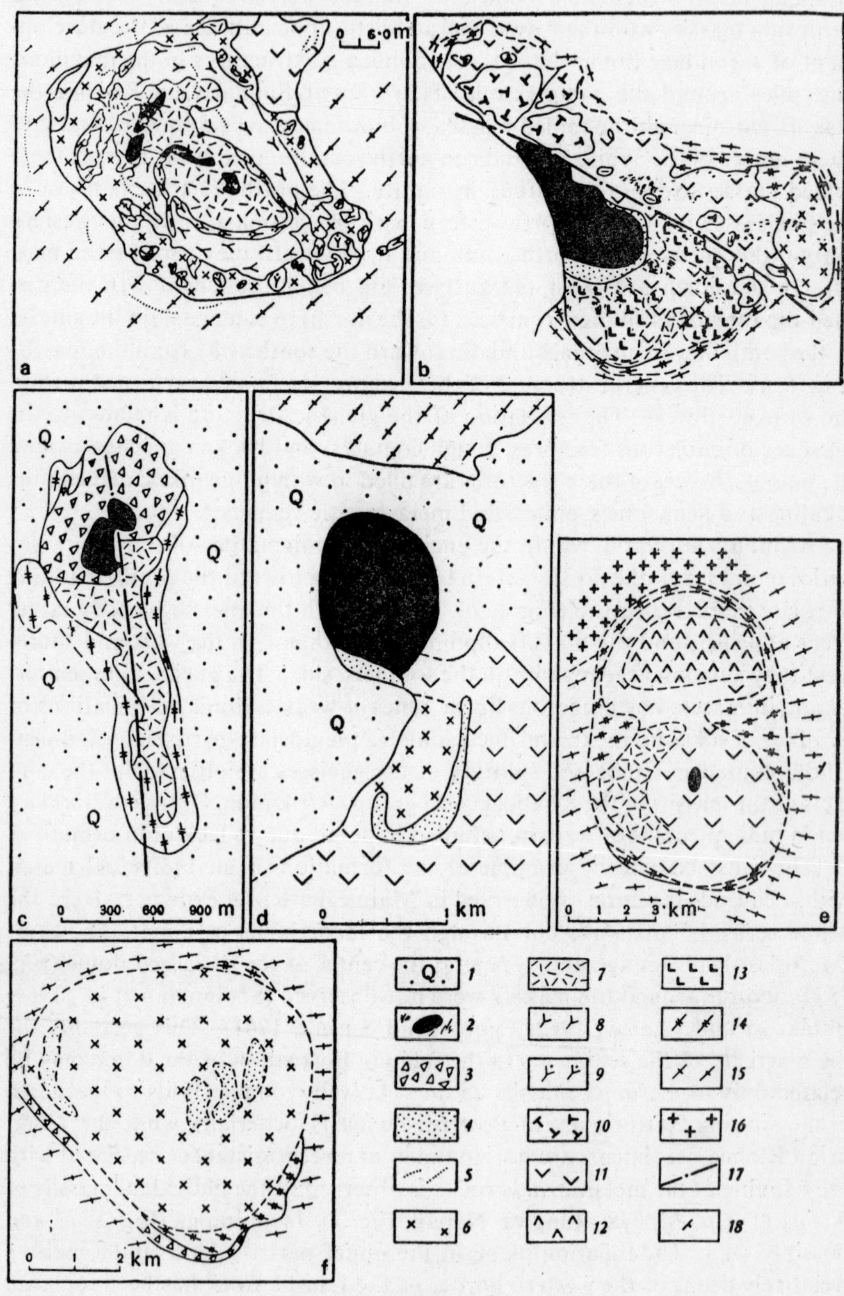
0 60m
a
b
Q
c 0 300 600 900 m
d 0 1 km
e 0 1 2 3 km
f 0 1 2 km
1
2
3
4
5
6
7
8
9
10
11
12
13
14
15
16
17
18

Fig. 8.

argillaceous minerals (sillimanite, spinel, corundum) are everywhere found to have disappeared at the beginning of the process. Formation of local dome structures is typical for complex massifs of hypabyssal facies. But they are either poorly developed or not observed in association with massifs of superficial nature. Relatively deep-seated massifs traversing the folds without any marked influence on them are quite common. The massifs of Magnet Cove cut through the folded mountain approximately east-west without bringing any change in the composition of the rocks (Erickson and Blade, 1963). The East African massifs (Muambe, Nkombwa, Mbeya and others) that occur within the ancient gneisses have no influence on their structure (Fig. 7). However, frequent occurrences of well-formed concentric ring-dikes around the carbonatite bosses are found in Tundulu, Kangankunde, Mwambuto, Toror, and Lake Chilwa, etc. These show the frequent association of carbonatites with the circular pattern of tectonic deformations.

Forms and structures of the superficial massifs depend very little on the structures of the mixed region. But in hypabyssal massifs of dome-shaped anticlines, the forms and distribution of characteristic rock types show some dependence on the mixed structures. The Vuoriyarvi and Kovdor massifs show some affiliation to the direction of mixed structures. One of the Siberian massifs shows its own stretched asymmetric body oriented parallel to the general trend of the mixed anticlinorium (Frolov et al., 1969). The carbonatites in them form on the flanks of the linearly tapered system of bodies (Fig. 5, *g*). Only a few adjoining massifs show some rounded forms even when they run in the same direction (Fig. 5, *f*). Several massifs in Kazakhstan show dike-like bodies confined within the zone of regional tectonic deformation (Letnikov and Zagumennova, 1962; Letnikov, 1966). Well-known deep-seated massifs are cited as examples. They form rounded bodies. Their formation does not depend on the mixed structures (Magnet Cove, Jacupiranga, Grönnedal-Ika and others). Numerous examples of these are found in Maimecha-Kotui Province, where one of the massifs, the Gulinskii (fractured body), has the structure of mixed layered sediments.

The structure, form and degree of dependence of the formation of massifs on the mixed region differ for massifs of different regions and different erosional surfaces. The dependence of structures on erosional surfaces may be

Fig. 8. Distribution of alkaline ultrabasic rocks and carbonatites in North and South American massifs.

a—Magnet Cove (Erickson and Blade, 1963); b—Iron Hill (Temple and Grogan, 1965); c—Sibruk Lake (Parsons, 1961); d—Tapira (Heinrich, 1967); e—Jacupiranga (Melcher, 1954); f—Serrote (Tuttle et al., 1967). 1—Weathered rocks; 2—Carbonatites; 3—Breccia; 4—Carbonatized rocks; 5—Dikes of alkaline rocks; 6—Nepheline syenites; 7—Ijolites; 8—Layered trachytes; 9—Phonolites; 10—Alkaline effusives; 11—Pyroxenites; 12—Olivinites, peridotites; 13—Melilitic rocks; 14—Fenitized rocks; 15—Mixed gneisses and schists; 16—Granites; 17—Faults; 18—Dip and strike.

considered individually and differs vertically. Vertical zoning of the carbonatite massifs is an indication of and one of the principal reasons for the different structures and compositions of the massifs. This is apparent if we compare the deeply-eroded ancient massifs with the younger ones. Multiphase massifs of these types are always found to contain several rocks formed in definite sequence. But in different massifs they are formed in different ways. Volcanic veins as a rule show simpler construction and contain a smaller number of silicate rocks, while in deep-seated massifs there is a larger number of rock types. In a single region individual massifs may be characterized by different deep-seated origins and a different number of intrusive phases. In this regard mention may be made of the Baltic and African provinces where multiphase and most complex massifs (Kovdor, Palabora, Spitzkop) as well as the simpler ones are associated with the series of small bodies and alkaline stocks and carbonatites (Tuimis, Sallanlatva, Napak, Kruidfontein, Nkombwa).

CHARACTERISTICS OF THE PRINCIPAL ROCK TYPES

Among the older rocks olivinites and dunites are found to occur in most massifs. Pyroxenites are also formed, and different complex alkaline rocks are found to occur along with them in the following sequences: turjaite, ijolite, melteigite, nepheline and alkaline syenites. Closely related in space, rocks of the carbonatite series, e.g. magnetite-forsterite, picrite-alnöite, damkjernite, independent carbonates and numerous alkaline rocks, are found to occur within a single stage. Alkaline gabbroids are found in some massifs but the age of these rocks is not clear. For example, trachytes in the Magnet Cove massif are considered much older than pyroxenites while alkaline rocks are much younger than trachytes (sodalitic and porphyritic).

Olivinites

Olivinites, peridotites, or dunites are formed at the first intrusive phase and are observed characteristically in the massifs of hypabyssal facies; they are rare in superficial type. Relicts of micaceous olivinites are found in alkaline lavas of the Toro-Ankole and Birunga-Bufumbira (Holmes and Harwood, 1932; Turner and Verhoogen, 1961) regions and in the Gulinskii massif (formed relatively at shallow depth, which is evidenced by their wider development near the alkaline effusives). Dunites form large bodies (larger than 500 km^2 at the present level of erosion, and geophysically larger than 2,000 km^2) of unknown thickness. According to Butakova (1962) these dunites develop fractured bodies. Similar gigantic dunite bodies accompanying thick ultrabasic effusive piles, as observed in the above region, are not found in other places. Olivinites are well known in most of the massifs of Maimecha-Kotui and Karelo-Kola Provinces (Afanaseev, 1940; Motichko, 1958; Butakova and

Egorov, 1962; Kukharenko et al., 1965). Ninety per cent of them are found in Lesnaya Varaka. In Kovdor and Bor-Uryakh they form a thick central nucleus. Xenoliths of olivinites (Figs. 6, 7) occur in the massifs of Vuoriyarvi, Odikhincha, Magan, Kugda, Pesochnyi and Salmagorsk. In Africa dunites are present in the Shawa massif, and in Jacupiranga thick dunite bodies occupying the northern part of the massif occur within pyroxenites and jacupirangites. Smaller bodies of olivinites are found in Stjernöy within the gabbros (Neier, 1964), but their relationships with the carbonatite complex are not clear.

Olivinites always occur characteristically at the center of the massifs. They are most significant in Kovdor and Bor-Uryakh, where they form the central nucleus with the relatively younger rocks on the periphery. It may be suggested that the nucleus or the stretched bodies of olivinites were formed, at least in these massifs, where they are now known as xenoliths (Vuoriyarvi, Sebl-Yavr, Pesochnyi, Salmagorsk and others). The original forms and sizes of such olivinite nuclei are difficult to ascertain because they have undergone intensive crushing and metasomatic changes with the formation of relatively younger rocks. There is no doubt that the sizes of the nuclei made ample room for the total development of the massifs. Using the geochemical-indicator method, Borodin suggested olivinites are heterogenic rocks, i.e. the primary olivinites rich in Cr and Ni (Kovdor, Lesnaya Varaka, Gulinskii, Bor-Uryakh and in other massifs) and the secondary olivinites devoid of these elements (Afrikanda). Considering the distinct geochemical specification and combining the general structures of the complex massifs of the earlier olivinites, Borodin (1965a) suggested that the yare aligned in space, but not genetically, with relatively older complex ultrabasic intrusives. Characteristically this type of olivinites, differing from other types of rocks, is exemplified in the Aldan massif where platinum and chromite-rich ultrabasites (dunites) of Proterozoic age are surrounded by alkaline bodies (sometimes ringlike, Inagli) of Mesozoic age. For lack of detailed research the problem of the absolute ages of the olivinites remains unsolved. Considering the spatial extension of the olivinites toward the carbonatite massifs of Kola and Maimecha-Kotui provinces, olivinites may be placed within the general rock sequence of these massifs, although their exact ages remain to be assigned. But this does not rule out the possibility of correlating relatively older alkaline rocks with the ultrabasites and basites (Bushveld Complex, Inagli and others), though the former (older alkaline rocks) are genetically unrelated to the latter.

Kukharenko (1958) suggested that the complex massifs of the first stage are developed as fractured intrusives. The elongated forms of the olivinite bodies in Lesnaya Varaka, Kovdor, and Pesochnyi definitely confirm this idea, while a concrete example is found in the Gulinskii massif. At the contacts, olivinitc bodies dip pronouncedly, and this resembles flattened stocks differing from typical fractured intrusions.

About 80–90% of the olivinites are composed of forsterite containing 10% (Vuoriyarvi, Lesnaya Varaka) to 15–17% (Salmagorsk, Gulinskii) fayalite molecules, indicating that these rocks differ from the ferrodunite-peridotites of gabbro-peridotitic formations of South Africa and Malaysia (Schneiderhöhn, 1941) but resemble the magnesium-rich dunites of Ural (Vorob'eva, 1962; Zavaritskii, 1956; Kuznetsov, 1956). The characteristic inclusion in olivinites is titanomagnetite (from 5% in Kovdor to 20–30% in Lesnaya Varaka and other massifs. Sometimes sideritic structures, small individual veins and rich impregnated zones of titanomagnetite (TiO_2 greater than 11%) occur as inclusions in olivinites. The impregnated zone often shows uneven banding oriented parallel to the contacts of the intrusions. In almost all the massifs of the Kola region olivinites contain unequal proportions of perovskitic impregnations that extend toward the titanomagnetite body and micaceous zone. Kukharenko et al. (1965) considered perovskite a typical mineral of olivinites, while Borodin (1963a) related it to the presence of alkali metasomatism in olivinites. The presence of late perovskite is observed in many cases, but at the contacts of perovskite-rich rocks with alkaline dikes it is replaced by sphene (Vuoriyarvi, Kovdor). In the olivinites of the Kola region only magnetites are known. Chromites (>15%) are widely distributed in the dunites of Maimecha-Kotui Province (Butakova and Egorov, 1962). Chromite nodules are also known from the Bor-Uryakh massif. They were formed by primary magmatic crystallization (Lapen and Zhabin, 1966). The occurrence of chromite resembles that in carbonatite massifs associated with dunite-peridotite of geosynclinal gabbro-peridotitic formation (Mg-Pt-dunite subformations of Ural, Kuznetzsov, 1964).

Intrusive olivinites occur in most regions. East of Gulinskii thick alkaline ultrabasic lavas are widespread. Within these lavas effusive equivalents of dunites, e.g. picritic porphyrites forming uneven strata in effusive piles of alkaline basaltoids of Arizonian suite (Butakova and Egorov, 1962), occur. Possible Maimecha group can be associated with this group. Formation of effusive picrite-porphyrites is preceded by intrusions of dunites that traverse the metamorphic Arizonian suite of rocks. Finally, it is noted that limited occurrences of picrite-porphyry dikes are genetically related to effusive bodies. Effusive picrite-porphyrites are composed of 80–90% forsterite (the Fe content is equal to that of the forsterite in dunites). But they are intensively replaced by secondary minerals like serpentine, chlorite, etc.

Intrusive olivinites as a rule undergo intensive brecciation and are replaced along the periphery. Micas are widely developed in them. Individual blocks of mica are transformed into a phlogopitic mass and completely surround the margin of olivinites. The thick micaceous zones in Petyaian-Vara Mountain (Vuoriyarvi) contain numerous rounded blocks of olivinites (from 0.1 to 1 m in diameter). In Kovdor, micatization of several stages is developed so widely that in some parts of Nizka Vara Mountain olivinites are almost completely transformed into mica rock. In this region diopside-phlogopite rocks mixed with apatite and calcite are formed around the olivinite nucleus. Melilitization and pyroxenitization took place at the contacts of alkaline rocks with phlogopitized olivinites. Moreover, in almost all the massifs olivinites are subjected to serpentinization. Such veins of serpentine, up to 10 m thick, are widely developed in Lesnaya Varaka. In Kovdor serpentinization is preceded by micatization, and in the serpentinized parts phlogopites are vermiculitized.

Pyroxenites

Pyroxenites are among the principal rocks of the formations in question. These are well known in all the massifs of hypabyssal facies (Kola Peninsula, Maimecha-Kotui Province, Eastern Sayan, Brazil) and in massifs that are transitional to volcanic facies (Shawa, Dorowa, Spitzkop). These rocks are often absent from superficial volcanic apparatus or are seen in the form of rare relics that were subjected to micatization or nephelinization. The massifs of Vuoriyarvi and Afrikanda are 80% composed of pyroxenites. So is one of the massifs or Sayan (Konev, 1960). These rocks are widely distributed in Sebl-Yavr and Jacupiranga. In Kovdor, Kovdozersk, Salmagorsk, Lesnaya Varaka, Gulinskii, and Sayan they constitute large bodies. Smaller bodies of xenoliths and relics of pyroxenites are well known in Ozernaya Varaka, Sallanlatva, Fen, Rocky Boy, and some massifs of Africa (Lalekek, Spitskop, Dorowa, etc.). Pyroxenites usually form independent circular bodies (in plan) that pass through the mixed structures. Pyroxenites have wider distribution and larger dimensions than the olivinites and often occur as hypabyssal complex massifs with alkaline rocks confined to the peripheral zones. Location and sizes of the pyroxenite bodies depend on the forms and sizes of the olivinites and on younger alkaline rocks. Pyroxenites that intruded after the olivinites occur as independent intrusive bodies (Afrikanda, Vuoriyarvi, Iron Hill and other massifs) or are interrupted in the circular zones around the olivinite nucleus (Kovdor, Lesnaya Varaka). Contact between olivinites and pyroxenites is intrusive by nature. But in Kugda and Gulinskii dunites in the peripheral zones are enriched with pyroxenes and contain schleiepen of isolated peridotites and pyroxenites (Goldburg et al., 1961; Butakova and Egorov, 1962), indicating the possibility that both types of rock were formed at the beginning of a single intrusive phase.

Pyroxenite bodies usually form zones. Peripheral zones of these rocks are fine-grained and sometimes show a trachytic texture with orientation of the pyroxene crystals parallel to the contacts of the massifs (Vuoriyarvi, Afrikanda, Lesnaya Varaka). The central part of the pyroxenite bodies is relatively coarse-grained. The grain size usually varies between 3 and 5 cm and sometimes between 10 and 15 cm. Compositions of primary unaltered pyroxenites are comparatively stable and constant in nature. About 80–90% of them are composed of augite-diopside assemblages. Diopside constitutes about 70–90%, hedenbergite up to 20%, and aegirine-augite up to 12–15%. The proportions of alkali, alumina, and iron in these rocks usually increases with the alkali metasomatism (Borodin, 1958a, b). Titanomagnetite and perovskite are unevenly distributed in pyroxenites. They form either zones of impregnation or small veins. Volotovskaya (1958, 1959, 1960) and Kukharenko et al. (1965) placed both of them in the group of primary minerals of pyroxenites, but Borodin (1962, 1963a), from his study of Vuoriyarvi and Afrikanda massifs, showed the presence of perovskite in the zone of micatization of pyroxenites and associated the presence of perovskite with the alkali metasomatism. The occurrence of perovskite as fine-grained aggregates with titanomagnetite (late) and its association with the formation of late micas are often noted along the periphery of pyroxenite. This supports the generalization regarding the genesis of perovskite.

The extraordinary characters of the secondary processes coincide with micatization of pyroxenites. In all the important massifs (Vuoriyarvi, Kovdor, Sebl-Yavr, Fen, Spitzkop, Magnet Cove and others) micas are always present in pyroxenites, and in some places they constitute up to 30–40%. Locally the rocks may undergo massive micatization. Micatization is usually confined to the central parts of the massifs, while the changes in the peripheral zones are negligible. Mica replaces pyroxenes marginally and develops to large poikiloblastic sizes of 20–30 cm. Besides the massive micatization, sharp linear veins of mica are found in more or less equally developed rocks and pyroxenites. Here the banding in mica 0.8–1 m (Vuoriyarvi) thick is usually oriented parallel to the contacts.

Besides micatization, constant development of multistage recrystallization is also seen in pyroxenites which, irrespective of their coarse or medium grain size (crystals of pyroxene up to 10–20 cm), form veins or veinlets within the fine-grained equivalents. In the peripheral zone of several pyroxenite massifs nephelinization took place. This is related to apatitization, briefly described below.

Ijolites

Nepheline-pyroxenite rocks are most important in the region in question and are present in most of the massifs. Their distribution, development, and morphology depend on the depths of the erosional surfaces. Ijolites occur as series of thin dikes or lava flows in poorly eroded subvolvances with stretched volcanic cones or in volcanic veins. Ijolites are either absent or rarely form dikes or lava flows in recent volcanoes of northeastern Africa, e.g. Lengan, Kerimasi, Kalyango, and in the stretched volcanoes of Tertiary and Mesozoic origin of Kaiserstühl. Changes in the composition of the rocks take place with the depth of the erosional surfaces and the exposure of all the deep-seated stages of the massifs. Dikes and stocks of ijolites are reported from the Miocene volcanoes, e.g. Kizingiri. In Chilwa, along with the formation of volcanic veins but without independent effusive facies, nepheline-bearing rocks are found in many places. Ijolites are found in the massifs of hypabyssal facies of all places without showing any volcanic influence. These are most important in: South Africa—Spitzkop, Lulekek, Dorwa; Baltic Shield—Kovdor, Sallanlatva, Kovdozero, Ozernaya Varaka; Siberia—Gulinskii, Odikhincha, Kugda and in other massifs; North and South America—Magnet Cove, Iron Hill, Tapira, Jacupiranga. Nepheline-pyroxenite rocks in different massifs show compositional variation to urtites or jacupirangites. The mode of occurrence of these rocks is also different. They form lava flows (in volcanoes), dikes, stocks, rings around ultrabasites, or independent massifs that are often composed of fenites or ultrabasites (Borodin, 1958a, b, 1959, 1960; Bostakova, 1959; Eckermann, 1948a, b, c, 1950, 1960; Gittins, 1961). Borodin divided the nepheline-pyroxenitic rocks into two groups: metasomatic and intrusive. Morphologically they constitute four types of structure:

1. Circular (arc formation) zones around the ultrabasites;
2. Independent massifs;
3. Dikes;
4. Effusive capping and flows.

The last type is negligibly developed in East Africa and has not been studied in detail, so it is not discussed below.

Ring zones of ijolites are characteristic of massifs of hypabyssal facies containing an ultrabasic nucleus (Kola Peninsula, Maimecha-Kotui province, Brazil). In volcanic formations of superficial nature these rocks are either absent or are insignificant. A complete ring (thickness 100–1000 m) of ijolite-melilite rocks surrounds the ultrabasic nucleus of the Kovdor massif (Fig. 6, *a*). In Pesochni (Fig. 6, *h*) pyroxenites occur in the central part (less than 25% of the area). The Ozernaya Varaka massifs comprise nepheline-pyroxenite rocks (Afanasev, 1939a, 1940) and the primary pyroxenites are well known in the form of nephelinized and apatitized xenoliths (Fig. 6, *d*). The Odikhincha and Magan (Fig. 5, *b*, *d*) massifs are entirely composed of ijolites. Arclike bodies of nepheline-pyroxenite rocks (thickness up to 500 m) occur in the western and northwestern part of Vuoriyarvi (Fig. 6, b). The interrupted arclike bodies of ijolite-melilite occur along the periphery of the ultrabasites in Afrikanda, Sebl-Yavr, Spitzkop and Jacupiranga, comprising jacupirangites and probably also nephelinized pyroxenites (Hussak, 1894b; Ödman, 1952). In Iron Hill and Magnet Cove ijolitic bodies occur within the pyroxenites (Larsen, 1942; Erickson and Blade, 1963), while in Alnö they occur within the mixed fenites (Eckermann, 1948a, b).

Nepheline-pyroxenitic rocks of the ring zones that form dikes and stocks differ from similar types of rocks not only in their general morphology but also in the structure and composition (Borodin, 1958a, b, 1966b; Lapin, 1963). These rocks in the rings are rarely consistent in composition (Kovdor) and cannot easily be isolated from the contact of pyroxenites. At the contacts, pyroxenites are recrystallized, apatitized, and amphibolitized. The thickness of the apatitized zones in Vuoriyarvi is more than 200 m, while in Afrikanda it is about 50–70 m. In Ozernaya Varaka and Pesochnyi apatite and amphiboles are found as xenoliths in pyroxenites. Similar apatitization is also noticed in East Sayan as well as in Spitzkop, Lulekek, and Jacupiranga. In pyroxenites that occur in close proximity to the contacts of ijolite veins accumulation of nepheline megacrysts has taken place and aegirine has developed at the periphery. The upper zones of pyroxenites are brecciated and cemented together with ijolites or ijolite-urtites. Such breccias are known to occur in the Kola Peninsula (Kovdor, Vuoriyarvi, Sebl-Yavr, Pesochnyi and others). Breccias of Ozernaya Varaka are placed with agmatites (Kukharenko et al., 1965). Fragments of pyroxenites in ijolites are angular in shape but often form a flattened system of shorter bands and lenses (banded taxitic configuration: ijolites-nephelinized pyroxenites are found in almost all the massifs containing these rocks). An appreciable part of the flattened accumulation of pyroxenes shows relics of pyroxenites and contains relics of perovskite. Banding is parallel to the contacts of ijolites.

Ring zones of nepheline pyroxenitic rocks, formed by independent nephelinization of the pyroxenites, are probably not known in all the massifs but they may be formed by intrusions. The rings of ijolites in Kovdor encircle the whole massif. Pyroxenites are absent from the northern and western boundaries and ijolites here differ from them by the presence of consistent thin layers, the presence of trachytoids, and uniform mineral assemblages. In Sayan ijolites and melteigites with schorlomites (of consistent composition and structure) form thick independent bodies near the northwestern part, containing relics of nephelinized and micatized pyroxenites with perovskite. Nephelinization that develops along the contacts of complex massifs invades not only the pyroxenites but also the fenites (Eckermann, 1948b, c, 1950, 1961; Gittins, 1961). In the Kola Peninsula and in Scandinavia melanocratic nepheline-pyroxenite rocks (often with cancrinite and feldspar) form marginal zones (up to 200–400 m thick) along the upper contacts of ijolites. In Sayan nepheline-pyroxenite rocks (containing albite, biotite, and calcite) are fenitized to quartz-sericite schists with the formation of sharp rhythmic bands (with relics of primary layers). In the fenitized schists porphyroblasts and veins of nepheline are formed along the schistosity. Nepheline-pyroxenite rocks formed by the process of nephelinization never show brecciated or gneissic textures. They are converted into massifs of equigranular rocks similar in structure and composition to intrusive ijolites but containing relics of minerals. These ijolites were intruded into the diabases at the northwestern contact of Sallanlatva (in a zone more than 400 m thick) and contain feldspar, calcite and, in places, abundant pyryhotite. Melanocratic relics rich in pyroxenes are characteristic and important in some parts.

Intrusive nepheline-pyroxenite rocks give rise to two morphological varieties: independent massifs (stocks), and dikes (series of veins). Independent massifs of these rocks are oval in shape (Sallanlatva, Magan, Odikhincha, Rangwa, Dorowa, Tapira and others). The contacts of these massifs dip toward the center (conical intrusion). Consistent composition and uniform distribution of minerals are characteristics of this type of ijolites. Sometimes they show banding defined by melanocratic layers (massifs of Siberia, Sallanlatva, Kovdor) or trachytization (Kovdor, Vuoriyarvi—in places). Ijolites are composed of prismatic pyroxenes and nepheline (20–40%). Mica, garnet, apatite, and sphene are always present as inclusions.

Ijolitic dikes 100–200 m thick and up to 1 km long (Kovdor) are well known in all the massifs. These dikes are located either in the middle or at the border zones of the massifs and cut through the fenites, the rock containing micatized pyroxenes with perovskites, and titanomagnetites, indicating the later origin of these dikes. Their distribution is strictly controlled either by prevalent linear zones (in this area) or radial fracture zones. Primary development of the dikes in the fractured zones is illustrated in the massifs of Vuoriyarvi, where they trend approximately east-west except in the fracture zone, where the prevalent trend is northeast-southwest. Similarly, in Kovdor, ijolitic dikes run primarily north-south and in Ozernaya Varaka, northeast. Radial ijolitic dikes are known to occur in almost all massifs and they are located within the mixed rocks (Tundulu, Mbeya, Oka). In some massifs primary superficial (East African volcanoes, Oka), cone-sheets (sometimes arched) are known to surround the carbonatite stocks (Tundulu, Rangwa, Chilwa, Toror; Fig. 8).

The structure and composition of ijolitic veins are relatively uniform and stable. These rocks are usually medium-grained and sometimes pegmatic in nature (ijolite-pegmatite massif of Afrikanda, Kovdor, Vuoriyarvi, Ozernaya Varaka; Bagdasarov, 1959). Individual veins of ijolite pegmatites show zoning, which is also characteristic of alkaline pegmatites with natrolite and calcite at the center of the zone. Besides nepheline and pyroxene, biotite and schorlomite are always found in ijolitic veins. Primary calcites (Zhabin, 1967), feldspar, wollastonite, cancrinite (Kovdor, Oka) and other minerals are also found to occur in them. Ijolite pegmatites are absent from superficial subvolcanic structures. The dikes are fine-grained and often contain different varieties of porphyrites. This rock group was probably formed at different times and in different phases.

Melilitic rocks

Occurrences of melilitic rocks are significant for the endmembers of differentiated groups of alkaline basaltoids. These rocks are widely distributed in the massifs in question. Genetically they are closely related to ijolite-melteigites. Melilitic rocks are well known in the massifs of Maimecha-Kotui, Odikhincha, Kugda, Gulinskii, Kareliya Kola, Kovdor, Magnet Cove, and

Oka provinces. These rocks are rarely found in the volcanic apparatus of the African massifs. They form independent bodies (Lokupoi), or often are present in the effusive series and dikes. Melilitic basaltoids are well known in the effusive bodies of Gulinskii (Shikhorina, 1959; Butakova and Egorov, 1962; Goldburg et al., 1961; Motycko, 1957).

Melilitic rocks are formed at different times at different levels of different erosional surfaces. Dikes and the effusive capping of the volcanic apparatus in hypabyssal massifs are transformed into thick bodies of holocrystalline rocks. Arclike turjaite bodies are well known in Gulinskii, Kugda, Kovdor, Odikhincha, Salmagorsk, Magnet Cove, Iron Hill. They are confined to the contact zone with ijolites. Small remnants of transformed melilitites were observed in one of the massifs of Eastern Sayan. Alkaline dikes containing melilitites are known to occur in all the provinces and in all the massifs of all facies from all depths.

Melilitic rocks are formed after the formation of ultrabasites. They often occur along with them (Orlova, 1959, 1963; Lapin, 1962; Egorov, 1963, 1966) and contain relics of olivinites and pyroxenites on the periphery. In Iron Hill the melilitic rock uncompahgrite is regarded as older than pyroxenites (Larsen, 1942). The pyroxenites here are characterized by veins of metasomatic phlogopite-pyroxene-rich rocks. These are illustrated in the massifs of Kola and Maimecha-Kotui provinces (separation of intrusive pyroxenites from metasomatic pyroxenitic rocks is difficult: in composition they are very similar). In Afrikanda melilitites contain megacrysts of banded olivinites with perovskites. Bodies of equigranular turjaites are chiefly composed of varying proportions of melilites, phlogopites, and pyroxenes. But in all cases they are found to occur near the olivinites and are always associated with ferruginous forsterites (kovdorites), magnetites, and perovskites. Near the contact with ijolites they are associated with nepheline and schorlomites. Contact zones of turjaites with ultrabasites are relatively sharply outlined with the characteristic presence of micas and melilitization of olivines. But demarcation of contacts between turjaites and ijolites is difficult. The rocks in this zone contain nepheline and melilite and the veins of turjaites and ijolites intersect each other. The close relationship between nephelinitic and melilitic rocks is indicative of similar age. Melilitization outstrips the formation of ijolites or accompanies them (Orlova, 1959; Lapin, 1962; Egorov, 1966). At the southwestern border of the Kovdor massif, within the ijolitic ring zones, angular xenoliths of apomelilitic rocks (amphibole-monticellite-garnet) have been reported from some open quarries. The ijolites here show uniform distribution of large brown phlogopites, which are indicative of melilitites but not of ijolites. The intrusive relation of turjaites with ijolites here as well as in other massifs indicates that ijolites are later in origin than melilitic rocks.

Melilitic rocks are usually either massive or banded, with alternation of melanocratic and leucocratic layers. Their textures often show a reaction relation, e.g. mica replaces pyroxene and forsterite, magnetite replaces garnet, etc. At the bottom layer dark-colored minerals disappear, giving rise to leucocratic medium and coarse-grained melilitites. Melilitites are similar to akermanites in composition and contain 10–35% melilite. They also contain a small proportion of gelatinous material (Zlatkind, 1945; Kupletski, 1948; Orlova and Kukharenko, 1962). Melilitic rocks are more alkaline in the form of dikes, as in Tura Bay (Belyankin et al., 1924; Belyankin and Vlodavatz, 1932). The unstable composition of melilites is responsible for the complete replacement of these rocks (Western Sayan) or the formation of different rocks from them (Kovdor), such as garnet-amphibolitic, amphibole-monticellitic, micaceous and wollastonitic rocks, whose formation is related to alkali metasomatism at contacts under the influence of carbonatites (Kukharenko et al., 1965). Melilites in dikes are sometimes completely replaced by aggregates of phlogopites, cebollites, and calcites (Kovdor, Vuoriyarvi).

In recent years there has been much discussion of the problem of the origin of melilitic rocks. Most authors (Orlova, 1959, 1963; Kukharenko et al., 1965; Lapin, 1962) believe they were formed due to metasomatism under the influence of an alkaline solution associated with ijolites. But the constant development of many dikes and effusives in many African (Toro-Ankole: Holmes and Harwood, 1937; Bowen, 1938; Holmes, 1950; Elgon: Davies, 1952; Searle, 1952; Rangwa: McCall, 1958, 1959, 1963) and Gulinskii massifs (Butakova, 1956, 1958; Goldburg et al., 1961; Butakova and Egorov, 1962) under primary magmatic conditions is a bit doubtful. Egorov (1963, 1966) suggested magmatic origin for the melilitic rocks of Maimecha-Kotui province, where there is evidence of magmatic or metasomatic replacement of the ultrabasites.

Alkaline gabbroids

Rocks of this group are less important than ultrabasites and nepheline syenites in the massifs in question, but they play an important role in other massifs. Alkaline gabbroids are less common in complex massifs than they should be. Sheinmann (Sheinmann et al., 1961) and Kukharenko (1966) show that alkaline gabbroids are absent from the composition of the massifs of older shields but present in the massifs of folded regions. This phenomenon is illustrated in the massifs of Stjernöy, Magnet Cove, Kaiserstühl, and Iron Hill, where alkaline gabbroids are found in the massifs. Most of the carbonatite massifs occurring in the folded region (massifs of Siberia, Yenisei Mountain Ridge, Sikhote Alin Range) and the massifs of Mountain Pass and the Chilwa group (where pulaskites are present) situated within the ancient platforms are characteristically devoid of these minerals. A few nepheline-syenitic massifs of Kuznetzski-Ala-Tau and Tuva contain gabbroids, but they are quite barren of carbonatites. In such cases alkaline gabbroids in carbonatite massifs rarely depend on the spatial disposition of the latter. The massifs in which the carbonatites are associated with gabbroids are characterized by the constant occurrence of pyroxenites and nepheline syenites (Stjernöy, Rocky Boy, Iron Hill, Magnet Cove).

Among the alkaline gabbroids of the massifs in question pulaskites, essexites, theralites, tephrites, and also shonkinites, monzonites, and their effusive equivalents are well known. These rocks occur in different erosional surfaces under hypabyssal conditions (Stjernöy, Rocky Boy) to superficially (Kaiserstühl) and are associated with intrusive bodies and lavas or tuffs. In Kaiserstühl the yare chiefly composed of plagioclase, orthoclase, and pyroxene with forsterite, apatite, magnetite, leucite, nepheline, sodalite (Wimmenauer, 1959). In the massifs of the Chilwa series Palula, Kapiri, Nsengwa, Nailuwa and others) they contain microcline, pyroxene, and biotite (syenites). Unstable composition and a tendency to transform into syenites and quartz syenites are characteristics of shonkinites of Mountain Pass (Olson et al., 1954). They are very similar in composition to melanocratic syenites. Their unstable composition (from shonkinite to granite) and the preponderance of smoky quartz in shonkinites allies them with fenites, as does the presence of quartz with alkali amphibole and pyroxene in the rocks of Mountain Pass. But no genetic relationship between carbonatite veins and granitoids obtains in this case.

In Stjernöy there are some well-known occurrences of genetically related gabbroids with carbonatites and nepheline syenites. The carbonatites form independent bodies and banded carbonatized zones in schistose and amphibolitized gabbro (Heier, 1964). Possibly gabbroids (their ages are not known) do not belong to the carbonatite complex but to the magmatic group of Caledonian geosynclinal facies and are genetically not related to carbonatites and alkaline rocks (spatially associated). It is not possible to establish a genetic relationship between carbonatites and typical gabbroids, but the rocks that are regarded as alkaline gabbroids may be of heterogeneous origin.

Typical alkaline basaltoids (effusives) are known from Gulinskii, but here they are not related to the normal series of basaltoids (Butakova and Egorova, 1962). Rocks regarded as gabbroids formed at early intrusive or effusive phases and consequently changed into alkaline and nepheline syenites or their effusive equivalents. In Kaiserstühl essexites were transformed into phonolites (melanocratic sodalite syenite) and tuffaceous lavas of leucite, haüyne, tephrites and other rocks. Young ring dikes and stocks of nepheline and alkaline syenites are formed along the periphery of pulaskites in the massifs of Chilwa series and Magnet Cove.

Nepheline-cancrinite and alkaline syenites

Even in recent times feldspathic syenites were not considered as important rocks for complex massifs. Sheinmann (Sheinmann et al., 1961), Kukharenko (Kukharenko et al., 1965) and Kuznetzsov (1964) made divisions between alkaline ultrabasic and nepheline-syenite intrusives, although the relation between the two types of magmatism remains static in space. Borodin (1963b) observed the close genetic relationship of carbonatites with nepheline syenite and classified the carbonatites into different subformations on the basis of the presence of nepheline syenites. In recent times definite nephelinitic and alkaline syenites have been found in most of the massifs. The influence of the erosional surface is reflected in the distribution of these rocks. In the deep-seated massifs of Kola, Maimecha-Kotui, and North American provinces they are almost devoid of ultrabasites and ijolites. In the massifs of superficial or volcanic origin syenites often prevail.

This influence is well illustrated in the East African group, where the massifs are composed of carbonatites and nepheline (cancrinitic) syenites (Lokupoi, Toro Hills, Tundulu, Homa, Kalkfeld, Lueshe, Kruidfontein). Among these only the rocks of Lueshe are supposed to be of deep-seated origin (Meyer and Bethune, 1960), which is improbable (Kapustin, 1971), while the rest show typical volcanism with the retention of effusives. The question of assuming a genetic relationship between carbonatites and nepheline syenites is difficult because of their double characters. Almost all the carbonatite massifs are accompanied by feldspathoid or alkaline syenites. But typical nepheline-syenite massifs rarely contain carbonatites. Some 10 massifs of this type are known where carbonatites are either absent or weak carbonatization is prevalent (in association with the minerals of late hydrothermal carbonatite veins). Carbonatites are absent from the massifs of North Prebaikal, Kuznetzski-Alatau, Minusinski basement, the southern part of Yenisei Mountain Ridge, South Norway and from serveral African massifs. Large Khinbinski and Lovozovski alkaline intrusives are totally devoid of any carbonatite veins. Attempts were made to explain this fact as the differences in composition of the original magmas of different massifs. But this can hardly be considered for a whole province where carbonatites are known to occur sporadically. In Tuva, of 20–30 alkaline massifs only three contain carbonatites (Harlinski, Dahunurski, and Solbelderski). In the classical Chilwa massifs carbonatites are either well known in the form of small veins (Palula, Kapiri, Nsengwa) or are totally absent. But in the Chilwa Lake region, south and west of the lake, the whole series of thick veins unexpectedly appears (Kangankunde, Songwe, Tundulu). In nepheline syenites carbonatization is always present but typical carbonatites are not always found. Nephelinites and syenites in the carbonatite massifs are usually post-ijolite but pre-carbonatite in age.

Morphologically, syenites of different compositions form individual stocks and thick bodies in relatively deep-seated massifs or in the dike system of volcanic apparatus. The most characteristic features of the syenites are the ring structures and arched dike systems. Stocks of carbonatites are associated with them (Tundulu, Toror Hills). These types of structure in association with central types and bodies of nepheline syenites in many massifs (Chilwa, Nsengwa, Eastern Sayan, Mbeya, Iron Hill, Magnet Cove) surround the periphery of ultrabasites and other earlier rocks. In the hypabyssal massifs of Kola and Siberian provinces dikes of nepheline syenite occur in conformity with the contacts of ultrabasites and ijolites. They are also known in the massifs of Magan, Bor-Uryak, Kovdor, Vuoriyarvi, or in mixed fenites (Odikhincha, Vuoriyarvi, Eastern Sayan, Kovdor). In Vuoriyarvi and Bor-Uryak massifs radial cancrinite dikes, nepheline and aegirine syenites occur.

The structure and composition of syenites of different morphological groups are not identical. Stocks and large syenitic bodies are usually composed of coarse- to medium-grained varieties and trachytoids (foyaites, tinguaites). The composition of the latter tallies fully with this group of rocks. In some massifs (Eastern Sayan, Chilwa, Tuva) gradual transition between nepheline-bearing and nepheline-free rocks takes place. Cancrinite occurs along with nepheline in Lueshe as well as in small dikes of the Kovdor massif. The porphyritic texture of these rocks, their prominent trachytization, and the total absence of nephelinitic relics suggest cancrinite is the primary mineral. However, in one massif of Eastern Sayan the reverse relationship is reported, with occurrence of secondary cancrinite replacing nepheline. Probably the formation of effusive rocks like sodalite and haüyne-phonolite is related to nepheline syenite (Kaiserstühl) and leucitic rocks to syenites (Eastern Rift, Africa), and these are unstable at greater depths.

The compositions of these rocks are quite normal. The principal minerals in them are potash feldspars, nepheline, biotite, hastingsite-kataphorite, augite-diopside, and accessories like apatite, zircon, sphene, and pyrochlore. Nepheline syenites show a miascitic character, but independent dikes and veins of pegmatites nearer to the massifs are endowed with agpaitic accessory minerals, e.g. in Kovdor with eudialite and rinkolite, in Gulinskii with lovozerite and eudialite, and in Sayan with loporite. In fine-grained nepheline-syenite dikes of Vuoriyarvi sphene is replaced by ramsayite, while in Kovdor accessory zircon is replaced by eudialite. Pyroxenes are well-zoned in both cases: the colorless augite nucleus is surrounded by green aegirine. Pegmatitic dikes are younger in age than stocks of alkaline rocks. Possibly differentiation took place, giving rise to an alkaline solution as the ultimate product.

Rocks of the dike facies

The development of the massifs and of the intrusive bodies that accompany the formation of different complex dikes is simultaneous. Dikes of varied composition are well known in all the important massifs. The composition of these dikes also varies with the general variation in the composition of the magmas. The scatter of the dikes indicates the depth of the erosional surface. A few of them are formed in superficial subvolcanic structures (Tundulu, Toror, Napak, Kizingiri, Hudini). Distribution of the dikes controls the general structure of the massifs, but the influence of the structures of the mixed zones is also prominent. In Kovdor, Vuoriyarvi, Sebl-Yavr, and Iron Hill hundreds of dikes are found whose orientation conforms with the general strike of the region (toward the northeast in Vuoriyarvi, north-south in Kovdor, northwest in Iron Hill, etc.).

Complex dikes are divided into three groups on the basis of age:

a) Nepheline-pyroxenite rocks;

b) Nephelinitic, alkaline syenites, and pegmatites;

c) Alnöites, picrites, and damkjernites.

The principal compositions of alkaline dikes are listed above. Due to their close petrological affinities with carbonatites alnöites and damkjernites will be considered together with carbonatites.

Fenites

In the massifs investigated mixed rocks of variable composition were subjected to intensive alkali metasomatism at the contact zones. This is widely reported from the massifs of Scandinavia (Brögger, 1921; Högbom, 1895; Eckermann, 1948b, 1950), Africa (Smith, 1956; Tuttle et al., 1967) and America (Larsen, 1942; Heinrich, 1967) and is known to have occurred in all the massifs of the USSR (Gaidukova et al., 1962; Pozaritzkaya, 1966; Kukharenko et al., 1965). The general principles of this process were studied by Sergeev (1959, 1962, 1963, 1967), while Tikhonenkov (1962) studied only the alkaline massifs. Due to metasomatism the mixed rocks acquire massif-like configuration and their primary structures and textures disappear. But compositionally they resemble alkaline or nepheline syenites and are difficult to isolate from their intrusive equivalents. The thickness of the fenitized aureoles varies between 20 m and 2–5 km. A thinner aureole is characteristic of steep contacts of the massifs but the thickness is greater when intrusive alkaline rocks are believed to be present underneath. In the eastern and northern contacts of Vuoriyarvi the fenitized aureole is about 200 m thick along a stretch of 100 m or more, retaining the primary gneissic structures. But in the southwestern contact zone, where the mixed rocks gently plunge into ijolites, the thickness of the fenitized aureole is more than 2 km. Moreover, the primary gneisses here are converted into massifs of syenitic composition intersected by thick networks (palingenetic) of alkaline and nepheline-syenitic veins. Similarly, in north and northwestern Kovdor the primary gneisses preserve their own characteristic textures right up to the contact, but in the south the textures show variation along a stretch of more than 2 km. Around several massifs of Afrikanda, Ozernaya, and Lesnaya Varaka fenitization is weakly developed and confined to a region 250 km (sic) from the contact, but in all these massifs small veins of alkaline amphibolite, pyroxenes and albites occupy large areas. Fenites are accompanied by subvolcanic stocks and volcanic pipes in Africa (Hudini, Kruidfontein, Lengai, Napak, and others), but their thickness does not exceed 0.5 km.

The thickness of the fenitized aureoles depends mainly on the structure of the region and to a lesser degree on the composition of the intrusive rocks. Fenitization is well developed around the massifs composed of olivinites (Lesnaya Varaka, Shawa), pyroxenites (Afrikanda) and carbonatites (Oldonyo, Lengan, Mazomba, Kizingiri), but it is more prominent around ijolitic massifs or in contacts with them. Differences in the composition of newly formed fenites and other types of rock at the contact zones are not established. In all cases of fenitization there is a gradual change to alkaline amphibolic rocks or to diopside-aegirine-augites, whose formation accompanies the overall process. During the leaching of the dark-colored minerals from the massifs minute veins (1–5 mm thick) of biotite and other dark-colored primary minerals are developed near the contact zone. In this vein rock (chiefly melanocratic biotite gneisses rich in quartz, and quartzites) replacement of quartz by pyroxene takes place and the rocks form cavity-like openings in which pyroxenes are formed after the alkalization of quartz. Melanocratic amphibolites with relics of primary pyrrhotites (Kovdor, Ozernaya Varaka) are the transformed products of monomineralic pyroxenites.

In the long run, albite and potash-feldspar are also formed and the pyroxenites are converted into leucocratic alkali syenites. Sergeev (1967) showed the occurrence of such alumina-rich minerals, e.g. spinel, corundum, or sillimanite, which are replaced by albite or mica in the long run. Lastly, the rocks thus formed cannot be differentiated from their intrusive equivalents and pyroxenites. At the last stage of this process nepheline, cancrinite, sodalite, aegirine, and rare metallic minerals like eudyalite, woehlerite, ramsayite, schorlomite, etc. are formed. In all the massifs the same process of post-fenitization is observed. This involves zeolitization, calcitization, biotitization, and other processes that develop along the late fractures.

Chapter III

ROCKS OF THE CARBONATITE SERIES

In this series we have grouped the rocks that formed later than ijolites and nepheline syenites and are petrologically very similar as well as closely associated in space. The most important feature is the close spatial relation of these rocks with carbonatites and the presence of minerals typical for early carbonatites (forsterite, magnetite, apatite, and calcite). This rock series is again divided into three independent groups:

a) Magnetite-forsterite rocks;
b) Picrite alnöite-damkjernites;
c) Carbonatites proper.

MAGNETITE-FORSTERITE ROCKS

Besides the magnetite-bearing ultrabasites, another type of rock similar in composition to magnetite dunites (magnesium-rich rock type) but later than ijolites and syenites occurs in various massifs. This type of rock is found in Palabora (Russel et al., 1954), and in Magnet Cove (Erickson and Blade, 1963). It is also well known in Arbarastakhe (Stoyalov, 1961) and has been studied in Kovdor and Vuoriyarvi (Hackman, 1925; Reinskaya and Korsakova, 1947, 1963; Kukharenko et al., 1965).

Magnetite-forsterite rocks develop independent geological units that intersect the alkaline and ultrabasic rocks and are closely associated with carbonatites. In Vuoriyarvi these rocks give rise to two morphological types: (i) a linear system of veins running approximately east-west between 0.5 and 2.5 m thick in Neske-Vara and (ii) stocks more than 150 m thick (Tuxta-Vara). These veins intersect the pyroxenites, running for a distance of 400–600 m and at depths greater than 250 m. They are confined to the system of echelon fractures that dip 75 to 85° toward the south. Stocks of magnetite-forsterite rocks (Tuxta-Vara) were originally of ellipsoidal form in the northeastern direction but their forms in this direction have since been changed by the presence of large relics of blocks of early carbonatites (Fig. 6b). In all the blocks of magnetite-forsterite rocks a single compact primary banding (along which the blocks are oriented) is retained, dipping 70–75° toward the northwest in the northeastern part of Tuxta-Vara. The contacts of the other rocks with magnetite-forsterite rocks are sharp and linear and there is no evidence of transitional contact with the mixed pyroxenites.

In Kovdor, magnetite-forsterite rocks form thick bodies and a series of small veinlets that occur at the southwestern contacts of the massifs and run north-south (Fig. 6, *a*, *k*). In the north these rocks are confined to the contact zones, intersect the ijolitic rings, and pass through the mixed fenites. It is now difficult to determine the exact dimension and forms of magnetite-forsterite rocks, because these rocks are intensively carbonatized and are intersected by bodies of picrite porphyrites whose carbonatization also forms calcite-forsterite-magnetite rocks. But the general primary structure of magnetite-forsterite rocks is determined by the presence of ijolites and fenites that are marked by characteristic micatization and forsteritization. Bodies of magnetite-forsterite rocks that run more than 1.5 km with a thickness of 600 m in the south gradually extend north with the plunge toward the south. In the south the top is exposed. This is composed of leucocratic fenite intersecting a large number of north-south trending mica veins and magnetite-forsterite rocks. Individual veins and banded rocks of the main body dip 70–80° toward the east. Most parts of the smaller veinlets of magnetite-forsterite rocks show dike-like forms and sharp linear contacts, while their main body is surrounded by contact zones (100 m in width and up to 200 m in length) composed of breccias (Fig. 9). In these zones fragments of ijolites and fenites are cemented together with fine-grained phlogopite and forsterite masses and contain inclusions of apatite, magnetite, and clinohumite. Individual fragments of ijolites and fenites are surrounded by reaction rims. They are composed of tetraferri-phlogopites, richterites, and calcite. Bodies of magnetite-forsterite rocks show well-developed zones whose peripheral parts are massive fine-grained aggregates of forsterite and apatite. The central parts are rich in magnetite (up to 60%), more coarse-grained and distinctly banded by nature. The orientation of the banding is parallel to the contact of the body and is characterized by alternate magnetite-rich and magnetite-poor layers. Spinel, apatite, and accessory baddeleyite are always present in these rocks, while phlogopite and clinohumite are present at the periphery.

Among all the rocks of complex massifs magnetite-forsterite rocks are closely related to carbonatites in space and are always restricted to definite parts or to one or several similar structures. The linear veins of these rocks in Vuoriyarvi are in structural conformity with the carbonatite bodies. Stocks of these rocks in Tuxta-Vara city are confined to the center of the semicircular carbonatite body (Fig. 6, *b*). In both massifs segregations of forsterite, magnetite, phlogopite, and apatite resembling relics of magnetite-forsterite rocks (carried up from the depths?) are found in carbonatite veins about 1–2 km from their centers. Close association of these rocks is observed in Palabora (Fig. 7, *a*), where carbonatite stocks intersect the pyroxenites and are themselves surrounded by consistent concentric zones of magnetite-forsterite-phlogopite rocks. Here (Palabora) pyroxenites at the contact zone are transformed into pegmatoid forsterite-vermiculite-pyroxene rock. Probably these are recrystallized and micatized pyroxenites with mica-forsterite veinlets (Russel et al., 1954).

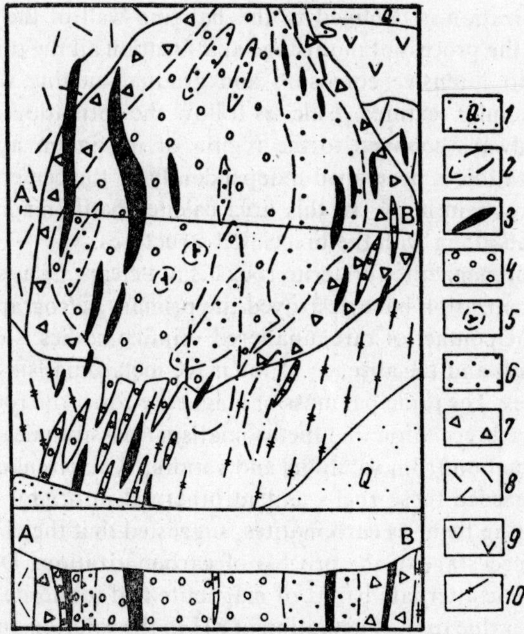

Fig. 9. Distribution of magnetite-forsterite rock bodies in Kovdor massif.
1—Quaternary deposits; 2—Boundary of shtaffelitic zones; 3—Early carbonatite veins; 4—Carbonatized magnetite-forsterite rocks; 5—Picrite porphyrites; 6—Zones of intensive apatitization; 7—Brecciated ijolites and fenites with veins of micatized-forsteritic rocks; 8—Ijolites; 9—Pyroxenites; 10—Faults.

Magnetite-forsterite rocks are carbonatized and apatitized. According to Valovom the composition of the rocks in the carbonatized zones is similar to that of normal carbonatites, but brecciated structures are observed and bedded relics of magnetite-forsterite rocks are preserved. It is quite likely that the magnetite-forsterite rocks were more widely distributed than is believed today. The Siberian carbonatite massifs often contain segregation of magnetite, forsterite, phlogopite, and apatite in which calcite is present in the form of rare megacrysts. It is possible that this segregation gives rise to relics of magnetite-forsterite rocks not superficially but at greater depths of recent erosional surfaces. Transformation of such relics within carbonatites is found in Vuoriyarvi, where carbonatite veins intersect the magnetite-forsterite rocks at a depth of 70 m in all directions and contain phlogopitized fragments of these rocks (southeastern slope of Neske-Vara town).

According to Glagolev (1962) apatitization of magnetite-forsterite rocks is closely related in space to carbonatites but precedes carbonatization (pre-carbonatites). Normally apatitization precedes brecciation of magnetite-forsteritic rocks and apatite occurs either as veins or as cemented fragments. In Kovdor, apatitization is confined to the hanging wall of the main body of these rocks. In the process of multistage apatitization all the primary minerals are subjected to intensive corrosion and gradual melting while the rocks develop equigranular textures. Calcites follow the formation of apatites but they are not always confined to the region of maximum apatitization. In Kovdor calcitization is developed independently at the center as well as the periphery of the main body. In this area calcite-apatite-magnetite-forsterite rocks are formed along with the brecciated structures.

The origin of magnetite-forsterite rocks is not clear. Consistent apatitization and carbonatization have destroyed the primary petrographic features of these rocks. The contact of rare, unaltered veinlike bodies is obscure. Their distinct structures and the absence of intensive metasomatism classifies them as intrusive dikes. The principal mass of magnetite-forsterite rocks in Kovdor, with its intensive brecciation and metasomatism (massive micatization), is an example of formation from solutions and vapors. Kukharenko (Kukharenko et al., 1965) regarded these rocks as hydrothermal in origin. Pozharitzkaya (1966), considering them as carbonatites, suggested that they had been formed at an advanced stage of the process of carbonatization. Development of banding (rhythmic alternate bands of magnetite and forsterite), according to Pozharitzkaya, is due to the fluctuation of pH in the solution and independent deposition sometimes of Mg and sometimes of Fe. But his assumption is hardly justified since the peripheral zone of the magnetite-forsterite rock body, about 70 m thick, contains massive fine-grained aggregates of forsterites with an appreciable amount of magnetite, and rhythmic layers are formed at the center of the rock body.

The genetic relationship between magnetite-forsterite rocks and carbonatites is obvious, but the mineralogical composition of these rocks by itself is not enough to classify them as hydrothermal. Conversely, in all cases hydrothermal activity in olivine-bearing rocks transforms the olivines first. The presence of magmatic magnetite-forsterite rocks within the intrusive rocks (dunite-peridotite series) as well as their equivalents (picrite) in complex massifs is indicative. However, intensive association and later metasomatism also have great roles in the formation of these rocks. So the solution of such a simple problem as the origin of these rocks remains difficult because of insufficient data.

PICRITIC PORPHYRITES-ALNÖITES-DAMKJERNITES

Picrite porphyrites, the dike equivalents of dunites, although known in most of the carbonatite massifs, have not been properly studied. Due to their inconsistent composition and structure these rocks are referred to by different names as picrite-porphyrites (Lavrenev and Pozharitzkaya, 1958; Frolov, 1960; Frolov et al., 1967), alnöites (Högbom, 1895), damkjernite (Brögger, 1921), kimberlite (Davidson, 1964), kimberlite-carbonatites (Eckermann, 1963; Heinrich, 1967), picrite porphyry, vescelyites (Kovalski, 1963; Milashev et al., 1963). These rocks form small volcanic plugs and dikes, often crowded with foreign rock fragments (eruptive breccia). These are similar to kimberlites in composition and structure but differ from them conspicuously in the absence of diamond, pyrope, ilmentite, rhombic pyroxene, and chromite and the presence of perovskite, calcite, monticellite, and alkaline minerals, e.g. nepheline, melilite, richterite, hastingsite-barkevikites. Alnöite-picrites are found in the massifs of Alnö and Fen (Högbom, 1895; Brögger, 1921; Eckermann, 1948, 1960). Turi Mis (Bulakh, 1959, 1962; Shurkin, 1960), all the massifs of Kola (author), in Siberia (Epshtein, 1958; Frolov, 1960; Butakova and Egorov, 1962; Kovalski, 1963; Kovalski et al., 1969; Milashev et al., 1963) and in several massifs of Africa and America (Christman et al., 1959; Heinrich and Dahlem, 1965; Heinrich, 1967). These rocks were first classified as pre-carbonatites (Lavrenev and Pozharitzkaya, 1958; Frolov, 1960), although Frolov (Frolov et al., 1967) showed the occurrence of intracarbonatite dikes and Zhabin regarded them as post-carbonatites. Within the picrites of several massifs carbonatite fragments are found, e.g. Mbeya, Ngualla, Igwisi (Heinrich, 1967), Fen (Saether, 1958), Kovdor, Vuoriyarvi and a few massifs of Siberia. Numerous blocks of picrite-porphyrites occur at the center of several large massifs of southeastern Siberia. These were formerly regarded as a single mass (thickness up to 500 m) that cuts across the pyroxenites (Frolov, 1960) and is thereby broken and carbonatized. We can report picrite veins intersecting the carbonatites in these and other massifs (Vuoriyarvi, Kovdor, Sebl-Yavr, Pesochnyi, Turi Mis, and the Siberian massifs). The study showed that two types of rocks similar in structure and microscopic features but different in composition and age were formed.

Rocks of the first type are similar to picrite alnöites. They are composed of forsterite (monticellite), pyroxene (Tiaugite), phlogopite, and magnetite, with variable proportions of melilite and nepheline and an admixture of perovskite and apatite. Rocks of the second type primarily contain phlogopite and calcite and also magnetite, richterite, serpentine, chlorite, zeolite, needles of aegirine, apatite, and disseminated augite, forsterite, barkevikite, nepheline, and melilite (often with total substitution) and resemble in composition early melanocratic carbonatites. These rocks should be classified as an independent group so that the nomenclature of damkjernite (Brögger, 1921) may be retained. Both types of rock are equigranular or are characterized by different varieties of porphyries (with fine-grained or with principal microlitic masses) and contain thin opaque inclusions responsible for the black color of these rocks.

Picrite-alnöites

Rocks of the first type form either stretched or circular pipe-like bodies within the carbonatite massifs or away from them (up to 7 km), and comprise fragments of mixed and foreign rock materials (Fig. 10, *a*). In the Kola Peninsula these rocks occur in all the massifs, either as thin viens (Sebl-Yavr, Afrikanda, Lesnaya and Ozernaya Varaka) or as pipes up to 50 m thick (Kovdor, Turi Mis). In Vuoriyarvi thin veins (from 5 cm to 3 m) of these rocks occur either within the pyroxenites (Neske-Vara) and magnetite-forsterite rocks (Tuxta Vara) or form a stock-like system over an area exceeding 200 × 300 m (Petyaian Vara). Picrites in Kovdor intersect the main apatitized magnetite-forsterite body and give rise to two pipe-like structures (up to 120 m in diameter) that dip 80° to the east and are not associated with the carbonatites or the process of carbonatization (making it difficult to reconstruct their primary forms). In Turi Mis pipes and small dikes of these rocks intersect the sandstone, fenites, and alkaline rocks.

Several circular subvertical volcanic pipes (up to 250 m in diameter) saturated with picrites and eruptive breccias occur in the Anabar Shield (Milashev et al., 1963; Marzsheitzsev et al., 1966; Kovalski, 1963; Kovalski et al., 1969) and in the Priclensky region (Rabkin, 1960; Krutoyarski et al., 1959). These pipes are concentrated in some areas and are associated, in space, with carbonatites and kimberlites. Picritic and alnöitic pipes and dikes are also reported in the massifs of Maimecha-Kotui province, especially from Gulinskii (here a part of these pipes is genetically related to effusive bodies of Aridzansky suites of rocks and are preceded by the formation of alkaline rocks) and south of it (Butakova and Egorov, 1962; Polkin, 1958). Similar rocks are found in many massifs, e.g. Magnet Cove (Erickson and Blade, 1963), Iron Hill (Larsen, 1942; Rust, 1937), Ngualla (Heinrich, 1967), Alnö (Eckermann, 1958, 1960, 1963, 1964), Fen (Brögger, 1921; Saether, 1948, 1958). The composition of these rocks is more or less constant but is specific to the region to some extent. The principal rock-forming mineral in them is forsterite containing 2 to 10% of FeO. It is found in more than 85% of the veins of Vuoriyarvi (Petyaian Vara) and in the individual dikes of the White Sea and Siberia (Gulinskii massif). In Kovdor forsterite constitutes about 70% of the northern

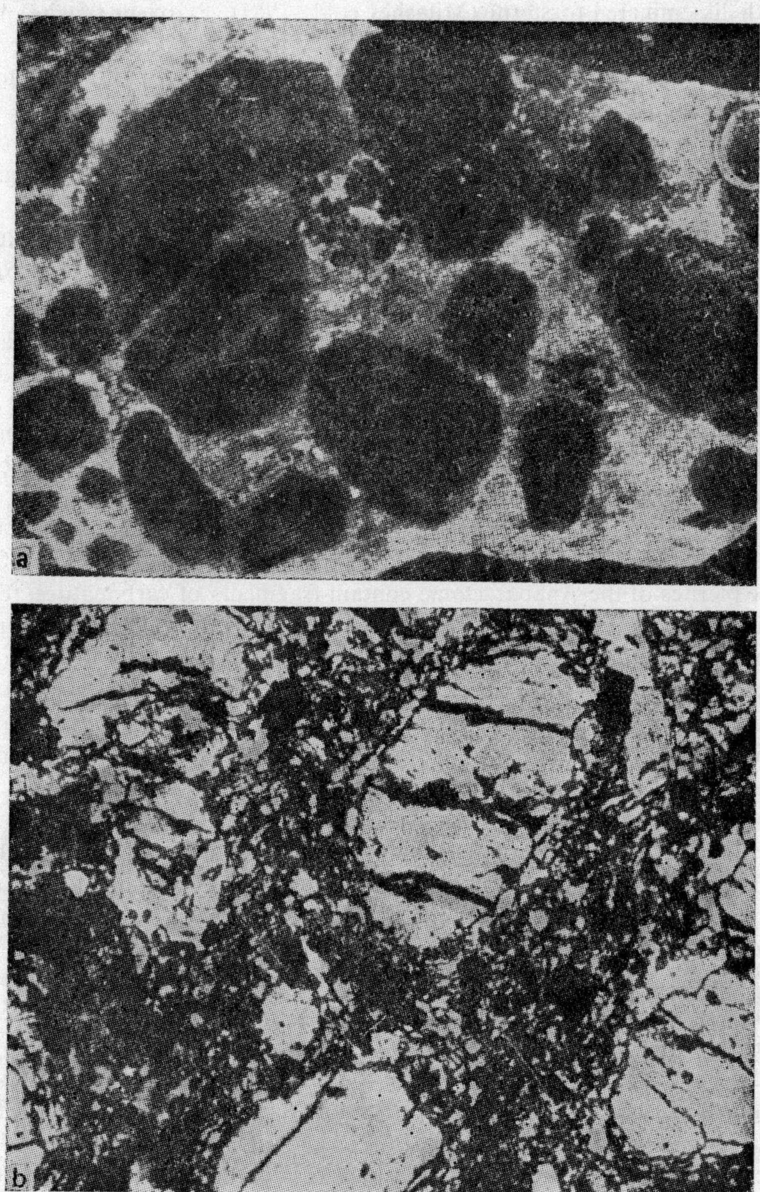

Fig. 10. Picrites of Kovdor massif.

a—Olivine fragments (black) in picrites; b—Porphyritic texture of picrite (in forsterite)—under crossed nicol, magnification ×24.

body, while pyroxene predominates in the south. Both the disseminated and principal masses of Anabar pipes contain monticellite intimately associated with disseminated forsterite (Milashev et al., 1963). Pyroxene (augite) predominates in the porphyrites of southeastern Siberia, Afrikanda, and Alnö, but occurs in smaller amounts in all the other massifs. The picrite-alnöites are brecciated and either porphyritic or porphyrite-like (Fig. 10, *b*). In the disseminated body of picrite-alnöite forsterites monticellite or pyroxene occur. The principal mass is composed of fine-grained aggregates of phlogopite, pyroxene, forsterite (rarely monticellite-Anabar), magnetite, perovskite, and secondary minerals like serpentine, chlorite, richterite, and calcite. Melilite is rare in the forsterite-bearing variety and is usually not more than 20%. Nepheline is practically absent. Pyroxene-rich rocks are more fine-grained. They contain impregnated phlogopite rich in melilite (0–30%) and nepheline (0–20%) and form typical alnöites (Alnö, Kovdor, and the Siberian massifs).

Pyroxenitic and forsteritic rocks usually form independent dikes in picrite-alnöites, but dikes of mixed composition are also observed (the Siberian massifs, Turi Mis, Afrikanda, Kovdor, Lesnaya Varaka).

Fragments of mixed rocks are always present in picrites, and these occur at a depth below the present erosional surfaces (sometimes greater than 500 m). The picrites of the Anabar Dome contain fragments of carbonatites, fenites, gneisses and schists, but these are absent at the superficial level. The pipes in Kovdor contain xenoliths of olivine at the superficial level. They are not found if we drill even to a depth of 500 m. Similar cases are reported from Turi Mis (Shenkin, 1960). These xenoliths are often sharply angular, sometimes ball-shaped and without any traces of flotational contacts (rounded during transportation and friction). The presence of picritic xenoliths in these pipes is not so important (in a zone up to 1 cm). The composition of the picrites does not depend on the composition of the mixed rocks. But with the rounding and friction of xenoliths the picrites were contaminated with small fragmented materials (forsterite in Kovdor, pyroxene in Vuoriyarvi, phlogopite in Vuoriyarvi and Siberian massifs). Independent small volcanic veins full of tuffs and lavas of vitreous peridotites occur in the massifs of Igwisi in Tanganyika (Sampson, 1956; Fozzard, 1956). These are composed of serpentinized forsterite with an admixture of volcanic glass, serpentine, calcite, magnetite, and perovskite. They also contain xenoliths of labradorite and fragments of barkevikite. Maimechaites of Gulinskii massif (Goldburg et al., 1961; Butakova, 1958; Butakova and Egorov, 1962) may be similar to these rocks, but the age of these rocks is not clear (if maimechaites are preceded by dunites correlation with picrite-alnöites is impossible).

Picrite-alnöite rocks are not everywhere intersected by early carbonatites. In Kovdor calcite-forsterite-magnetite rocks similar to carbonatized magnetite-forsterite rocks were formed along with the picrite-alnöite.

Damkjernites

These rocks were first reported from Fen (Brögger, 1921). Later, in the parent massifs, they were considered along with picrite porphyrites (Frolov, 1960; Frolov and Bagdasarov, 1967; Gaidukova et al., 1962; Lavrenev and Pozharitzkaya, 1958), with which they have morphological characters in common (circular pipes of eruptive breccia) and similar mineral assemblages such as phlogopite, forsterite, pyroxene, hastingsite-barkevikite, melilite, and nepheline (constantly changing assemblage). Damkjernites everywhere intersect the schistose and dolomitized parts of the earlier carbonatites and contain fragments of the latter as well as the principal rock-forming minerals such as calcite and phlogopite (Fig. 11, *a*, *b*).

Pipes of eruptive breccias cemented with black, fine-grained carbonatites occur in the Anabar Mountain Ridge. They contain numerous fragments of different rocks, among which coarse-grained calcitic or dolomitized carbonatites with accessory minerals like pyrochlore or fragments of individual crystals of accessory minerals like baddeleyite, pyrochlore, apatite, magnetite, and columbite (Ilupina, personal communication) are important. The structure and composition of these rocks differ sharply from typical carbonatites and rather resemble damkjernites. In the Kola Peninsula damkjernites form small linear veins 1–5 cm thick. Sometimes these occur as dikes up to 5 m thick and intersect the pyroxenites (Afrikanda, Vuoriyarvi, Kovdor, Salmagorsk), magnetite-forsterite rocks and early carbonatites (Kovdor, Vuoriyarvi). In Kovdor damkjernites are rich in ball-shaped fragments of ijolites and fenites. In Vuoriyarvi they are full of small fragments of pyroxenites (and pyroxene) or carbonatites. Several steeply dipping stocks, pipes and small dikes of volcanic breccia occur in the north White Sea (Turi Mis, White Sea Island—Bulak, 1959, 1962; Shurkin, 1960; Kukharenko et al., 1965). These bodies, up to 15 m thick, contain fragments of Precambrian sandstones, granites, and gneisses (part of which lie below the recent erosional surfaces). Individual dikes of Turi Mis are so rich in such fragments that the cementing material constitutes less than 10% (by volume) of the total.

Damkjernites are widely known in the Fen massif (Brögger, 1921; Bergstöl and Svinndal, 1960), particularly in the southeastern part of Lake Nordse at a distance of 6 km from the massif, and are closely associated with tinguaite dikes. Here damkjernites occur as subvertical pipes, either circular or elongated, and contain fragments of migmatitic granites and gneisses. Saether (1948) determined the age of the damkjernites of Fen as post-sövites, considering them contemporary to rauhaugite. According to him rauhaugite is both earlier and later than the damkjernites and is probably associated with both earlier and later dolomitized carbonatites. Small bodies of damkjernites, kimberlites, kimberlitic carbonatites and alnöites rich in calcites occur in Alnö (Eckermann, 1948a, 1960), Nagulla (Heinrich, 1967) and in other massifs (Daly, 1925; King and Sutherland, 1960a, b, c; Valachi and Kopp, 1965).

Fig. 11. Damkjernites.

a—Intersection of damkjernite by early carbonatite veins (Siberian massif);
b—Carbonatite fragments (white) in damkjernites (Vuoriyarvi massif)—normal magnification.

Numerous small pipe-like bodies of eruptive breccias with fragments of mixed gneisses and schists, carbonatites, and lapilli of melanocratic rocks cemented with carbonatites and dark-colored materials are reported from the USA (particularly from Missouri, Colorado, Arkansas—Christman et al., 1959; Heinrich and Dahlem, 1965; Singewald and Milton, 1930).

In all these cases the damkjernites are remarkably similar in composition. The principal constituents of the main damkjernite body are fine-grained aggregates (0.1–0.001 mm and even finer) of calcite, apatite, richerite, phlogopite, serpentine, magnetite and minor dark inclusions. We did not observe volcanic glasses but they are reported in the pipes of Evon (Heinrich, 1967). The proportions of these minerals (up to 1.5 cm thick) of phlogopite, calcite, forsterite (usually serpentinized), and almost totally replaced nepheline and melilite are almost invariably found to occur in these rocks. Similarly, fragments of kataphorite-barkevikites (Alnö, Fen, massifs of Eastern Sayan, Kovdor, Vuoriyarvi, Afrikanda), surrounded by marginal aggregates of magnetite, calcite, phlogopite or chlorite are regular constituents. Aegirine and zeolites also occur in the dikes of Turi Mis. Shurkin (1960) observed the presence of decomposed material of mixed rocks. Here about 80% of the total mass shows the presence of small decomposed fragments of feldspars and quartz formed from the mixed polymictic sandstones and granites, while calcites were formed from the principal mineral constituent of damkjernites.

Fragments of all the rocks (except carbonatites) in damkjernites are replaced and surrounded by minerals like calcite, phlogopite, chlorite, or serpentine. In the dikes of Turi Mis fragments of quartz are replaced by aegirine at the periphery, while feldspars are albitized.

The volcanic pipes studied are localized in certain parts of the individual massifs. Dikes of the Kandalaksha region probably do not belong to any massif but are confined to a wider deformational zone that controls the formation of carbonatite massifs (Kukharenko, 1967). Nor are the volcanic pipes of the Russian Platform related to any concrete massif of alkaline ultrabasic rocks. Ultrabasic breccias with fragments of monchiquites and odinites occur in Priazove (Ruzitzki, 1963), where the principal mass is composed of calcite, serpentine, micas, and impregnated ores.

Occurrences of fragments of mixed rocks and other rock fragments at great depths are significant for picrite porphyrites and damkjernites. In Kovdor the picritic body is full of fragments of olivine at a depth below 500 m (indicated by core samples from a borehole). In Vuoriyarvi the subvertical damkjernite dikes lying within the pyroxenites contain fragments of fenites that occur at depths greater than 300 m. The volcanic pipes of Anabar massif contain fragments of eclogite, carbonatite, ultrabasites, and other rocks at depths greater than 300 m. Constant occurrences of fragments of ultrabasites and the presence of impregnated amphibole, pyroxene, forsterite, melilite, monticellite, apatite, and other minerals of alkaline ultrabasic rocks in the main mass of the Anabar massif indicate a genetic relationship of the volcanic pipes with these rocks and their formation in complex massifs rich in Ca and CO_2. Occurrences of such intrusive bodies confirm the possibility of the existence of silica-carbonatitic melts.

The typical damkjernites also disappear completely with the formation of their mobile melts, i.e. veins (probably extraordinarily rich in volatiles, chiefly CO_2 and H_2O). We observed such veins of consistent composition (up to 1–2 cm thick) intersecting different rocks along a length of 30 m. Often these veins are branched, extending to 3–5 mm. Shurkin (1960) reported the presence of decomposed material of these veins in the dikes of Turi Mis.

Chapter IV

CARBONATITES

The term 'carbonatite' was introduced by Brögger (1921) for the carbonate rocks of Fen. He considered these rocks as magmatic in origin. Since then the term has been enriched by numerous interpretations and the sedimentary carbonate rocks, meta-sediments (Daly, 1918), and an important part of the rocks of pneumatolytic-hydrothermal origin came to be included under the head "carbonatites". With the discovery of rare-earth elements in carbonatites, the carbonate veins containing minerals of TR, Sr, Ba, and Th were also placed under this head. Within this group were also placed typical carbonates, carbonate-fluorite veins (Petrov et al., 1946), carbonate veins with apatite and ilmenite (Ilmensk Mountain) or with pyrochlore and sulfide (Cherry Blossom Mountain; Zhabin, 1961), and almost monomineralic calcite veins usually accompanied by nepheline syenites (Konev, 1960). Calciphyritic lenses containing silicates (Andreev, 1958) and recrystallized marbles containing zircon and pyrochlore (Tuva) were also classified as carbonatites.

On the other hand, subdivision of the carbonatites and carbonate veins containing rare-earth elements was advocated by Semenov (1963). He subdivided the carbonatites into independent hydrothermal groups genetically related to grano-syenites (Mountain Pass and Tuva) and alkaline nepheline syenites (Yenisei Mountain Ridge). The term 'carbonatites' therefore has wider connotations. Now the term 'carbonatites' means associations of rocks of different origins. Detailed discussions on the origin of these rocks are concerned with different geological factors, variable composition, and peculiar mineral assemblages. It is difficult to bracket synonymous or other types of rocks with carbonatites even in a complex massif where carbonatites constitute one of the characteristic phases.

In many complex massifs of carbonatites the ultrabasites (chiefly pyroxenites) contain primary calcite and are enriched by melilitic- and nepheline-pyroxenitic rocks. In almost all the massifs where the process of nephelinization (Kovdor, Vuoriyarvi, massifs of Eastern Sayan, Odikhincha) is well developed, calcite together with apatite forms xenomorphic coarse-laminated segregations in ijolites, filling the interstices of the silicates. Calcite along with amphibole is formed at the zone between pyroxenites and ijolites or in the region where amphibolitization of pyroxenites is prominent (connected with ijolites in space and origin). Its formation in this case is due to the excess of calcium liberated during the process of amphibolization of pyroxene, as evidenced by its close association with hornblende (Ural). Calcite-pyroxene-amphibole rocks occur in Vuoriyarvi, Kovdor, Pesochnyi, and Afrikanda. In the beginning normal carbonatites are formed, although sphene and perovskite (entrapped in mixed rocks) are also observed in these rocks. Still, these are more akin to early carbonatites.

Studies of carbonatites in recent years show that these rocks are exclusively characterized and individualized by their complex nature. By their geological position and chemical composition they are similar to calciphyres or hydrothermal veins. Even the association of carbonatites with magmatic rocks is not as prominent as was earlier thought. Sometimes in some particular massifs several rocks become isolated from the general rock sequence. In other cases rocks of different characters or individual bodies of carbonatites, not accompanied by alkaline rocks, are formed (Kaluwe) within the same general rock sequence. The absence of similar or dissimilar types of rocks in the massifs may be explained by the following factors:

a) Tectonic configuration of the region;
b) Nature of the parent magma and the degree of contamination;
c) Level of erosional surfaces of the massifs (vertical zoning);
d) Spontaneous development of magmatism of other types.

Minor development of silicate rocks in carbonatites makes it difficult to analyze their formational history. In the absence of characteristic mineralization in carbonatite bodies it is very unconventional to place them in the group of carbonatites (veins of pyroxene-calcite, biotite-calcite, hematite-carbonate, and carbonate-fluorapatite of Tuva, Yenisei Mountain Ridge, Ukraine and other regions). It is difficult to differentiate the carbonatites from the pneumatolytic-hydrothermal carbonate veins that accompany the massifs rich in calcium miascites (Ural, Tuva, Yenisei Mountain Ridge, Prebaikal, Norway, Canada). A few authors (Zhabin, 1959; Sheinmann et al., 1961; Heinrich, 1967), however, assign these veins to independent groups of carbonatites. Thus the history of the formation of carbonatites is quite complex: only some of these rocks show characters corresponding to their true nomenclature.

We also studied other types of carbonatites, i.e. carbonatites forming intrusive or metasomatic bodies or lava flows. These carbonatites accompanying alkaline ultrabasic rocks contain specific rare-earth metals and show characteristic different mineral assemblages. On this count contact-metamorphic, sulfide-hydrothermal, and skarn rocks are to be excluded from the group of carbonatites. But the carbonate veins containing rare-earth mineralization (Mountain Pass) and indicating different origin resemble carbonatites by different convergent features.

The distribution and, particularly, the degree of development of carbonatites depend on many factors. By analogy, it is expected that along with the intrusive formations the volume of carbonatites should increase with the increase in the volume of the massif as a whole. But in large complex massifs, although carbonatites form large bodies, they cannot be compared to the volume of the general intrusive rocks. In large massifs: Gulinskii, Odikhincha, Magan, Kovdor, Magnet Cove, etc., where carbonatite bodies are 0.5–3 km thick, even then they represent a small part of the total volume of intrusive rocks. At the same time the relatively small massifs of Sayan, Sallanlatva, Alnö, and the African volcanic vents are either totally composed of carbonatites or contain 20–30% (in area) of intrusive silicate rocks. Dependence of the volume of carbonatites on erosional surfaces of the massifs is often observed. In the hypabyssal type of massifs (North Siberia, Kola Peninsula) carbonatites form bodies similar to the dimensions of the silicate rocks. The volcanic rocks and vents of East Africa are often grouped together with carbonatites (Chilwa, Mrima, Muambe, Nkombwa) or accompany the series of ring dikes of alkaline rocks (Bukusu, Sukulu, Toror, Kerimasi, Tundulu, Napak, and others). The dependence on erosional surfaces controls the structure of the carbonatites, their interrelation with the associated rocks, and the composition and distribution of minerals in them. Vertical zoning indicates the dominance of different types of carbonatites (see below).

CLASSIFICATION OF CARBONATITES

In recent years the term 'carbonatite' has been used in a collective sense, and all carbonate rocks of complex massifs or volcanic veins, regardless of their structure and composition, are grouped under carbonatites. However, Brögger (1921) showed the occurrence of at least two varieties of these rocks: calcitic (sövites) and dolomitic (rauhaugites) equivalent to dikes (corresponding to alvikites and beforsites). Recent works on carbonatites mainly deal with their genesis. The study of their classification and mineral paragenesis started only a few years ago. These rocks are thought to be composed of forsterite, pyroxene, mica, serpentine, chlorite, zeolite, magnetite, sulfide, etc. and evidently do not belong to the same mineral paragenesis. The various genetic propositions and detailed discussions on the origin of carbonatites are of little use for classifying them. Most of the African massifs have been very little studied in this context. Different stages of the formation of carbonatites and the subsequent development of their structure and composition have been studied in detail for the massifs of Alnö (Eckermann, 1948a, 1958), Fen (Brögger, 1921; Bowen, 1924; Saether, 1948), Africa (Dixey, 1946; Dixey et al., 1955; Bailey, 1958, 1960; Dawson, 1962a, b; de Kun, 1961; James, 1956; Garson, 1955, 1958, 1962, 1963) and North America (Tuttle et al., 1967; Heinrich, 1967; Landes, 1931; Larsen, 1942; Olson et al., 1954). Several seminal studies on the classification of carbonatites and their mineral assemblages have been carried out by Soviet geologists. On the basis of the works of Borodin, Bulak, Volotovskaya, Ginzburg, Gaidukova, Egorov, Kupletsky, Kukharenko, Pozharitzkaya, Sheinmann, Epshtein and other petrological considerations the classification of carbonatites was now possible.

Brögger's (1921) division of the carbonatites into types prevailed for a long time. It was, however, observed from detailed studies of the new massifs that carbonatites may be divided into more varieties differing by complex features. At the beginning of the formation of carbonatites several calcitic and dolomitic stages were present. In classifying the carbonatites most workers considered their mineralogical assemblages and petrographical features. Kojireva and Ilinski (1959), Bulakh (1961), Bogachev (1958), and Volotovskaya (1958, 1959) classified the different massifs of the Kola Peninsula into the following varieties: *calcitic dolomitic*, *ankeritic*, *pyroxene-calcitic*, *amphibole-calcitic*, *apatite* (or *magnetite*)*-calcitic*, *magnetite-carbonatic*, *quartz-carbonatic*, *sideritic*, and others. Frolov (1960), Pozharitzkaya (1960), and Epshtein (1959) explained the difference between the ore-bearing and ore-free calcitic carbonatites and divided the carbonatites according to their texture into fine-, medium- and coarse-grained. Borodin (1965a) suggested the genetic classification of carbonatites and distinguished different types genetically related to different silicate rocks. Borodin's classification of carbonatites distinguishes three types of rocks differing in composition and temperature of formation (500–700, 300–500, and 100–300°C). The mineralogical composition of the first group (high temperature) corresponds to the *early carbonatites* and the third to *late carbonatites* (see below). Rocks of the intermediate group, according to Borodin, contain minerals of two other groups of rocks (apatite, pyrochlore, dysanalytes on the one hand, and monazite, burbankite and rutile on the other).

In all these classifications, grouping of the rocks is based on their mineralogical composition, particularly on the principal rock-forming minerals—the carbonates. This principle, introduced by Brögger, carried genetic significance, because changes in the composition of the carbonates indicate changing physicochemical conditions of formation. Study of these rocks shows that the changes in composition of carbonatites are always accompanied by changes of the paragenesis of the minerals. Carbonate-magmatitic, apatitic, pyroxenitic, phologopitic, and other varieties of rock may occur within a single geological unit with local concentrations of either of these or other minerals (the individual mineral content of the carbonatite massifs of Kovdor, Vuoriyarvi and Eastern Sayan varies between 20 and 40% and depends markedly on the contents of relics and fragments of mixed silicate rocks). However, stable mineral associations are formed and these help a great deal in classifying the carbonatites. Carbonatites are characterized by sharp sequences within the changing mineral associations and each of the sequences contains characteristic minerals (Pozharitzkaya, 1960, 1966; Epshtein, 1958, 1959; Gaidukova et al., 1962; Kapustin, 1960, 1961, 1964, 1965a; Zdorik et al., 1966). Pozharitzkaya and Epshtein (1963, 1964) divided the process of formation of carbonatites into four stages: *early* and *late calcitic*, *calcite-dolomitic*, and *ankeritic*.

Pozharitzkaya and Epshtein suggested the metasomatic origin of carbonatites, considering their sequences of different varieties as the sequences of zones within a single metasomatic column. These authors repeatedly showed the presence of concentric (in stocks) or linear-symmetrical (in linear veins) zones with early rocks at the top and later rocks at the center of the carbonatite bodies. Such zonings are present in metasomatic bodies, indicating the formation of carbonatites within a single metasomatic column, and are found to occur in skarn, phologopitic veins, and gneisses (Korzhinskii, 1947, 1953). Similar zonings in carbonatite stocks were reported by Epshtein (1959) and Pozharitzkaya (1966) in Gulinskii, and by Frolov (1960) and Frolov et al. (1967) in the massifs of South and Eastern Siberia and also in Sallanlatva, Chilwa, Mbeya, and Spitzkop. However, a large number of massifs are known where carbonatites are formed or are dominant within one or more stages with or without being distorted and the carbonatites of different stages are widely scattered. Moreover, where the carbonatites develop all the stages within a single metasomatic column the presence of zoning is expected in each of the carbonatite bodies. But hundreds of carbonatite veins in Vuoriyarvi, Kovdor, Lesnaya Varaka, Ozernaya Varaka, Alnö, Fen, Tundulu, and South Siberia do not show zoning and are composed of equigranular rocks (chiefly sövites).

From a detailed geological and structural study of the Fen Mountain, Eckermann (1948a, 1958) has shown for the first time that carbonatites are characterized by definite structural elements. Rocks of different composition control the joint system. Examples of these are found in several massifs of Africa (Garson, 1953, 1955, 1958, 1959, 1962, 1963; Holmes, 1953; Du Bois, 1959) and are also described in detail by Frolov (1960, 1962, 1966a, b), Frolov and Gagdasorov (1967), and Frolov et al. (1969) from the Siberian massifs. We reported similar cases from the Kola Peninsula (Kapustin, 1960, 1961, 1964) and mentioned that formations at different stages (distinguished by Pozharitzkaya and Epshtein) cannot be compared by size. More than 90% of the total material introduced at the beginning of the formation of carbonatite confined to the first two stages. The earlier stages are composed of independent bodies of hundreds and thousands of meters in size and give rise to abundant mixed rocks retaining their own specific composition. The carbonatites in the intersecting veins contain up to 99% of the material, and in metasomatic bodies up to 90% of the material at the center. Near the peripheral zones they are rich in relics and reactivated minerals. In the third stage independent bodies of carbonatites are not generally formed. Frolov showed from the Siberian massifs and the Kola Peninsula that the typical mineral assemblages of this process are linked with early carbonatites along their margin. In mixed rocks the process develops weak amphibolization or micatization (Vuoriyarvi and Eastern Sayan), and redistributes the materials within the carbonatites or between the carbonatites and mixed silicate rocks.

The composition of carbonatites of the fourth stage depends mainly on the composition of the mixed rocks. Such carbonatites are not comparable in volume with those of the earlier stages. With the formation of these rocks surrounding the early carbonatites the volume of these bodies increases significantly. Around the silicate rocks they form small veins or metasomatic zones where the carbonatites comprise less than 30% of the total mass (Namo-Vara, Kovdor, and Eastern Sayan). In most massifs 90% of the material belongs to the first and second stages while in the later stages 70–80% of the components (CaO, BaO, SrO, FeO, SiO_2, TR_2O_3, TiO_2) are derived from the mixed rocks. Similarly, the differences in the morphology and volume of carbonatites forming in different stages do not permit us to consider these stages as equally important. They show differences in the process of formation and composition of the material from which they are derived.

We (Kapustin, 1964, 1965a, 1966a, b) distinguished two principal types of carbonatites—*early* and *late*. Each of these is characterized by some specific features and wide variations (Tables 2 and 3). The principal structures, compositions, and distribution of these carbonatites are given below.

The sequence of formation of the rock-forming minerals of carbonatite is very important. In all the massifs that we studied directly and also in the literature it is found that calcite is preceded by dolomite. Independent bodies of dolomitic carbonatites occur in Sebl-Yavr (Bulakh, 1960), Lesnaya Varaka, and Shawa (Dickey, 1946). Dolomitic carbonatites of these massifs contain more or less uniformly distributed minerals like apatite, magnetite, phlogopite and sometimes pyroxene, forsterite, and clinohumite and accessory minerals like dysanalyte and pyrochlore. In early carbonatites the dolomites form equigranular aggregates. Isolated equigranular dolomitic dikes without relics of calcite but with phlogopite, clinohumite, and accessory pyrochlore occur in Vuoriyarvi and Kovdor, but in these massifs they are directly intersected by early carbonatite bodies. Special research on these and similar massifs may indicate the existence of primary dolomitic carbonatites similar to early calcitic ores. But in any case early dolomitic rocks may appear with anomalous characters. In the majority of the massifs dolomite is formed later than the calcite, replacing it metasomatically.

The presence of early dolomitic rocks in most of the massifs prompts us to classify the carbonatites on the basis not only of their varying mineral

Table 2. Carbonatite system

	Carbonatites	stages	Typomorphic minerals: Rock-forming	Typomorphic minerals: Accessory	Morphology	Examples (massifs)
Early	Calcitic	I	Calcite-phlogopite, biotite, augite, apatite	Dysanalite, calzirtite, sphene	Stocks	Vuoriyarvi (Tuxta-Vara), Kaiserstühl
					Linear veins	Kovdor, Kaiserstühl, Siberian massifs
					Linear metasomatic veins	Kovdor (Mogo-Vidi), Oka, Siberian massifs
		II	Calcite, phlogopite, forsterite, aegirine, magnetite, apatite	Pyrochlore, baddeleyite	Conical-ring-like vein system	Vuoriyarvi, Alnö, Tunduly, Arbarastax, Hudini, Rangva
					Conical stocks	Gulinskii, Napak, Mrima, Serrote, Siberian massifs
	Dolomitized	I-II	Calcite, dolomite, richterite, tetraferriphlogopite	Niobozirconolite, ilmenite, zircon	Linear metasomatic zones	Vuoriyarvi, Sebl-Yavr, Iron Hill, Siberian massifs
Late	Calcitic	I	Calcite, phlogopite, pyrrhotite	Burbankite, Ba carbonate	Independent linear veins	Vuoriyarvi, Kovdor, Sebl-Yavr
	Ankeritic dolomitic	II-III	Ankerite-dolomite, chlorite, sulfides, barite, quartz	Strontianite, ancylite, brookite	Linear and stock like metasomatic bodies	Namo-Vara, Sallanlatva, Alnö, Chilwa, Nkumbwa, Kangankunde, Spitzkop, Gulinskii, Siberian massifs
	Calcitic	IV	Calcite, zeolite, hematite	Vinogradovite, catapleiit	Independent linear veins	Vuoriyarvi, Kovdor, Gulinskii, Sallanlatva

Table 3. Mineralogical composition and sequence of carbonatite formations

Minerals	Early carbonatites				Damkjernite dikes	Late carbonatites			
	Calcitic		Dolomitized			Calcitic	Ankeritic-dolomitic		Calcitic
	I Stage	II Stage	I Stage	II Stage		I Stage	II Stage	III Stage	IV Stage
1	2	3	4	5	6	7	8	9	10
Rock-forming and secondary	Calcite, augite, biotite, phlogopite, monticellite, forsterite, melilite, nepheline, apatite, magnetite	Calcite, forsterite, phlogopite, diopside, aegirine, albite, apatite, magnetite	Calcite, clinohumite, tetraferri-phlogopite, cancrinite, pyrrhotite, chalcopy-rite, pentlandite	Dolomite, richterite, brucite	Calcite, richterite, serpentine, forsterite, apatite, magnetite	Calcite, phlogopite, orthoclase, arfvedsonite, alstonite, barytocalcite, norsetnite, natrofair-childite	Dolomite, paraankerite, albite, quartz, serpentine, strontiobarite, podolite, pyrite, marmatite, millerite, molybdenite, gold, valleriite	Ankerite, chlorite, quartz, siderite, magnesite, breunnerite, barite, vivianite, collinsite, jamesonite, bournonite, boulangerite, tetrahedrite, galenite, cleiophane	Calcite, fluorite, hematite, aegirine, natrolite, mesolite, manasseit, hydrotalcite, sellaite, pyrite, marcasite, anglesite

1	2	3	4	5	6	7	8	9	10
Accessory	Dysanolite, calzirtite, schorlomite, sphene, niccolite	Pyrochlore 1, pyrochlore 2, baddeleyite, eudialite, lavenite	Pyrochlore 3, niobozirconolite, lueshite, thorianite	Ilmenite, zircon	Perovskite	Labunzovite, thorite, wadeite, burbankite, cerite	Columbite, fersmite, anatase, brookite, zircon, monazite, carbocernaite	Ilmenorutile, Sr-Ba-pyrochlore, aeschynite, huanghoite, strontianite, florencite, ancylite, gorceixite, goyazite, parisite	Orthite, niobo-labuntsovite, ramsayite, katapleite, rhabdophane, svanbergite, bastnaesite

composition but also of their complex features. The most important, in this context, is the composition of dark-colored minerals. These dark-colored minerals in dolomitic carbonatites of Lesnaya Varaka and Shawa are similar to those of early carbonatites. If early dolomitic carbonatites of similar age and origin occur, like early calcitic rocks, there is a possibility of compositional inversion among the principal rock-forming carbonates, i.e. dolomite is the first to come out, followed by calcite. In the dolomitic carbonatites of Lesnaya Varaka weak and local calcitization is noticed and the veins of calcite contain scattered tetraferriphlogopite, which indicates the development of secondary dolomitization in the calcitic rocks. We are not justified in establishing the characters of the calcites of this massif on the basis of superficial studies of small exposures, when dolomitization and ankeritization, which correspond to different stages of formation of late carbonatites, are well developed in this area. Rare occurrences of independent primary dolomitic rocks in typomorphic association with early carbonatites and the inadequate study of this type of rock prompted us to make a further division of the early calcitic rocks of our classification.

EARLY CARBONATITES (SÖVITES)

Calcitic carbonatites, formerly known as 'sövites', are placed under this head. They form large bodies within and on the periphery of the alkaline ultrabasic massifs. Carbonatites of most of the massifs (Gulinskii, Odikhincha, Kovdor, Vuoriyarvi, Alnö, Kaiserstühl, Iron Hill, Magnet Cove, Oka, Jacupiranga, Palabora, Napak, Toror, Tundulu, and the Siberian massifs) belong to this group of rocks. Only in a few cases are these of smaller size than the late varieties (Sallanlatva, Mbeya) or totally absent (Kangankunde, Fremont County, and Ravalli County). Later rocks form large bodies after the formation of early rocks (Chilwa, Gulinskii, South Siberian massifs). It is only recently that a complete classification has been established, but this classification is not widely known in countries outside the USSR. In most of the massifs of other countries sövites are looked upon as an independent type. The other varieties surrounding sövites can be approximately isolated if these rocks are depicted by their characteristic mineral constituents and interrelations.

Early carbonatites of the 1st stage

Carbonatites of the 1st stage form independent massive bodies around any kind of rock or thick metasomatic zones within or at the periphery of the parent massif (Fig. 12). Quantitative evaluation of their distribution is complicated by the formation of part of these rocks along with the parent massif. The following features are important for early carbonatites of the 1st stage:

a) Linear or stock-like form of the body;

b) Intensive association with metasomatites;

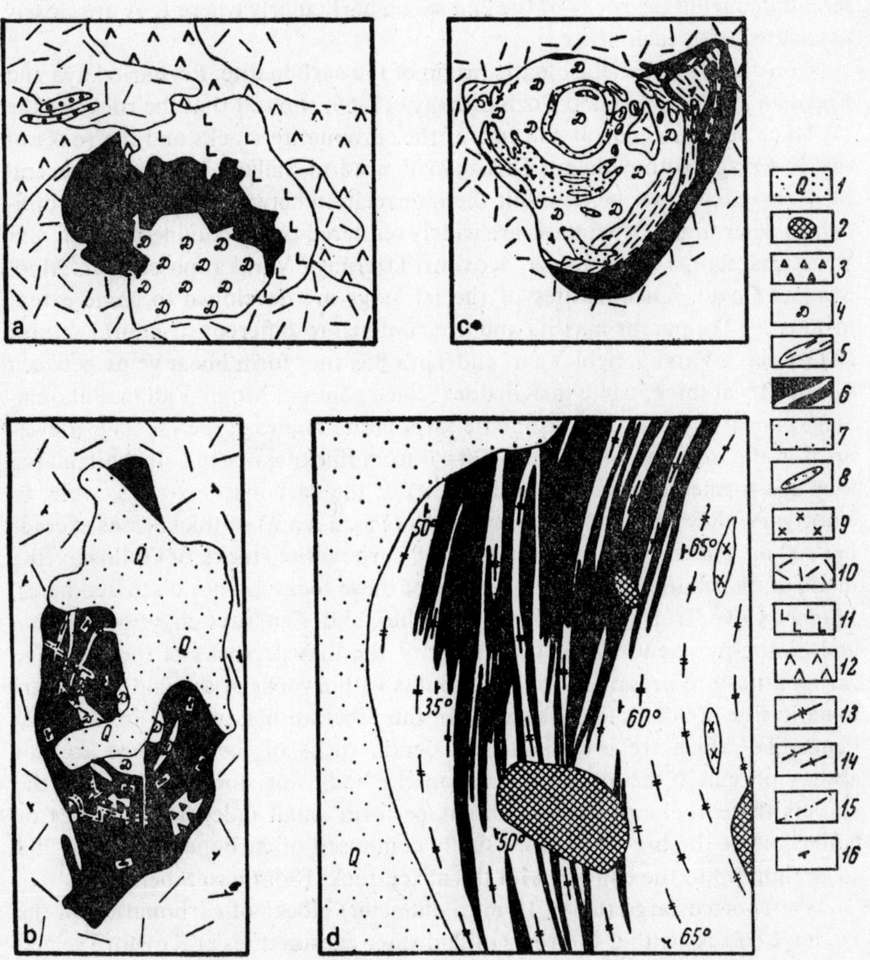

Fig. 12. Structural map of carbonatite bodies.

a,b—Stocks of Gulinskii massif—northern and southern (Epshtein, 1959); c—Stocks of Spitzkop massif (Tuttle et al., 1967); d—Veined-zone of carbonatites in Kovdor massifs. 1—Quaternary deposition; 2—Staffelitic breccias; 3—Breccia; 4—Late ankerite-dolomitic carbonatites; 5—Dolomitized carbonatites; 6—Early carbonatites; 7—Parts rich in apatite; 8—Dikes of alkaline rocks; 9—Nepheline and alkaline syenites; 10—Ijolites; 11—Melilitic rocks; 12—Olivinites; 13—Fenites; 14—Mixed gneisses and schists; 15—Faults; 16—Dip and strike.

c) Frequent development of poikiloblastic texture;
d) Presence of augite-diopside, dysanalyte, sphene, calcite, schorlomite, and absence or relics of magnetite (Table 3).

With the presence of these features the rocks of the 1st stage are easily differentiated from the rocks of the 2nd stage, particularly where they are closely associated with each other.

Considering the metasomatic origin of the carbonatite, Pozharitzkaya and Epshtein (1963, 1964) and Pozharitzkaya (1966) showed that the rocks of the 1st stage should occur at the top of the carbonatite stocks and the rocks of the 2nd stage within them. This is evidenced in Sallanlatva and in several Siberian massifs (see below). But the interrelation between these rocks is difficult to determine. Often these are widely scattered or are confined to different structural setups (Vuoriyarvi, Kovdor, Ozernaya Varaka, possibly in Alnö, Magnet Cove). Carbonatites of the 1st stage are developed to some extent in most of the parent massifs and are confined to different structural setups. In Ozernaya Varaka, Sebl-Yavr, and Tura Bay they form linear veins between 0.1 and 15 m thick, while in Kovdor (veined zones of Mogo-Vidi or Pilkoma-Selga) linear veins and metasomatic carbonatite bodies of the 1st stage (developed in the zone of brecciation) 20–80 m in thickness occur. In Sallanlatva they are formed at the top (to the west) of the carbonatite stocks, while in Vuoriyarvi they form independent stocks (Tuxta-Vara) of thicknesses exceeding 300 m. These rocks are found in the carbonatite stocks of Gulinskii (the mode of distribution and the extention of these rocks are not discussed here), Magnet Cove, Iron Hill, Kaiserstühl, Alnö, and Fen (dysanalytic-pyroxene and biotite-pyroxene sövites). In most of the massifs rocks of the 1st stage carbonatites are present in small amounts within rocks of the 2nd stage carbonatites or are completely absent. In the Siberian massifs and in the Kola Peninsula, which we investigated in detail, rocks of the 1st stage are not always present at the top of the carbonatite bodies or stocks. In most of the massifs these rocks are either absent or form small independent zones or bodies, while the big stocks are usually composed of carbonatites of the 2nd stage right up to the contact with the mixed rocks (Southern Siberia).

We reported large (up to 10 m in diameter) blocks of carbonatites of the 1st stage (black) within the veins of 2nd stage carbonatites at Kovdor (veined zones of Botsu-Vara and Pilkoma-Selga), but these blocks are mostly confined to the centers of the veins and show a rounded form resembling xenoliths.

Carbonatites of the 1st stage form stocks more than 300 m in diameter in Vuoriyarvi (Tuxta-Vara), and contain numerous large thick-banded blocks of magnetite-forsterite rocks. The banding is sharply intersected by independent, approximately north-south veins of carbonatites. In Kovdor rocks of the 1st stage form rounded metasomatic bodies around ijolites (Mogo-Vidi body), and are well developed in thick zones of magnetite-forsteritic rocks (the principal body) and fenites in the southern part of the massif (Pilkoma-

Selga). In Ozernaya Varaka a north-south trending body of carbonatite 5 m in width and 50 m in length on the eastern flank of the massif is located along with the rocks of the 1st stage. This body surrounds the fenites along a stretch of 10 m and is highly mylonitized, calcitized, and biotitized. Similar mylonitization is also noticed in other areas. One of the Siberian massifs (Frolov, 1960) contains fragments of pyroxenes, while in other places (Frolov et al., 1969) they form carbonatized schists and ijolites. Probably the wide zones of altered metasomatic melilitic rocks of Gulinskii (recrystallized skarn—Epshtein, 1959) and Oka are associated with these carbonatites and contain dysanalyte (latrappite).

Where the carbonatites of the 1st stage (sövites) are distinguished from the rest it is observed that these carbonatites are localized in a large mylonitic zone (linear or tube-like) and are either preceded by or associated with rocks of the 2nd stage. Intensively mixed metasomatites associated with carbonatites are responsible for the brecciated appearance to the carbonatites. Aureoles around the carbonatites of the 1st stage sometimes reach 10 m in thickness and contain numerous carbonatite veins. These aureole rocks are always composed of fragmentary relics of mixed altered rocks and often constitute more than 60% of the total volume (Kovdor, Pilkoma-Selga, Ozernaya Varaka, Vuoriyarvi, Tuxta-Vara). It is often difficult to differentiate between pure carbonatites and carbonatized mixed rocks like ijolites, micatized fenites, and mica-magnetite-forsterite rocks.

Carbonatites of the 1st stage can be differentiated by their intimate association with the mylonite zones, the presence of fragments of mixed rocks, non-uniform structures, taxitic textures, and well-defined zones. Central and subcentral parts of the bodies are usually leucocratic ($SiO_2 < 30\%$), equigranular, and consistent in composition. But along the periphery and central parts silica and apatite contents increase up to 40–60% and become even higher deep within the aureole. In Kovdor (Pilkoma-Selga) carbonatite zones are composed of fragments of micatized fenites (up to 7 m in diameter) at the upper level, grading to brecciated fenites and, at still higher levels, pinch out (40 m vertically). Below these carbonatite zones weak micatized fenite vugs, calcite veins, apatite (with biotite and sphene), and apatite veins (with biotite and pyrrhotite) occur. The proportion of these fragments remains unchanged to a depth of 100 m. In carbonatite of the 1st stage fragments and relics of mixed rocks are flat or rounded in shape and are oriented parallel to the contact of the body, giving rise to banded structures.

The composition of carbonatites of the 1st stage (sövites) is relatively simple (Tables 2 and 3). Large leucocratic bodies are composed of calcite (60–80%), apatite (5–10%), pyroxene (0–10%), mica (biotite or phlogopite, 5–15%), and magnetite (0–15%). Sometimes monticellite, melilite, schorlomite, nepheline, and forsterite are also present. Silicate minerals are dominant in the metasomatites of the contact zone and fragments of mixed rocks are present.

The prevalent rocks may be grouped into three facies:

a) Micaceous-pyroxenitic;

b) Monticellitic;

c) Phlogopite-forsteritic.

Carbonatites of *micaceous-pyroxenitic facies* are located within the fenitized gneisses (Ozernaya Varaka), fenites (Kovdor, Vuoriyarvi, and probably Alnö), ijolites and nephelinitic pyroxenites (Siberian massifs, Kovdor, and Sallanlatva). The proportion of mica and pyroxene in carbonatite varies. On the margin of micaceous-pyroxenitic veins wollastonite (Kovdor, Gulinskii) is occasionally present. Apatites costituting 5–10% and sometimes up to 25% are concentrated at the marginal and apical parts. Magnetites are either totally absent (Kovdor, Ozernaya Varaka) or form small relics (Oka and southern massifs of Siberia). These relics constitute not more than 15% of the total (excluding the parts rich in relics of magnetite-forsteritic rocks, e.g. Kovdor, Vuoriyarvi). Possibly the wide metasomatic zones of Gulinskii belong to this facies. They are carbonatized and altered to melilitic rocks comprising diopside, phlogopite, schorlomite, and wollastonite (recrystallized skarn—Epshtein, 1959).

Carbonatites of the *monticellite facies* are rare. Thin veins (up to 3 m) occurring at the center of Kovdor massif and possibly the veins of Kaiserstühl and Magnet Cove belong to this facies. These veins are more widely distributed in Oka, where they contain biotite (in places they are dominated by monticellite) and melilite (Gold, 1964; Maurice, 1957; Nickel, 1956) and, in places, wollastonite. In Oka the carbonatites occur around the melilitic rocks and are surrounded by zones of silica-metasomatites containing melilite.

Frolov (1960) studied the carbonatites of *phlogopite-forsterite facies* in the Kovdor, Vuoriyarvi, and Siberian massifs. They are composed of phlogopite, forsterite, magnetite, and sometimes diopside and schorlomite. They are often gray (Silurian massif) or black (Kovdor, Vuoriyarvi) in color and cut across the thick blocks of magnetite and serpentine (chrysotile). Serpentines are developed along the margin of forsterite crystals and, without any forsterite relic, always penetrate thc calcite crystals (Fig. 13, *a*). In the carbonatized zone of magnetite-forsteritic rocks serpentines occur in small amounts. If present they are not embedded in calcite. In Vuoriyarvi and in the south Siberian massifs ferruginous forsterite (FeO 7.32–8.04%) occurs within the carbonatite of the 1st stage. It is surrounded by reaction rims of serpentine, richterite, and magnetite or is totally replaced by aggregates (Fig. 13, *b*) of these minerals with or without richterite. These carbonatites also occur within the pyroxenites (Siberian massif) and magnetite-forsteritic rocks (Vuoriyarvi), where the ferruginous nature of the forsterites is not established. Probably these forsterites were derived from much deeper horizons.

In all the carbonatites of the 1st stage the most important feature is the presence of complex accessory minerals like schorlomite (in Vuoriyarvi—zircon; Borodin et al., 1960), dysanalyte (in Oka—latrappite), sphene, calcite, and niccolite (Oka). Sphene and dysanalyte (and schorlomite) occur in a reaction relation. There is an antipathetic relation between Zr-schorlomite and calcite. Niccolite is associated with latrappite (activity of Nb is inversely proportional to the activity of Ti). The principal distribution of the individual minerals and the geochemical specification of the carbonatites are discussed below.

The presence of the above mentioned or other calc-silicates in carbonatites indicates the conditions of formation of the rocks, i.e. the depth (pressure) and the potentiality of components like CaO and CO_2. Diopside is always present with melilite and monticellite, but always shows an antipathetic relation with wollastonite. Probably the crystallization of melilite-monticellite-calcite took place at a shallow depth or at higher temperatures (similar to skarn). Formation of wollastonite is preceded by carbonatites or it is formed by the decomposition of melilite, indicating thermal influence of carbonatites. The absence of bedding in calcined quartz rocks and replacement of quartz by diopside recall the similar process associated with deep-seated facies of the metasomatic rocks of Aldan Shield and Baikal (Korzhinskii, 1947).

At the contact of carbonatites of the 1st stage there is frequent occurrence of metasomatites. The characters of these metasomatites depend on the composition of the mixed rock and principally on the degree of deformation. The contact effect in all cases leads to recrystallization, meltiin of rocks, and recurrence of reactive minerals. At the contacts with the gneisses around the carbonatite veins (Ozernaya Varaka, Vuoriyarvi) biotite-pyroxenitic, pyroxenitic, or albite-pyroxenetic bands between 1 and 2 cm thick and occasionally up to 30 cm are formed. Similar replacement is also found in contacts with fenites (leucocratic) and nepheline syenites. But when they contain nepheline at the contact zones, biotites are formed and the pyroxene becomes less than 20% (Kovdor). All nepheline-bearing or melanocratic rocks are subjected to intense metasomatism. The contact zone may be up to 1–2 m wide and apatites are always present (up to 20% and more—Kovdor), sometimes forming monomineralic rock. Pyrrhotite, although not so significant in carbonatites of the 1st stage, occurs in some veins of Kovdor at the contact zones without replacing the carbonatites and is associated with apatite and biotite. Probably these are derived from the mixed fenitized amphibolites in which the pyrrhotite content increases to 15%. Melanocratic pyroxenites and olivinites at the contacts with carbonatites of the 1st stage are subjected to partial melting, apatitization, and calcitization with recrystallization and segregation of magnetite. The thickness of the alteration zone around ultrabasites is 5–10 cm on an average (Kovdor, Vuoriyarvi). Sometimes it is up to 1–2 m (in pyroxenites and ijolites of Eastern Sayan).

Melilitic rocks at the contact zones with carbonatites are subjected to mild but extensive replacement. Consequently these may be divided into two

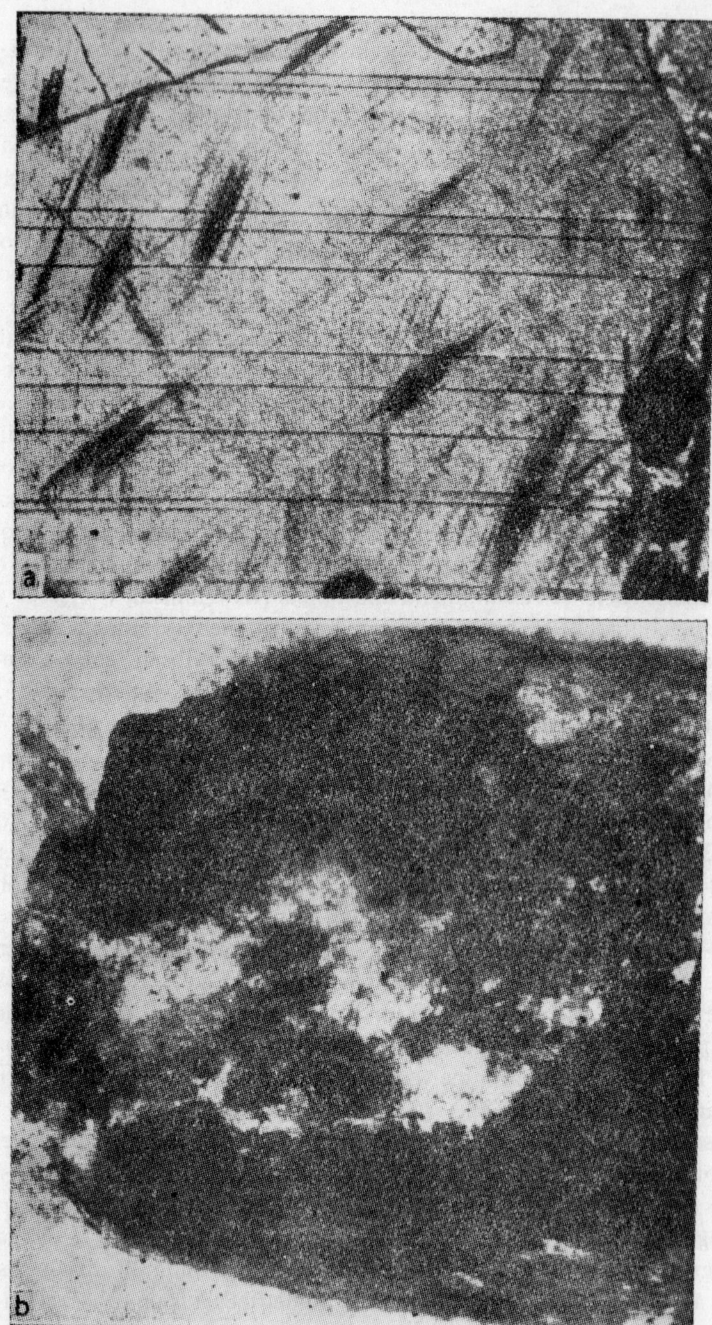

Fig. 13. Carbonatites of 1st stage.

a—Needle-shaped crystals of magnetite and serpentine in calcite (Kovdor massif, under crossed nicol, ×128); b—Reaction rims of richterite, dolomite, and serpentine (gray) around forsterite crystals (black) (Vuoriyarvi massif) natural magnification.

types: Wide distribution of fine-grained aggregates of diopside, phlogopite, and wollastonite in melilitites, comprising the *first type* of replacement, is well known in Kovdor, Gulinskii, and Salmagorsk (Borodin et al., 1963). The above mineral assemblage recrystallizes near the contact with carbonatites and is gradually converted to melanocratic carbonatites, retaining the same silicates in their composition. With calcitization of the rocks recrystallization of the minerals takes place and wollastonite as well as diopside start melting. Principally this characterizes the replacement of the *second type*, which develops at the contact of these rocks with carbonatites of monticellite facies, where melilitic rocks are subjected to melting without decomposition of melilite. This second type of replacement associated with carbonatites occurs in Oka (Maurice, 1956, 1957) where the paragenesis melilite-calcite-monticellite is known to occur at the zone of carbonatization. Similarly, stable mineral assemblages like pyroxene, mica, forsterite, and magnetite are formed in these rocks at the contact of carbonatite bodies. The thickness of the contact zone is usually up to 0.5 m but in cataclastic parts of the mixed rocks the thickness of the aureole is five to ten times of this (for each rock).

Early carbonatites of the 2nd stage

These rocks are widely distributed in the massifs we studied and constitute from 30–40% to 80–95% of the total volume of carbonatite rocks. Except in Magnet Cove, Iron Hill, and Gulinskii (rocks of the 1st stage predominate there), carbonatites of the 2nd stage are predominant in the rest of the massifs like Maimecha-Kotui, Eastern Siberia, Sayan, Fenno-Scandinavia, and the African provinces. In the superficial massifs of Eastern Africa the role of the rocks of the 1st stage becomes negligible due to the dominance of later carbonatites.

As stated earlier, in most of the massifs clear subdivision of the groups of early carbonatites (sövites) is impossible. This makes it difficult to evaluate the distribution and interrelation of the individual groups. But the distinct geological structures of the rocks of the 2nd stage and the presence of characteristic minerals (chiefly pyrochlore) helped us to draw an analogy between the massifs observed and other massifs abroad. As a whole the carbonatites of the 2nd stage are characterized by the following:

a) Localization principally within the system of conical, ring-like fractures;
b) Prevalence of metasomatic bodies;
c) Hypidimorphic texture;
d) Presence of magnetite and accessory pyrochlore.

A definite geological setting is most important for early carbonatites of the 2nd stage. In most cases these are developed in a conical-ring system of fractures occurring at depths (at the focus). This characteristic is one reason for drawing an analogy between the magmatic carbonatites and the ring dikes of Scotland, Iceland, and FRG (Federal Republic of Germany). Conical-ring dikes are widely known from various massifs of Africa, Siberia and Fenno-Scandinavia.

For example, when these rocks are localized within the linear fractured system a concentration of massifs, rare in nature, occurs in linear regional tectonic zones (Siberia—Frolov et al., 1969; Kazakhstan). In such cases, all the rocks of the massifs are distinctly oriented along this zone. In most cases carbonatites of the 2nd stage not only form their own independent system of conical-ring bodies, but the formation of this system depends very little on the structure of the massif or the structures of the mixed region. This may be illustrated from the massifs of the Kola region, where the centers (focal axis and focus) of the ring-dikes usually coincide with the general center. In Vuoriyarvi the focus is situated at the southern contact, while in Kovdor it is in the southeast and in Sallanlatva in the north (Fig. 6). This is more conspicuous in the massifs of hypabyssal facies, whereas in superficial conditions independent stocks of carbonatites (Tundulu, Toror, Napak, Chilwa) or central types of structures (Siberian massifs, Sallanlatva, Mbeya, Lolekek, Spitzkop, and others) are formed. The carbonatites in them are either concentrated at the center or are slightly mixed up. Formation and development of a conical system of fractures in which carbonatites of the 2nd stage are localized do not depend on the structures of carbonatite bodies that cut across the monoclines (Kovdor, southern contact; Vuoriyarvi, eastern contact; Arbarstakh) and the folded structures (Eastern Siberian massifs). But in the latter case the primary development of carbonatite bodies occurs where the orientation of the conical dikes coincides with the orientation of the layered rocks. In Ozernaya Varaka most of the carbonatites form gently dipping strata or cross-cutting veins within the fenitized gneisses. In Kovdor a thick, stretched carbonatite body lies in the southwestern part within the fenitized gneisses, showing poor stratification and containing numerous fragments of fenites. To the south and to the north where the trend of the ring structures sharply differs from the trend of the metamorphic rocks the thickness of the carbonatites gradually decreases to zero.

In Vuoriyarvi carbonatite bodies of the 2nd stage strike northeasterly and are mainly restricted to folded structures in which the same strike is present. Influences of mixed structures on the configurations of the carbonatite of Siberia and Scandinavia as well as that of the surficial volcanoes of Central Africa are not so conspicuous. In Kovdor, Vuoriyarvi, Ozernaya Varaka, and Siberia carbonatite veins from mixed fenites, traced within ijolites and ultrabasites cutting across the contacts of the massifs and early pseudo-ring structures, are alkaline in nature. Carbonatites of the 2nd stage either spontaneously cut across the rocks of the stocks of the 1st stage or develop along with them (Kovdor, Vuoriyarvi). But as mentioned earlier, interrelations between them are not always clear. In one of the massifs of Siberia the contacts of the 1st and 2nd stage rocks are always tectonic in nature, but Pozharitzkaya showed the spontaneous development of rocks of the 2nd stage along with the rocks of the 1st stage in this particular massif. Occurrences of accessory pyrochlore (characteristic of rocks of the 2nd stage) occur in the carbonatites of the 1st stage in Vuoriyarvi (Tuxta-Vara). Further field work will show whether it is possible to consider the rocks of both stages under the same phase or facies of formation of early carbonatites.

Early carbonatites of the 2nd stage form *two morphological* varieties: *stocks* (nucleus) and the system of *conical-ring* bodies (layered) (Dixey, 1946; McCall, 1958, 1959, 1963) that accompany the stocks. Stocks (nuclei) are more common in the superficial massifs (Africa and South Siberian massifs, Gulinskii, Sallanlatva, Mbeya, Lolekek, Toror, Chilwa, Tundula, Lueshe). Massifs of transitional facies (between volcanic and hypabyssal) similarly contain stocks (Alnö, East Siberian massifs). But hypabyssal massifs rich in ultrabasites often form a conical vein system (Kovdor, Vuoriyarvi, Lesnaya, and Ozernaya Varaka). The stocks show their usual conical forms with layering, the latter indicating the concentric configuration in conformity with their contacts. The focal axis of the stocks and veins is usually the same, but the focus is different (the focus of the stock is higher than the focus of the conical vein), as shown by the classical example given by Eckermann (1948a) from Alnö (Fig. 6, *i*) and by our example from Sallanlatva, where the focus of the central stock is placed higher than the focus of the series of veins. Occurrences of vein-like bodies of carbonatites within a single conical fracture-system and with a single focus indicate the constant flattening of the veins in the direction of the focal axis. In Kovdor, near the focal axis, the veins of carbonatites are almost vertical (dipping about 75–85°W) and in the extended part (Pilkoma-Selga, Votzu-Vara) the dip of the veins varies from 60 to 50 and even to 25° (Niske-Vara). A similar change in dip (from 65–70 to 35–40°) is observed in Vuoriyarvi and Sallanlatva. The structures formed at the central stock and in the system of conical ring dikes are often independent and their focal axis is oriented away from the center of the massifs, forming individual concentric zonal groups. If there is a known occurrence of carbonatites at the center of the volcanic massifs, the structures developed fully agree with the central type of massifs. The focus of the silicate rocks and of the carbonatites are different and the orientations of their directive textures usually do not coincide.

Unlike the rocks of the 1st stage, carbonatites of the 2nd stage form distinct fractured veins with uniform contacts (Fig. 14) confined to the zone of brecciation; the amount of the fragments of mixed rocks in them is not so large. In the thick carbonatite veins of Kovdor (Votzu-Vara) large (up to 100 m) individual blocks of fenites and fenitized amphibolites occur. Such blocks are, however, rare in the stocks (both southern and northern) of Gulinskii (Butakova and Egorov, 1962) but occur at the contact zones

(Epshtein, 1959). In a comparatively pure carbonatite body (Kovdor, Gulinskii, the Siberian massifs) and thick veins the amount of the fragments of mixed rocks increases. In Vuoriyarvi and in Sebl-Yavr, where the thickness of the individual veins does not exceed 150 m (on an average 20 m), the amount of fragments of mixed pyroxenites does not exceed 15–20%. Only in a particular vein does it reach 50%. Carbonatization of the region belonging to the principal zone and the intensively crushed magnetite-forsterite rocks show their own typical breccias full of fragments of these rocks (Kovdor, Vuoriyarvi). All the carbonatite veins of such a region contain relics of magnetite-forsterite rocks. Thick carbonatite bodies of the 2nd stage show relatively constant composition and calcite constitutes 70–80% of them. A consistent admixture of apatite constitutes about 10–20% while silicate and magnetite

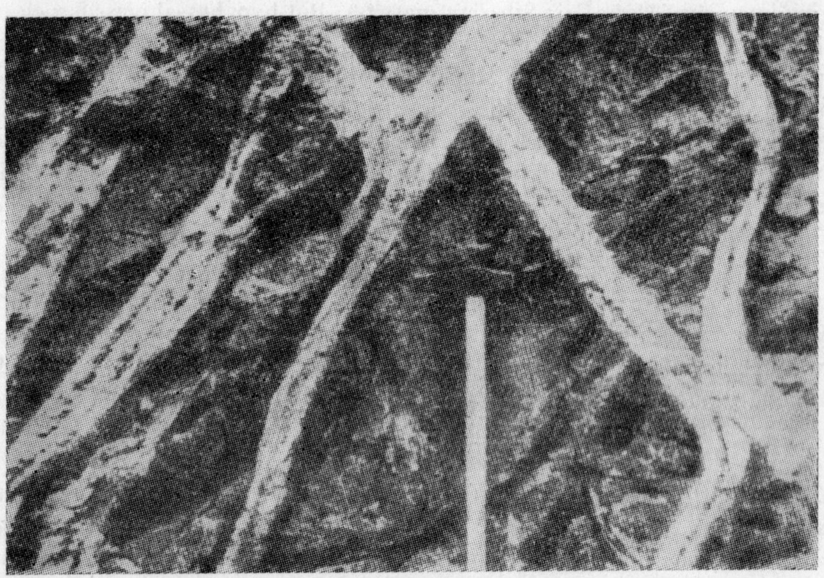

Fig. 14. Veins of early carbonatites of 2nd stage (with sharp contact but without prominent replacement near veins) in ijolites—Kovdor massif.

contents rarely exceed 20%. Minerals in such bodies are uniformly distributed (Kovdor, Pilkoma-Selga and Votzu-Vara, South Siberian massifs, Gulinskii, Alnö, Fen, Mrima, Chilwa, and others). Carbonatites confined to the zone of brecciation and containing selective fragments of mixed rocks show compositional and mineralogical variation over the same body. The peripheral carbonatite veins rich in silicates and magnetites between 1–2 cm and 1–2 m thick are more or less constant in composition, but here the veins contain relics and decomposed material of mixed rocks. At the center of the thick carbonatite body local segregations of silicates and magnetite always occur. In large carbonatite bodies of Kovdor (Votzu-Vara) segregation of magnetite (0.5×0.5 m to 5×10 m in dimensions) is found in some places. In the carbonatite nucleus of one of the Sayan massifs segregations of pyroxenes and micas occur over an appreciable part from the contact inward (up to 1 km). Along the southern part of the eastern thick carbonatized massif of Kovdor (Votzu-Vara) several zones rich in magnetite, forsterite and apatite occur (total up to 40%), while in the north the minerals do not exceed 20–25%.

Comparatively coarse-grained textures (grains up to 3–5 cm in size) are developed in the central parts of the thick carbonatite bodies of Vuoriyarvi, Kovdor, Sallanlatva, and the Siberian massifs. Calcite crystals (up to 3–5 cm) are enclosed within the fine-grained mass of apatite. Calcite and phlogopite form coarse-grained granoblastic aggregates. Apatite occurs uniformly but is confined to the central part of the body. However, no segmented zone controlling the occurrence of apatite could be isolated. Probably apatites in carbonatites are segregated after calcite during the same episode of mineral formation. Apatites are closely associated with accessory pyrochlore and reddish-brown phlogopite. But apatites may often be free of these minerals (Kovdor-Pilkoma-Selga). Coarse-grained carbonatites are well known in Alnö, Fen, Kaiserstühl, and Iron Hill, where they are regarded as "pegmatitic sövites" or "sövite-pegmatite" (Brögger, 1921; Eckermann, 1948a, 1958, 1966; Heinrich, 1967). Most of these massifs show their own characteristic laminated structures and form aggregates of calcite crystals 5×5 cm in size flattened in the direction of (0001). The transparent minerals (see below) are emplaced between them. The laminated parts are more melanocratic and the amount of apatite in them usually does not fall below 15%. The silicate content is higher than 20–25%. In these parts the laminated calcites are uniformly idiomorphic in nature, while the crystals of all the transparent minerals at the junction of calcites are rarely uniformly developed in the carbonatite bodies. Often these minerals form schlieren and pockets or are uniformly developed in the central parts.

Carbonatites of the 2nd stage differ from those of the 1st stage in mineral composition. Carbonatites of the 2nd stage are marked by constant presence of calcite (about 60–99%) and apatite (10–30%). The other minerals are segregated between them and include the different dark-colored characteristic ones like:

a) Phlogopite-forsterite;
b) Diopside-phlogopite; and
c) Aegirine-biotite.

Carbonatites of phlogopite-forsteritic facies are known to occur in almost all the massifs (Kovdor, Vuoriyarvi, Sebl-Yavr, Gulinskii, the Siberian massifs, probably Lolekek, Marima, Toror, Alnö, Fen, Kaiserstühl, and others) of hypabyssal and volcanic facies that occur at depths. The rocks are more persistent in composition and are characterized by conspicuous assemblages of mixed rocks (ultrabasite—Kovdor, Vuoriyarvi; ijolite—Sayan; fenite—Kovdor, Mrima, Toror), with the exception of nepheline syenites. At the margin of carbonatite veins of phlogopite-forsterite facies, forsterite is usually absent and gives way to phologopite and sometimes diopside. Pozhaitzkaya and Epshtein (1963, 1964) showed the replacement of foresterite by diopside near the contact zones and diopside by forsterite at the center of the carbonatite veins. Phlogopite-forsteritic and diopside-forsteritic facies are very similar to and are associated with interrelated transitional minerals. But as a rule in most carbonatite bodies forsterites are more prevalent.

Carbonatites of the diopside-phlogopitic facies are more frequent in occurrence, while the forsteritic rocks are more abundent. These are illustrated in the massifs of Eastern Sayan, Vuoriyarvi, and Kovdor. Occurrences of diopside along with phlogopite are reported from the massifs of Kaiserstühl (Wimmenauer, 1959), Alnö (Eckermann, 1948a, 1966), Fen (Brögger, 1921; Saether, 1958), Iron Hill (Larsen, 1942), and from other massifs (Smith, 1953; Heinrich, 1967).

Carbonatites of aegirine-biotite facies are frequent in the form of small individual veins, but in some cases they form large massifs as well. Carbonatites of this facies are widespread in Lueshe (Meyer and Bethune, 1960), and also occur in one of the massifs of Siberia (Frolov et al., 1969) and in Alnö (Eckermann, 1948a), Fen (Brögger, 1921), Kaiserstühl, Iron Hill (Larsen, 1942; Grogan, 1960), Oka (Maurice, 1956; Gold, 1963), Mbeya (Faroley and James, 1955; Jager, 1959) and in several other places (Tuttle et al., 1967). All the carbonatite bodies of this type are confined within nepheline (and cancrinite) syenite (Lueshe and the Siberian massifs), nepheline-bearing fenites (Kovdor, Vuoriyarvi, Alnö), ijolites (Iron Hill), and in equivalent alkaline effusives (Kaiserstühl). Forsterite and magnetite are usually absent from carbonatites of this facies and albite or albitized microcline are quite common, principally in the contact and central regions. Biotite decreases toward the center and is replaced by aegirine. Microcline and albite occur as relics from metasomatized feldspathic rocks. Both these minerals are absent from carbonatites that occur within the non-feldspathic rocks. Pyrite relics inherited from the schists occur in the contact zones and in some veins of one of the massifs of Eastern Sayan, and are associated with magnetites on the periphery.

Accessory minerals like pyrochlore (and hatchettolite), baddeleyite (in the first two facies), or zircon (in the rocks of aegirine-biotitic facies) occur in all the facies of carbonatites. Zircon probably originates as a result of magmatization with nepheline syenites. In carbonatites it is not replaced by other minerals because it is more stable (Lueshe and the Siberian massifs).

With the increase of contact activities carbonatites of the 2nd stage are converted into rocks of the 1st stage, but the thickness of the contact zones increases very little (in Vuoriyarvi hundreds of veins are encountered with thickness varying between 1 and 5 cm). Fenites and gneisses are to some extent transformed. These rocks, along with little albitization of the microcline, occur in Kovdor, Vuoriyarvi, and Ozernaya Varaka. Intensive replacement is noticed in melanocratic and nepheline-bearing rocks, i.e. pyroxenites, pyroxene-fenites, ijolites, and nepheline syenites that were subjected to massive micatization and are sometimes marked by the presence of pyroxenes (Kovdor, Siberia). The mineralogical composition of the contact zones depends wholly on the composition, thickness and intensity of tectonic activities of the mixed rocks. At the margin of diopside and aegirine-diopside, quartz-pyroxene-hornblende (Eastern Sayan) and biotite-pyroxene-fenites are formed with a negligible amount of micas (Fig. 15, *a*). But micas, almost in monomineralic aggregates (sometimes with admixtures of pyroxene and apatite, Fig. 15, *b*), are formed in rocks containing nepheline, cancrinite, and feldspars. This process is more conspicuous in one of the Sayan massifs, where carbonatites of different compositions occur in fenitized gneisses accompanied by biotitized and pyroxenitic rims. The iron content of the micas depends on the alkalinity of the mixed rocks. Micas rich in magnesium are formed at the contact with ultrabasites. Those rich in iron are formed at the contacts with nepheline syenites, nepheline-bearing fenites, and ijolites (Samoilov and Gormasheva, 1966; Pozharitzkaya, 1966; Chernisheva and Gormasheva, 1966; Landa, 1966). Micatized rims are also formed around the melilitic rocks.

Replacement without recrystallization is not so widespread in olivines at the contacts with carbonatites, and forsterite crystals are formed near the contacts (Fig. 15, *c*). From ferruginous primary forsterites iron separates out in the form of very fine magnetite and such forsterites show optical characters indicating the absence of Fe. Development of rims of magnetite crystals is a common feature at the contact of carbonatites of the 2nd stage with magnetite-bearing ultrabasites, magnetite-forsterite rocks, melanocratic fenites, and pyroxenites (without primary magnetite, Fig. 15, *d*). This suggests the fixation of iron at the contact zones of the veins (Pozharitzkaya, 1966). It is interesting to note that magnetite is not formed at the contacts of carbonatites with alkaline rocks and its place is taken by ferruginous biotite.

Intensive calcitization and apatitization, which are found everywhere, are the effects of contact metasomatism induced by the emplacement of carbonatites. Both these processes occur in the melanocratic and alkaline rocks. In leucocratic rocks they are negligible. In all these cases the intensity of metasomatic activity decreases in steeply dipping carbonatite bodies and increases in gently dipping bodies. In Ozernaya Varaka gently dipping metasomatic carbonatite veins show rings of different thicknesses in different facies (horizontally 1–2 cm and vertically up to 15 cm) at the contact zone. Contact replacements of fenites and schists under the carbonatite bodies at depths were

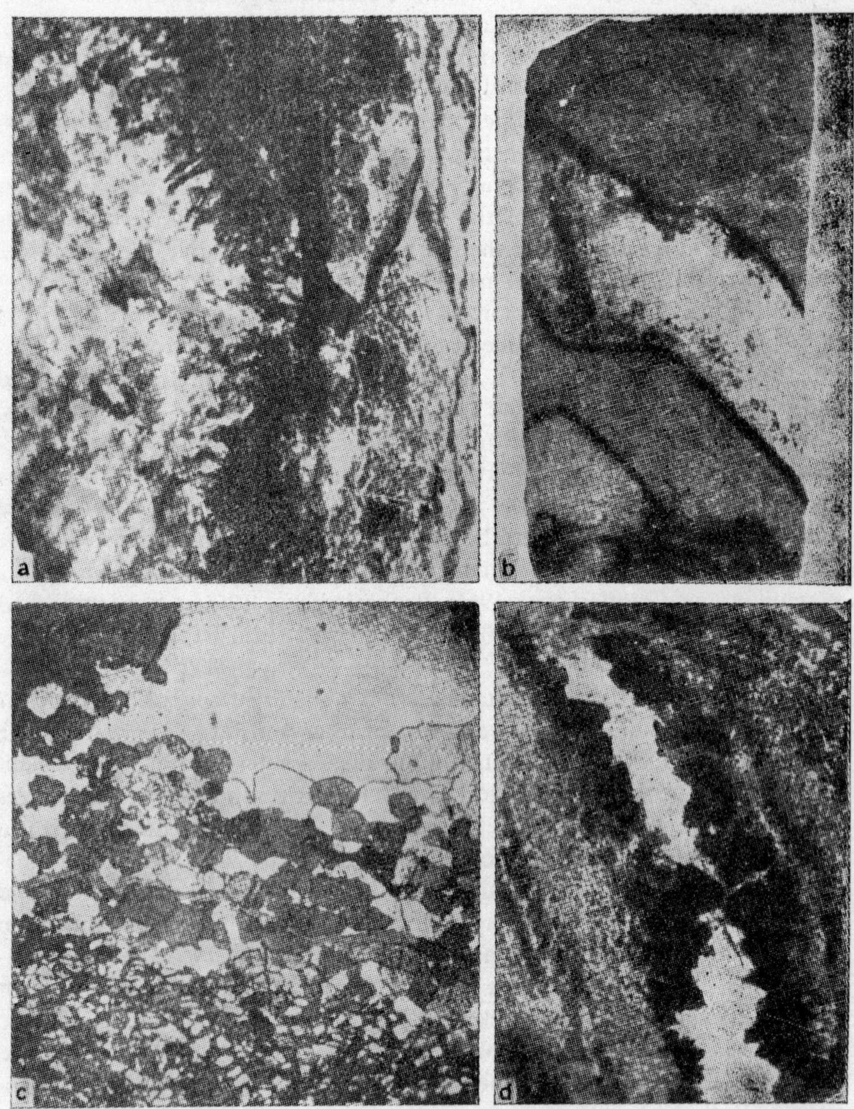

Fig. 15. Reaction rims at contacts of early carbonatites of 2nd stage.

a—Pyroxenitic (at contact with fenites)—Ozernaya Varaka; b—Biotitic (at contact with schists)—Siberia; c—Forsteritic (at contact with olivinites)—Kovdor; d—Magnetitic (at contact with pyroxenites)—Vuoriyarvi; a, b, d—Natural magnification; c—Under crossed nicol, mag. ×24.

observed in Vuoriyarvi and in Siberian massifs. In both cases fenites and schists are converted into albite-biotite-pyroxene metasomatites, with apatite constituting about 5–25%. In leucocratic fenites of Vuoriyarvi strong albitization is marked. In the melanocratic massifs of Siberia albite quickly disappears with the formation of either vesicular pyroxenitic rocks (along with quartz-rich schists) or masses of biotite (along with biotite-albite fenites and chlorite-sericite schists) near the carbonatites.

Apatitization is developed in association with carbonatites. Intensive apatitization sometimes occurs in considerable areas where it is localized around carbonatite stocks (Sukulu, Bukusu) and it is often found associated with magnetite-forsterite rocks. The latter in Kovdor, Vuoriyarvi and Lulekop not only contain apatite (5–25%) but are also subjected to massive apatitization accompanied by veins of carbonatites ('Karbonatite'—according to Glagolev, 1962). According to several workers these apatite-magnetite-forsterite rocks (Rimskaya-Korsakova, 1947; Volotovskaya, 1959; Kukharenko et al., 1965) formed earlier than the carbonatites. Only the spatial association of these rocks with carbonatites and the development of accessory minerals like baddeleyite and (sometimes) pyrochlore together with the apatite in them testify to the relation of apatitization with carbonatites.

The volume of metasomatic replacement of the mixed rocks at the contact zones with carbonatites is relatively not so great; it cannot be compared to the total volume of carbonatites. As mentioned earlier, replacement is minimum in leucocratic rocks (fenites). Carbonatite veins (Kovdor) within fenites (Pilkoma-Selga) between 150 and 200 m in size develop contact rims (only 1–5 cm thick) which may gradually die out (Votzu-Vara). In melanocratic rocks reaction rims are often found, varying between 10 and 15 cm thick, rarely 5 m and most commonly between 2 and 3 cm. Hundreds of such veins occur in Vuoriyarvi, Sebl-Yavr, Sallanlatva, and Southern Siberia. Sometimes thicker replacement zones also occur (up to 2–5 m, rarely up to 10 m). But in such cases they show recrystallization, calcitization, or apatitization of the crushed zones (Kovdor, Vuoriyarvi, Lolekek of Eastern Sayan). The sizes of carbonatite bodies are 2–3 km (Gulinskii massif) to 5 km (Siberia), with the thickness of the metasomatic zones increasing to 10 m. Replacement zones with thicknesses greater than 20–30 cm are as a rule formed near tectonicallydi sturbed regions. These zones with metasomatic activity cannot be related to the zones of brecciation that are closely associated with carbonatites. In fact the total thickness of such zones rises to 10 m or more. The zone of carbonatized magnetite-forsterite rocks of Kovdor is an example of this type. This zone is brecciated in all directions and contains individual calcite crystals everywhere. Carbonatites of the 2nd stage are relatively less developed in such zones where rocks of the 1st stage are more prominent.

Structural-textural characteristics of early carbonatites

Structures and textures of early carbonatites of both stages are similar and therefore these are considered together. The structural configuration of the carbonatites changes with the morphology of the bodies as well as their geological setup. Large bodies of carbonatite, localized within big fractured zones, develop sharp contacts retaining the configuration and composition of the fractured zone. Minerals in these carbonatite bodies are either uniformly distributed or segregated locally (schlieren and richer parts). Such bodies are massive in texture and banding develops in them very rarely (Kovdor, Pilmoma-Selga, Botzu-Vara; Gulinskii, Sallanlatva, and East Siberian massifs). This configuration, as mentioned above, is typical for most of the large carbonatite stocks of Africa (Mrima Hill, Toror, Tundulu). But the distribution of minerals as well as their quantitative relation in these carbonatite bodies is not mentioned in the literature. Only fragments (relics) of mixed rocks occur in the carbonatites of Africa, Scandinavia, and the USSR. These fragments are crushed and calcitized. Breccias cemented with calcite are well known in all the massifs, but are more common in the massifs of superficial (subvolcanic) facies. The classical works of Brögger (1921) and Eckermann (1948a) showed the occurrence of xenoliths of mixed rocks in carbonatites of Alnö and Fen. Bailey (1960), Dixey (Dixey et al., 1955), Garson (1955, 1959), and Garson and Smith (1958) showed wide distribution of xenoliths in the carbonatitic cores of Northern Rhodesia (Mwambuto, Hasveta, Nachomba Hill) and Nyasaland (Chilwa, Nsengwa, Songwa, Tundulu), and Heinrich (1967), Tuttle, and Gittins (Tuttle et al., 1967) refer to the consistent wide occurrences of xenoliths in carbonatites of the USA and Canada. Pozharitzkaya and Epshtein (1963, 1964) observed the relics of mixed ultrabasites in carbonatites of Eastern and Northern Siberia, where they are chiefly concentrated in the contact zones of large carbonatite cores. Rimskaya-Korsakova (1947), Volotovskaya (1958, 1959), and Kukharenko (Kukharenko et al., 1965) showed the formation of breccia cemented with carbonatites in Kola Peninsula.

Garson (1955, 1958, 1959) observed characteristic orientation of the xenoliths of mixed rocks and the formation of layered carbonatite. The crushing and melting of individual xenoliths caused continuation of the carbonatite mass. Frolov (1960, 1962, 1966a, b) studied in detail the internal configuration of the Siberian carbonatites and observed the wide development of two characteristic types of banding in them: *primary* and *secondary* (confirmed by our observation; Kapustin, 1960, 1964). Primary banding is related to the crystallization of carbonatites and originates at the beginning. Secondary banding is developed at the cataclastic zone. Both types of banding are characterized by different orientations in space and by different structures of the mineral aggregates in them, and differ from each other by the time and mechanism of formation. Primary banding is chiefly developed in small carbonatite bodies, localized in the zone of brecciation. They contain numerous fragments of mixed rocks. The individual fragments of mixed rocks in primary banding sometimes reorient themselves without retaining their angular forms. These are often crushed into finer fragments (Fig. 16, *a*, *b*) or reaction (and relic) minerals that sharply orient themselves parallel to the contact of the carbonatite body. In such zones banding in carbonatites is thicker on the periphery of the body and thinner near the central part (Fig. 16, *c*, *d*). Banding usually occurs at intervals and, in places, is locally disturbed (corrugation). It may be bent along the contact or enclose large fragments oriented parallel to the banding.

The banding in Kovdor (Pilkoma-Selga) has obviously taken place in an open basin in the zone of carbonatization. The central part of steeply dipping carbonatites is full of rounded and flattened fragments of mixed fenites. At depths the amount and the size of these fragments decrease, while carbonatites develop more thin bands rich in biotite flakes. Development of similar banding occurs in the zone of calcitization of magnetite-forsterite rocks of Kovdor and Vuoriyarvi, where the whole rock mass appears to contain brecciated carbonatite bands that become thinner at depth.

Cases of distinct trachytization were observed in the rocks of the banded regions. Here the minerals generally do not show any preferred orientation. Although the pyroxene crystals and mica flakes are sometimes oriented parallel to the banding (angle between the banding and 'c' axis of the pyroxene crystal is 0 to $\pm 40°$, while the mica flakes are oriented in the direction of banding with the angle between 0 and $\pm 30°$), the other minerals do not show any preferred orientation. Only in a single instance (Vuoriyarvi and East Sayan) was it found that the stretched calcite crystals are oriented parallel to the banding.

The stretching and intermixing with carbonate fragments, the constant development of reaction rims of minerals at the contacts of carbonatites, the banding parallel to the contact planes, and streamlined fragments devoid of cataclastic remnants reflect the intermingling of the carbonatite mass with the engulfed fragments of mixed rocks. The intermingling took place during or after solidification of carbonatite (plastic flow in solid state). Only the development of tectonic strain in crystalline carbonatites may have caused cataclasis in crystals of primary minerals under the same strain (see below). Movement (even plastic) of the solid carbonatite masses within coarse silicate rocks has invariably given rise to stripes in the former at the contact zone, while the crystalline minerals of the contact zones are subjected to crushing. Similar features, if exhibited by the carbonatites occurring in the silicate rock fragments at the contact zone, are usually destroyed; and nothing similar to this takes place in carbonatite proper. Conversely, crystals forming rims near the contacts of carbonatite with the mixed rocks and their fragments are often oriented perpendicular to the contacts with no trace of cataclasis. It is

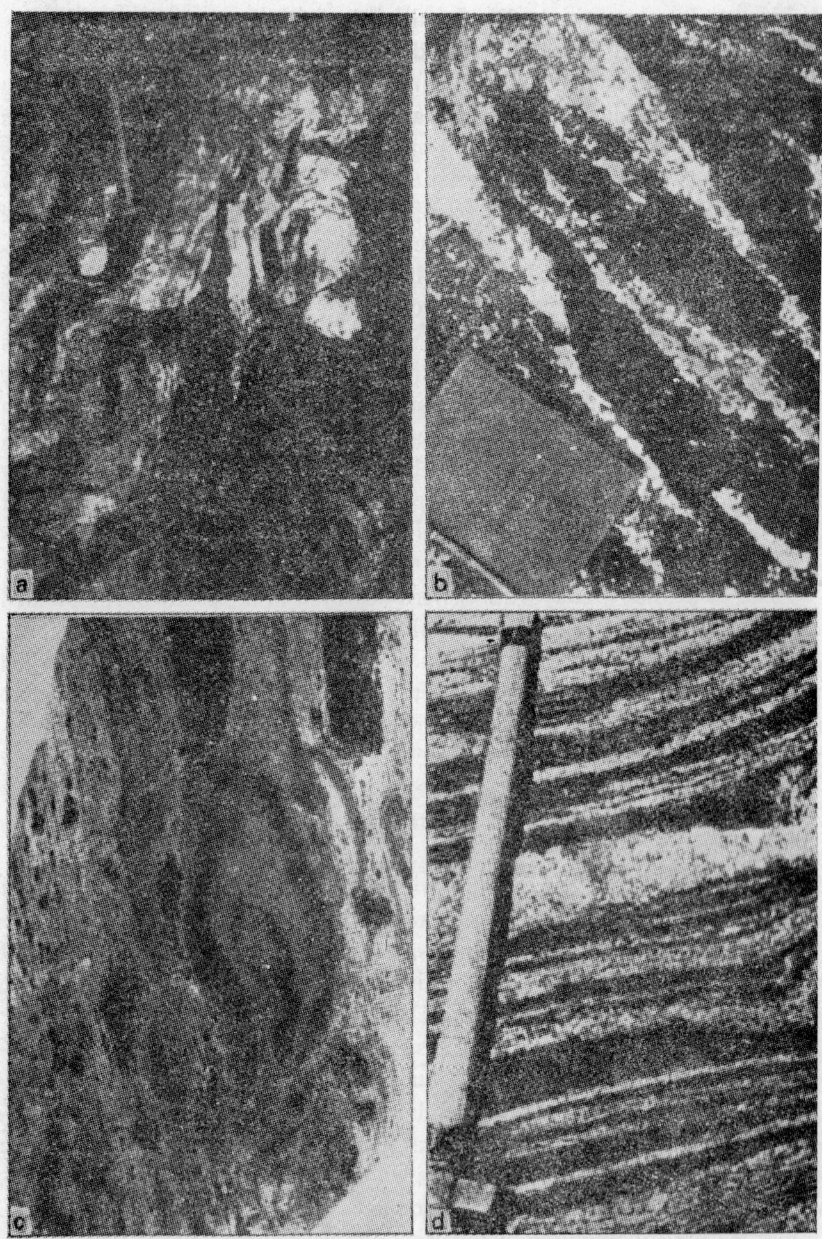

Fig. 16. Layered texture of early carbonatites.

a, b—Flattened micas and pyroxenitized fragments of fenites, in carbonatites (Kovdor); c—Flow of layered fragments (Sallanlatva); d—Thin-bedded carbonatites (Vuoriyarvi).

therefore suggested that the stretching of the fragments of relics of minerals parallel to the contact of the carbonatite body originates within the carbonatite mass from below. Banding in such cases may be related to fluidal texture, as illustrated by Garson (1955).

Primary structures of early carbonatites are often destroyed. Cataclasis and intermingling make it difficult to study them. In most of the massifs of Africa and America these primary structures have yet to be described. Detailed study of these massifs reveals the presence of three types of primary textures in these rocks: *poikiloblastic*, *hypidiomorphic granular*, and *idiomorphic granular* (laminated).

Poikiloblastic texture is typical only of vein-like (not banded) rocks of the 1st stage. Carbonatites having this texture occur in eastern and Southern Siberia (Pozharitzkaya, 1966) and in Vuoriyarvi, Kovdor, and Sebl-Yavr. These were also reported by us independently in exposures of Magnet Cove and Oka. Occurrences of poikiloblastic carbonatites have not been reported from other countries. But this type of texture in carbonatites may occur in Kaiserstühl, Fen, Alnö, Iron Hill, and in other massifs where early rocks containing dysanalyte are present. Carbonatites having this texture form thick leucocratic veins of consistent composition with rare impregnation of silicates and magnetites. Pyroxenes occur in them in small amounts while green phlogopite is the principal dark-colored mineral. Directional textures are not developed. Massive aggregates of calcite grains (0.5–5 cm in dimension) lend an allotriomorphic interlocking texture. Pyroxenes form poikilitic crystals full of inclusions of small rounded calcite and apatite grains, while phlogopites form subhedral grains (up to 5 cm) within the calcite aggregates (Fig. 17, *a*). This texture in carbonatites is formed early and indicates the intensity of interference during the growth of minerals.

Hypidiomorphic granular texture is more conspicuous in early carbonatites and occurs in all the massifs. Nearly 90% of the early carbonatites of southern, eastern and northern Siberia, Kovdor, Sallanlatva, Vuoriyarvi, Sebl-Yavr, Ozernaya Varaka, Alnö, Magnet Cove, Oka, and Nemogosenda show this texture. Possibly this texture is also typical for most of the African massifs, although there is no detailed description of the textures of carbonatites of this continent. Carbonatites of this textural type show mosaic aggregates of polygonal calcite grains 0.1–2 cm in size. The other minerals such as pyrochlore, pyroxene, forsterite, magnetite, apatite, and dysanalyte are idiomorphic and are interstitial to calcite (Fig. 17, *b*). Crystals of silicates and magnetite always contain inclusions of rounded calcite grains and idiomorphic prisms of apatite, while calcite does not contain any silicate inclusion. Inclusions of laths of magnetite and chrysolite are found in calcites of carbonatites of the 1st stage (see above) in many massifs. These are often thoroughly intermingled with calcite crystals. The overall structure of this variety of carbonatite does not differ from that of calciphyre and highly metamorphosed marble from

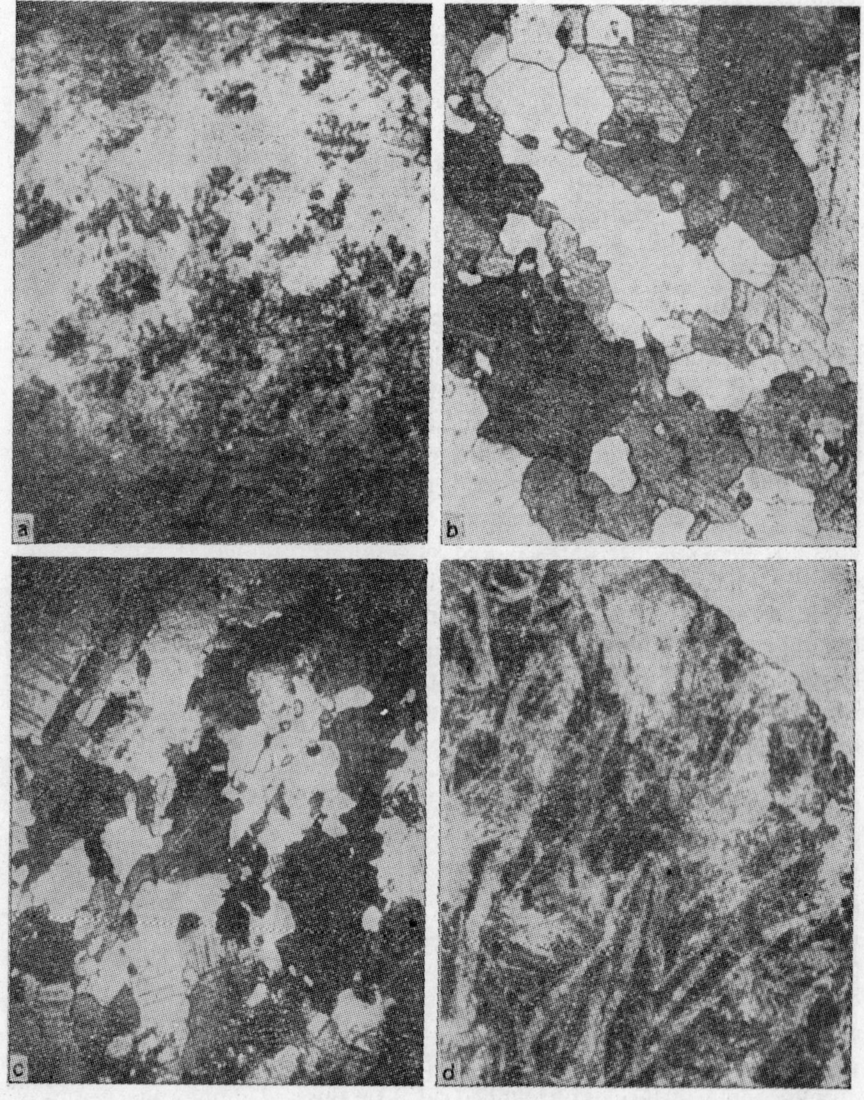

Fig. 17. Textures of early carbonatites, Siberia.

a—Skeleton crystals (dendrites) of micas in rocks of 1st stage; b, c—Mosaic texture of rocks of 2nd stage; d—Flattened calcite crystals (white) in aegirine mass; a, d—Natural magnification; b, c—Under crossed nicol, mag. ×24.

the Precambrian deposits of Aldan and South Prebaikal.

Idiomorphic granular texture is rare in carbonatites and is seen only in the 2nd stage carbonatite veins that are melanocratic and massive in structure, containing numerous relics of mixed rock. Carbonatites of this variety are more or less coarse-grained and contain aggregates of calcite crystals flattened along (0001) and transversely become 5–7 cm in length. Eckermann (1948a) regarded the highly laminated carbonatites as sövite-pegmatites. Dark-colored minerals in these rocks are distinctly xenomorphic in relation to calcites. The interstices of the coarse calcite grains are filled with relatively fine-grained material (Fig. 17, *c*).

This type of texture is formed in most parts of the 2nd stage carbonatite of Ozernaya Varaka and in one of the Siberian massifs (Frolov et al., 1969). In both these cases veins formed along the calcite lamination show no distinct contact relation with mixed rocks (fenites and syenites), while the laminated calcite crystals may develop spontaneously along with the mixed rocks. The amount of calcite decreases along the strike of the veins; near the contact the laminae are oriented more or less perpendicular to the contact (the angle between perpendicular to contact and lamination plane is 0 to $\pm 25°$). In Siberia the width of the transitional zone between one of the carbonatite bodies and nepheline syenites is about 30 m, showing recrystallization, calcitization, and cancrinitization of syenites. The microcline and biotite therein are laminated in nature, and near the typical carbonatites they gradually show a positive correlation with the calcite content (from 5–10% in syenites to 70–80% in carbonatites). The calcites here are also laminated in nature, but the laminae are not haphazardly oriented.

In the above example from Siberia calcite laminae are replaced by silicate rocks, the fragments and minerals of which show segregation. Wedge-shaped relics of mixed rocks occurring between the calcite laminae always occur in carbonatites at the contact zone.

Laminated calcites are probably formed at the upper zone of the carbonatite of the 2nd stage under intensive metasomatic replacement of the mixed rock, and occur as the principal constituents of the mixed rock. Coarse laminae of calcite and their orientations with no trace of former cataclasism indicate the metasomatic origin of calcite in such cases.

The laminated structure is usually formed in later stage. In different parts of the carbonatites of several massifs the laminated structures are present at the center of the veins, in which calcite forms mosaic textures. Richterite, pyrrhotite, and tetraferriphlogopite occur in such massifs. Pyrochlore is represented by the pure niobium variety ($Ta_2O_5 : Nb_2O_5 < 1 : 20$). Probably dolomite does not occur in such massifs, but the occurrence of the above-mentioned minerals indicates amphibolitization. It is possible that the laminated structure develops at the beginning of the process, when calcite starts recrystallizing and becomes soluble. The laminated structure indicates intensive growth of calcite with the melting of more stable minerals. Thus the rare development of idiomorphic crystal aggregates of calcite in massifs of any origin is highly significant. In laminated zones calcites are usually idiomorphic in texture. Such texture of calcite aggregates, characteristic of the metasomatically formed calcites and also of bodies of intrusive carbonatites, is not otherwise observed.

Process of autometasomatic changes in early carbonatites (amphibolitization-dolomitization)

Almost all the early carbonatites undergo metasomatic replacement with the formation of later minerals like dolomite, richterite, tetraferriphlogopite, and pyrrhotite mixed with primary minerals. Pyrrhotites are formed from magnetites and dolomites from calcites and silicates. Tetraferriphlogopites are replaced by richterites and are sometimes uniformly distributed, replacing calcites. Development of this type of mineral association in most of the veins of early carbonatites is closely related to the contact and central zones and zones of cataclasism and schistosity. Only in carbonatites of the 1st stage are richterite and dolomite often formed uniformly throughout the whole mass of the rock, totally replacing forsterite. Cataclasism is associated with small linear tectonic zones, often found parallel to the contact veins. The concentric veins of cataclastic zones are arranged along a linear zone which can often be traced for a small distance. Sometimes these minerals occur in the concentric zones of carbonatite veins along with the mixed rocks in which they gradually disappear. In Vuoriyarvi and in one of the massifs of Siberia we have observed, as mentioned by Frolov (Frolov et al., 1969), that the linear zones of cataclasism (area probably 10–30 m × 3 m) traverse the carbonatite body and occur along with the mixed rocks wherein micatization and richteritization have taken place with the development of small dolomitic veinlets. Orientations of such zones are usually in conformity with the orientations of the principal zones of fractures in individual parts. This is well illustrated in the individual massifs of Kovdor, where the orientation is approximately north-south, and in Vuoriyarvi where it is north-west, i.e. in marked conformity with the general trend of the traces of the mixed anticlinorium (Frolov, 1960; Frolov et al., 1969).

Early carbonatites are usually medium- to coarse-grained but in the zones of cataclasism fine-grained (grain size < 1 mm) allotriomorphic texture is formed. Silicates, magnetite, and pyrochlore crystals are crushed and corroded along the periphery of richterite. Calcites are replaced by dolomites, fine-grained microveinlets of which are formed at the interstices of calcite grains. These microveinlets intersect the calcites and sometimes penetrate them along their cleavages and twinning planes (Fig. 18).

As already mentioned, we did not find early dolomite similar in origin to calcite (Van der Veen, 1965; Kononova and Tarashan, 1968). Corrosion of

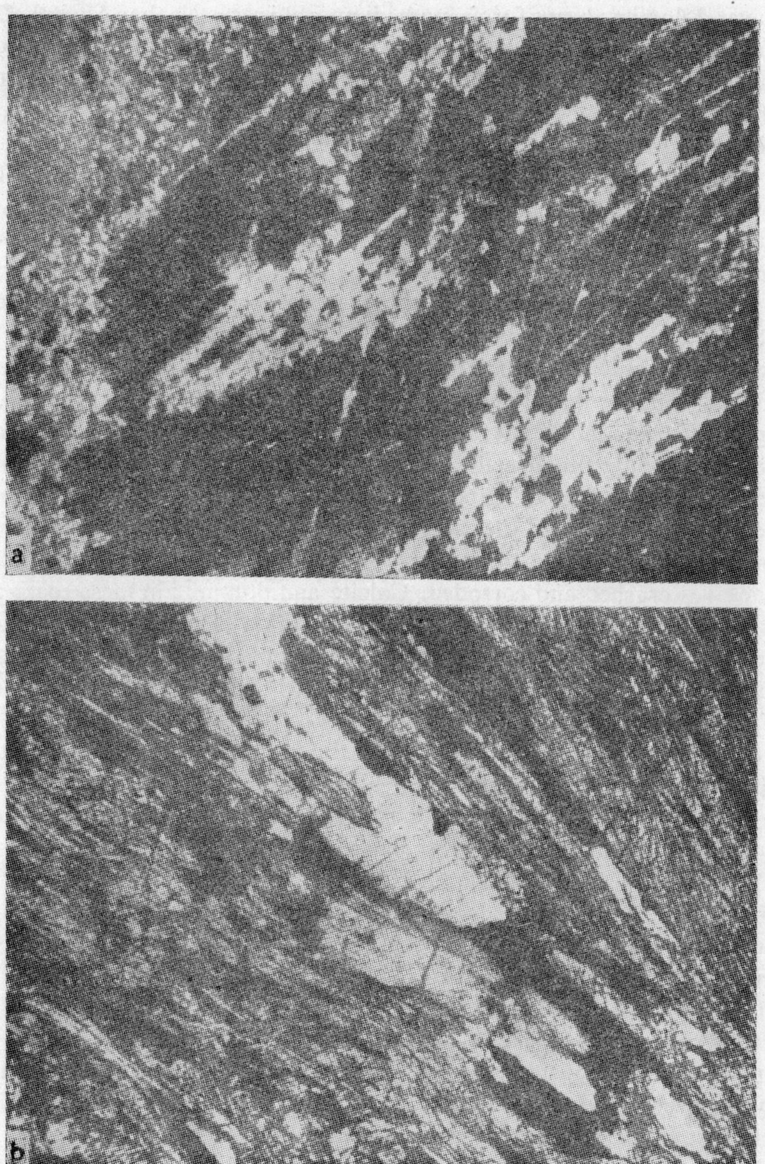

Fig. 18. Structure of dolomitized carbonatites.

a—Development of microveinlets of granular dolomite in calcite crystals (Siberia); b—Richterite-carbonate schist (Vuoriyarvi)—under crossed nicol, mag. ×64.

calcite by fine-grained dolomitic material is widely known to occur (this is because dolomite always forms more idiomorphic crystals than calcite). Dolomites occur near the cataclastic zones of carbonatites and are always accompanied by richterite, tetraferriphlogopite, and show other characteristic features, namely concordant relation of Ta/Nb in pyrochlore, presence of ilmenite and zircon, crushing and corrosion of primary silicates and magnetite (Table 3). In addition to the fine-grained veinlets, dolomites often form coarser (than the general mass of calcite and dolomite) idiomorphic crystalloblasts in the dolomitized parts and it is difficult to determine the time of formation. In such cases it is necessary to use other criteria, the first being the correlation of the structures with the composition of the primary early carbonatites containing dolomites. Pozharitzkaya and Epshtein (1963) grouped calcite-dolomite-amphibole-bearing carbonatites, in which calcite is paragenetically similar to dolomite. As observed earlier, this type of carbonatite does not form an independent body but always enters into the masses of early carbonatite bodies, intersecting them on the macroscopic as well as on the microscopic scale (Frolov, 1960, 1966a, b; Frolov et al., 1969). In almost all places the upper parts of the cataclastic dolomitized zones retain the relics of primary textures, while the primary minerals (magnetite, pyrochlore) are themselves crushed and corroded. Calcite and dolomite in these rocks have not formed simultaneously, since the interrelation between these minerals is reactional in nature (presence of replaced and replacing minerals is a constant phenomenon in any process where relics of early minerals are retained within the later ones).

Cataclasis and schistosity of early carbonatites are the result of tectonic and metasomatic replacement. On weathering, the schistose rocks show thin flakes of minerals. In many places rounded relics of primary massive rocks (Fig. 19) occur within the schistose parts.

Most of the small carbonatite bodies of Vuoriyarvi and Sebl-Yavr are completely shattered. In Sallanlatva the carbonatite nucleus has developed schistosity in the eastern part. In South Siberian massifs cataclasis is poorly developed and is chiefly confined to the central and marginal parts of the body, which are often replaced by and associated with mixed rocks. The western carbonatite veins of Votzu-Vara (Kovdor) occur as independent units all along the western contact. In the central parts of the eastern body they are overlapped by fenites and occur subhorizontally with a gentle slope to the east on the eastern flank and toward the west on the western flank.

The intensity of metasomatism cannot be correlated with the intensity of cataclasism: in different massifs the interrelation between them is different. The correlation between the typomorphic minerals varies in different massifs. In Lesnaya Varaka, Vuoriyarvi, and Sebl-Yavr numerous veins are totally dolomitized and tetraferriphlogopite and richterite are formed in every vein. In Sallanlatva and Kovdor dolomite and richterite are rare, and near the carbonatized magnetite-forsterite rocks small zone (up to 10 m long) occur where rocks are transformed, in places, into richterite-magnetite-carbonatite schists. In large Siberian massifs comprising ijolites and carbonatites (Frolov, 1960) both dolomite and richterite always occur, but in smaller massifs consisting of nepheline syenites and carbonatites (Frolov et al., 1969) richterite is widely prevalent and dolomite is rare. Richterite occurs in Mrima Hill (Coetzee and Edwards, 1959), Iron Hlli (Larsen, 1942), Oka (Maurice, 1956), and Alnö (Eckermann, 1950).

Fig. 19. Massive relic-like blocks of carbonatite in zone of micatization. Kovdor massif, carbonate body of Botzu-Vara.

In the massifs studied dolomitization and amphibolitization are prevalent. In the 1st stage apatite, niobo-zirconolite, tetraferriphlogopite, clinohumite, and pyrrhotite are formed (Kapustin, 1964) and in the second richterite, dolomite, ilmenite, zircon, thorianite, and leucite. The recrystallized pyrochlore becomes free of Ta, Th, and Ti (see below) and replaces niobo-zirconolite. The composition of the metasomatic rocks strictly depends on the nature of the substratum subjected to replacement and also on the surrounding rocks. Carbonatites occurring within ultrabasites rich in magnesium are subjected to intensive dolomitization and micatization (Vuoriyarvi, Sebl-Yavr, Lesnaya Varaka, Kovdor, Nizka-Vara). Richterite prevails in carbonatites that occur within magnesia-poor alkaline rocks and fenites, and the amount of dolomite and tetraferriphologopite is also less in such carbonatites (Siberian massifs). The metasomatites are localized at the intersection of tectonic zones. Independent carbonatite bodies were therefore not formed at the intersection of such tectonic zones in mixed silicate rocks. Micatization is developed in ultrabasites, while veinlets of amphiboles with minor inclusions of dolomite and calcite are formed in fenites and nepheline syenites (Fig. 20). The above facts do not tally with the initial presence of a significant amount of principal components (CaO, MgO, FeO, SiO_2) in the agent of metasomatism. Undoubtedly alkali, water, and sulfur are present at the beginning, but during the latter part of the process the other components are redistributed among rocks in the tectonic zones along which the solution circulated. CaO and CO_2 were driven out of the carbonatites to the silicate rocks while SiO_2, MgO, and Al_2O_3 were introduced into the carbonatites from the silicate rocks. The whole process gave rise to autometasomatism with mutual exchange of components between the carbonatites and the silicate rocks.

Metasomatic transformation of early carbonatites took place in all the massifs but with varying intensity. Carbonatites are always preceded by secondary dolomite, but it is not always possible to indicate to which group the

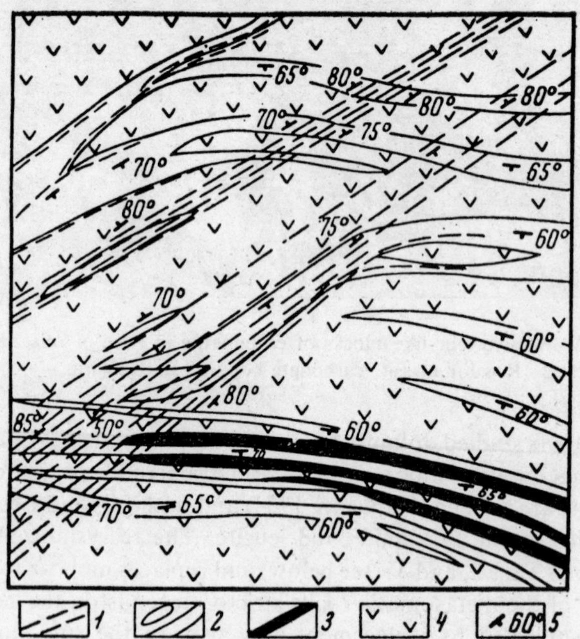

Fig. 20. Carbonatite veins and silicate rocks with intersected zones of dolomitization in Vuoriyarvi massif.

1—Zones of schistosity and dolomitization; 2—Early carbonatites (2nd stage); 3—Magnetite-forsterite rocks; 4—Pyroxenites; 5—Dip and strike.

dolomite belongs, as it is not possible to determine its paragenesis. Dolomitization is found in Fen, where dolomite precedes inner-damkjernites (Saether, 1958), and in African massifs (Van der Veen, 1965), where dolomites occur within suites (Mbeya, Palabora, Mrima Hill, Lueshe, Spitzkop) (Coetzee and Edwards, 1959; Tuttle et al., 1967; Meyer and Bethune, 1960). The structural characters of dolomites resemble the mixed structures of the massifs of Siberia and the Kola Peninsula.

LATE CARBONATITES

Under this heading we have grouped carbonatites that formed after inner-damkjernites and sharply cut across the dolomitized body of early carbonatites (Kapustin, 1960, 1964, 1965c, 1966b). These carbonatites constitute an independent group of rocks that are formed by a single tectonic deformation. They retain evidence of deformation and are characterized by the following features:

a) They are mainly confined to the linear zones of deformation.
b) The composition of these rocks depends on the composition of the mixed rocks.
c) These rocks are characteristically stratified in the following sequence: calcitic→ankeritic→dolomitic→calcitic rocks.
d) They are rich in sulfides and Sr and Ba minerals and are devoid of Nb, Ta, Zr, and U minerals.
e) Low-temperature processes like chloritization, serpentinization, silication, zeolitization, etc. have developed near the veins in these rocks.

Late carbonatites are as important as the early ones in all the massifs studied, but their volume varies widely. Early carbonatites are prevalent in hypabyssal massifs (Kovdor, Vuoriyarvi, Sebl-Yavr, and Ozernaya Varaka; in Alnö, Magnet Cove, Iron Hill, Oka—more than 90% in volume). In Sallanlatva (on the erosional surfaces of lower depths) late carbonatites occur. In Gulinskii (subvolcanic) both groups of rocks are equally developed, and in southeastern Siberia late carbonatites form thick bodies (Lavrenev and Pozharitzkaya, 1958; Frolov, 1960; Frolov and Bagdasarov, 1967; Frolov et al., 1969; Gaidukova et al., 1962). Late ankeritic, dolomitic, and baritic veins are well known in Alnö (Eckermann, 1950) and in Fen, the eastern half of which is full of ankerite and dolomite-ankeritic (hematitized) rocks (rauhaugites—Brögger, 1921; Saether, 1948, 1958; Björlykke, 1955, 1960). Several carbonatite veins with thorium-rare-earth mineralization occur in the USA. These veins are very similar to late carbonatites (Fremont County, Lemhi County, and Ravalli County—Heinrich and Levinson, 1961; Heinrich, 1967; Anderson, 1960, 1961; Sahinen, 1957; Tuttle et al., 1967). Carbonatite zones with fluorite and Tr, Th, Ti minerals occur near Iron Hill and Magnet Cove (Larsen, 1942; Temple and Grogan, 1965; Holbrook, 1947). Similar independent veins are well known in Colorado, Arizona, Montana, New Mexico, and in Alaska (Heinrich, 1967; Pecora, 1956). These veins are well developed in Mountain Pass (Pray and Sharp, 1951; Olson et al., 1954), where their relations with late carbonatites are obscure, due to the absence of any early carbonatites near these veins. The ankeritic zone of Lake Larder, Canada (Daly, 1936), and the small veins of alkaline and carbonatite massifs of Lake Memegosenda and Nipissing and similar veins in British Columbia probably belong to the group of late carbonatites (Parsons, 1961; Temple, 1959; Heinrich, 1967).

Late carbonatites also occur in several African massifs (King and Sutherland, 1960a, b, c; Smith, 1953; Tuttle et al., 1967). Most of these late carbonatites occur as stocks of volcanic veins. They are confined to the inner parts of the stocks, thereby forming zonal structures (Chilwa, Spitzkop, Tundulu, Kruidfontein, Lueshe). Conical strata (veins and metasomatic zones) of dolomite-ankerite rocks are formed in some stocks, and these conform with the general structure of the stocks (Williams, 1952; Smith, 1953; Davies, 1956; Garson and Smith, 1958; Hytönen, 1959; Garson, 1958; Johnson, 1961; Heinrich, 1967; Tuttle et al., 1967).

The volcanic veins of Nkombwa and Kangankunde are composed entirely of late carbonatites (Reeve and Deans, 1954; Phillips, 1955; Deans and McConnel, 1955; Garson, 1958; Mckie, 1962).

Peculiar features associated with these rocks are responsible for their independent distribution in space. Almost all the carbonatite massifs give rise to series of late veins that are formed within the boundaries of the massifs and these veins often run for several kilometers. Similar types of veins are known to occur in Siberia, Vuoriyarvi (Namo-Vara, Popova, 1964), Alnö, Africa (Tundulu, Toror, Chilwa, Karanga), and on Iron Hill, and are probably widely distributed (the veins are similar in mineral composition) in Mountain Pass, Fremont County, Ravalli County, and Lemhi County (USA). The structures of the late carbonatites control the structures of the veins formed in them, but the influences of mixed rocks are more prominent. Late carbonatites occurring within the silicate rocks often take the form of veins or develop a stock system following the general contour of the linear zone, even when they are surrounded by aureoles of metasomatically changed rocks, but when the later rocks occur around the early carbonatites they have wide zones of irregular structures. Some of the structures of early carbonatites are, however, retained in the form of stocks and conically layered veins.

Widely distributed rocks of different composition are described for most of the African massifs, but unfortunately the relations of these rocks with carbonatites are not mentioned. In the parent massifs we studied, the late carbonatite bodies are formed around the early ones (massifs of Eastern Sayan, Kovdor, Sallanlatva), following their contour lines, and not only retain the relict texture of the early carbonatites but have no sharp boundaries with them (early rocks). This is evidenced by relicts of calcite and magnetite often found to occur in early stages of metamorphism. The distribution of late minerals is entirely controlled by the preferred orientation of the grains in the early rocks. In most of the massifs the proportion of dolomites, ankerites, chlorites, and other minerals invariably increases at the contact zone of early carbonatites, and this marks the boundaries between these rocks (early and late). Cross-cutting ankeritic veins occur along the sharp linear contacts. Late carbonatites from a series of rock sequences with compositional change (Tables 2–3). At the first stage calcite is formed. This changes into dolomite (second generation) and ankerite, while at the late stage calcite reappears. The calcitic stage shows characteristics of late carbonatites. Pyrrhotite, burbankite and other carbonates containing Sr, Ba and TR, sulfides and sometimes hyalophane and labuntzovite (Table 3) are formed at the beginning of the calcite stage. Late calcitic veins are rare and negligible in Vuoriyarvi, Kovdor (Borodin and Kapustin, 1962; Kapustin, 1960, 1965a), and Bearpaw Mountain (Pecora, 1962). Thick ankeritic bodies are often surrounded by calcitic zones on the priphery (occurring in any rock).

In the second and third stages the development of late carbonatites gives rise to magnesium-iron-rich carbonatites and different minerals of Sr, Ba, TR and Ti. Carbonatites containing ankerite or dolomite are formed (Vuoriyarvi, Sallanlatva, Kovdor, Gulinskii, massifs of Eastern Siberia and Eastern Sayan, Fen, Kangankunde, Tundulu, Mbeya, Spitzkop, Chilwa). Some of these are characterized by the constant presence of siderite, rhodochrosite, breunnerite, and magnesite. Sometimes the proportion of some of these minerals sharply increases, developing thick bodies which also contain metasomatically formed siderite (Chilwa) or a significant amount of rhodochrosite (Nkombwa). Both siderite and rhodochrosite afterward from ankerite and dolomite (Table 3) and accompany chlorites which, in turn, partially replace most of the magnesium-iron-rich carbonatites (Fig. 21, *a*). At the 4th, concluding, stage magnesium-iron-rich carbonatites are replaced by aggregates of calcite and hematite, often forming pseudomorphic textures after carbonatites. This process is widely prevalent in Fen (Brögger, 1921; Björlykke, 1955). Weak hematitization occurs in most massifs. Often the process of hematitization is accompanied by the formation of fluorite and late quartz (Eastern Sayan). Possibly zeolite-calcitic veins (Vuoriyarvi, Kovdor, Sallanlatva, Gulinskii) were also formed at the same time. Typomorphic mineral assemblages of late carbonatites occur in all places, but their proportion varies sharply, depending on the changes in the composition of the mixed rocks. Late carbonatites that occur around leucocratic early carbonatites (Siberia) differ in their color index. They contain up to 20% silicates and sulfides (mostly pyrite), but with the increase in the color index of the mixed rocks the amount of silicates and pyrite sharply increases. Rings of chlorite are formed at the contact between carbonatites and the late melanocratic veins of

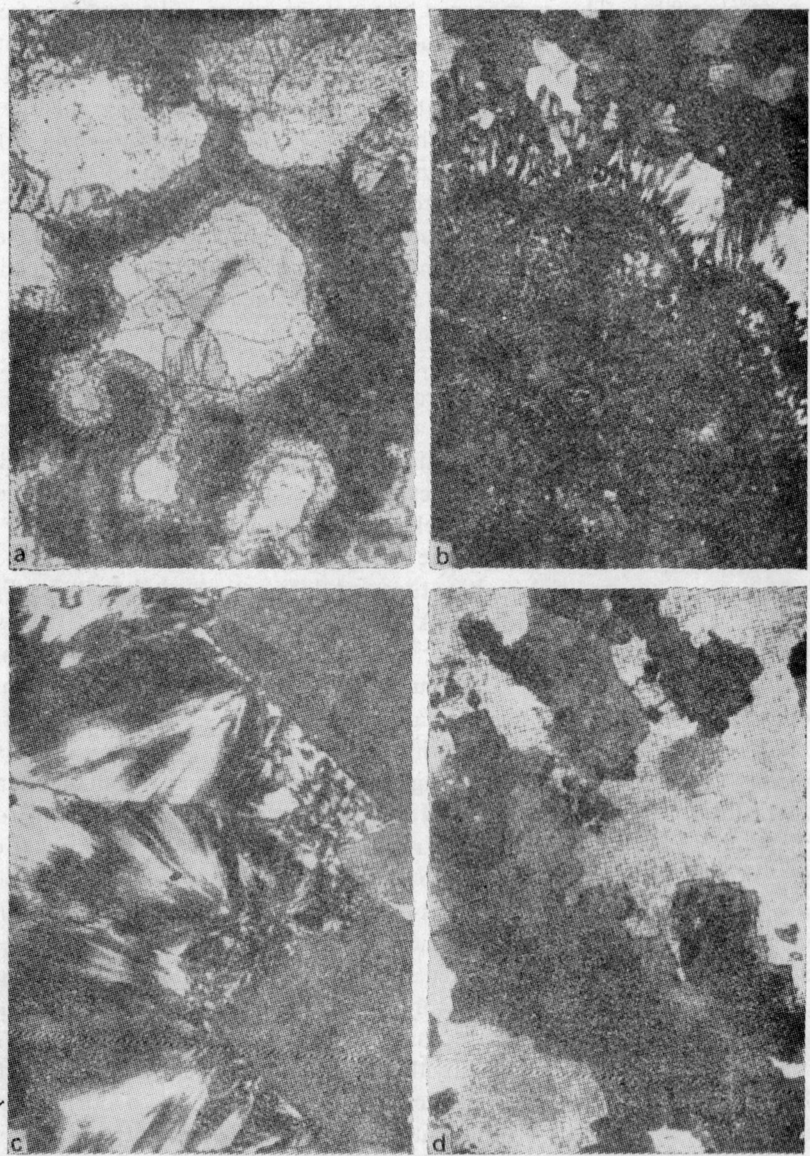

Fig. 21. Textures of late carbonatites.

a—Replacement of ankerite by chlorites (dark) with prominent zoned texture of chlorite with ferruginous zones, Siberia. Under crossed nicol, ×24; b—Texture of quartzose mass at contact with ankerite veins. Veined-zone of Namo-Vara. Under crossed nicol, ×24; c—Formation of radiated chalcedony in ankerite up to Vuoriyarvi. Under crossed nicol, ×48; d—Crystalline veins of ankerite in early calcitic carbonatites—Vuoriyarvi. Under crossed nicol, ×48.

pyroxenites, ijolites, and fenites; pyrite also increases up to 30–40% (Vuoriyarvi, Sallanlatva). Even the composition of the rock-forming carbonate changes: rock bodies occur around early carbonatites and mainly contain dolomite and paraankerite. When these rock bodies occur around ferruginous rocks, ankerite predominates and siderite and breunnerite are formed (Sallanlatva, Vuoriyarvi). Foreign materials are well developed in the thick series of veins of late carbonatites of Namo-Vara, where such veins are formed around ancient gneisses over an area exceeding 2 km × 1 km. More than 20 such veins with thicknesses up to 20 m (average 2 m) occur in this region, but isolation of these veins from the mixed rocks is difficult, as there is no definite boundary relation with the mixed rocks. Thicknesses of the carbonatite veins proper are between 1 and 2 m. Each of the veins is surrounded by aureoles of metasomatically transformed gneisses whose thickness is 5–10 times the thickness of the veins. The proportion of carbonate gradually decreases toward the periphery of the veins. Metasomatic changes cause intensive melting of the rocks and remove all the components except silica and iron. Gneisses are converted into vesicular aggregates of coarse-grained bipyramidal black quartz. The cavity is filled with druses of quartz crystals, carbonate, barite, and podolite. Free quartz content in the unaltered gneisses is about 12–20%, that of SiO_2 is up to 60–70%. In the altered gneisses the proportion of quartz goes up to 80–90%. In the vesicular rocks it constitutes about 60–70% of the initial volume of the rocks. Comparison of the above data indicates that with metasomatic changes the gneisses were freed from other elements except silica, which remained stationary in them. Of course, redistribution of silica took place, as is evidenced by the increase in the proportion of quartz to 85–90% in some parts. A still later generation of colorless quartz or amethyst or chalcedony was formed, filling up the cavities of the carbonatites (often with radiate structures, Fig. 21, *b*, *c*). Similar processes are observed in Fremont County, where carbonatite veins crowded with quartz and quartzose mixed rocks occur (Heinrich and Shapirio, 1966); carbonatite also occurs in the ore-deposits of Karonge, where the carbonate content is not high and quartz predominates (Thoreau et al., 1958). Possibly the amount of material during the formation of late veins was relatively small. With the movement of the solution toward the surface this material was quickly dispersed.

Veins that occur at shallow depths are chiefly of carbonatites. At the top they may be metasomatically transformed, incorporating foreign materials derived from mixed rocks. This indicates the vertical zoning of late carbonatite, whose carbonate content decreases from bottom to top. The bastnaasite deposits of Karonge (mineralized breccia), where carbonatites are almost absent, indicate similar types of veins at the top.

There has been migration of Ti, Nb, silica and iron from the mixed rocks into the late carbonatites. Late carbonatites that occur around perovskitic ultrabasites contain anatase. At the intersection of early carbonatite and the ultrabasites these late carbonatites are rich in pyrochlore that is replaced by aggregates of fersmite and columbite on the periphery (Fen—Sörum, 1955; Saether, 1958; Mbeya—Fawley and James, 1955; Ngualla—James and McKie, 1958; Verti—Hogarth, 1961; Heinrich, 1967; Hess and Trumpour, 1959; the Siberian massifs—Gaidukova, 1960a, b). Columbitized pyrochlore develops on the front of ankeritization and outstrips the formation of ankerite. The later veins show concentrations of TR, Sr, and Ba and lose their early calcite, which is replaced by ankerite, the other characteristic mineral.

The wide development of metasomatism and addition of material from the mixed rock to late carbonatites significantly increase the volume of late carbonatite bodies around the early carbonatites (Sallanlatva, Siberian massifs, Chilwa, Spitzkop, Lueshe) and replace the early rocks quite easily, but the veins of late carbonatites that occur around the silicate rocks are as a rule not so prevalent. They are restricted in occurrence to fractured zones and are surrounded by thick aureoles of vein-like metasomatites (Vuoriyarvi, Namo-Vara, Siberian massifs).

The structures of late carbonatites are similar to those of normal hydrothermal veins. They are either brecciated, vein-like, vesicular, or drusy, indicating formation from melts and material from mixed rocks (Fig. 21, *a*, *b*, *c*, *d*). Distribution of the minerals is not uniform; sometimes zones with a principal concentration of silicate and pyrite in gouge are formed. At the center of the veins solution, redeposition, and replacement of early minerals by later ones are found. In the cavity walls of the early minerals, chiefly burbankite and calcite, druses of barite crystals, quartz, chlorite, and other minerals are formed. Peripheral zones of veins and the zones of ankeritization are often full of relict minerals (quartzose, calcitic, phlogopitic), which makes it difficult to establish a definite boundary relation between the veins and the mixed rocks.

STAFFELITIC BRECCIA

Fragments of mixed rocks and cemented carbonate-apatite-staffelites filling the volcanic pipes are related to carbonatites both genetically and in space. With the formation of these pipes the formation of carbonatites is completed. Staffelitic breccias occur in several massifs of the Kola Peninsula (Vuoriyarvi, Kovdor, Sebl-Yavr, Lesnaya Varaka), Magnet Cove (McConnell and Gruner, 1940), and Gulinskii (Epshtein, 1959), and were also observed in the southeastern massifs of Siberia. They also occur in several African massifs, where breccias with apatite are well known (Mrima Hill, Palabora). Staffelitic breccias form oval-shaped tubes, more than 70% of whose volume is occupied by fragments of mixed rocks and materials derived from rocks that occur at depths. In Vuoriyarvi these tubes cut across the pyroxenites, in

Kovdor the fenites and carbonatites, and in Siberia the carbonatites. All these rock fragments are largely replaced near the mixed rocks. Calcite and apatite, replaced by staffelite, and forsterite replaced by serpentine, are all leached out from these tubes, while phlogopite is vermiculitized and sulfides are oxidized. All these rocks develop vesicular structures. The fenitic material and cavities in the Kovdor massif constitute more than 25% of the total volume. The walls of these cavities are filled with crystalline chabazite crusts and staffelite. The tubes cut across the fenites, while fragments of fenitized and serpentinized olivinites and carbonatites occur in them. The depth of these serpentinized olivinites and carbonatites is more than 500 m in this part of Kovdor. Accumulations of kidney-shaped masses (radiate structure) of staffelite, druses of chabazite crystals, natrolite, and angular calcites are found in almost all the massifs. The structure and composition of staffelitic breccias indicate formation by eruptions, deriving fragments of rocks at depths and later cementing them with staffelitic masses deposited from hydrothermal solutions.

EFFUSIVE CARBONATITES

Flows, bedded carbonate lavas and their encrustation accompanying carbonatite tuffs, phonolitic and nephelinitic lavas and their pyroclastic materials occur (Kerimasi, Oldoino Lengan, Kizingiri, Kalyango) in both recent and extinct volcanoes of East Africa. Similar subvolcanic carbonatite stocks rich in agglomerates and alkaline pyroclastic materials are well known (Hudini, Kruidfontein, Napak, Tororo Hills), but the composition of the agglomerates and the interrelation of the minerals in these subvolcanic carbonatites have not been properly studied. The composition of the effusive carbonatites has, however, been studied. It differs sharply from the composition of deeper and paleotypic analogs. In Kerimasi and Oldoino Dali bedded bodies (flows) of calcitic carbonatites occur (Heinrich, 1967; Tuttle et al., 1967). In Oldoino Lengan products of late eruptions are admixtures of complex Ca and Na carbonates (hydrated and dehydrated—Du Bois et al., 1963; Dawson, 1962a). Eruption of lava of this composition accompanies the discharge of a great volume of alkaline carbonate ashes. The lava becomes very mobile (lava type "a a"). Biotite, apatite, magnetite, and perovskite occur in these lavas and in the volcanic ash. On the surface, under the influence of air and water, these lavas become depleted in alkali and as a result aureoles are formed whose upper surface is contaminated by hydrated sodium (Lake Natron near Oldoino Lengan volcano). Heinrich (1967) showed the presence of one such ancient volcano in the USA (hot spring in Soda Lake), where sodium carbonates accumulate. Active volcanism is also known in association with early weathered carbonatite lava. In ancient volcanoes that underwent continued, deep erosion such lavas are not known. The presence of primary lavas (in the volcanic phases of developed massifs) is difficult to establish. Possibly eruptions of carbonatite lavas did not always take place (plugs of Laacher Sea and Bracciano Lake), while away from the large volcanoes, as in Oldoino Lengan, weathering may have destroyed them altogether (chiefly in inundated regions as in North Europe and Siberia).

Hydrothermal carbonatites are not known in association with effusive carbonatites. Solfataric activities increase significantly. Probably the hydrothermal process starts after the volcanic activity (postmagmatic phase), but it is also possible that independent hydrothermal phases do not occur in volcanoes and most of the volatiles escape immediately during eruption. In inactive and eroded volcanoes subvolcanic stocks later than carbonatites develop widely (Kangankunde, Nkombwa, Chilwa, Kruidfontein).

Chapter V

MINERAL CONSTITUENTS OF CARBONATITES

The mineralogical composition of carbonatites is very complex in nature. These rocks are genetically and geochemically distinct and contain several rare minerals (principally the rare-earth minerals zirkelite, baddeleyite, calzirtite, calkinsite, carbocernaite, and others) that are unknown or are very rare in other types of rocks. At present more than 200 species of minerals are known from carbonatites, but these minerals have been studied from different angles, and some of the factors responsible for their occurrence in carbonatite are doubtful because the detailed characteristics of the minerals have not been given. Frequent development of carbonatites in different mixed rocks and their wide assimilation of minerals or features of mixed rocks often render it difficult to isolate the actual minerals of carbonatite from those derived from the mixed rocks. It is quite likely that a few of the important carbonatite minerals (relic in origin) are stable at the beginning of the process of carbonatization. It is, therefore, very important to maintain a distinct limitation in the nomenclature of carbonatites so that alien rocks (hydrothermal veins, calciphyres, and others) are not confused with carbonatites.

From the collective research carried out under the guidance of Ginzburg (Ginzburg et al., 1958) and Kukharenko (Kukharenko et al., 1965), more than 80 species of minerals were reported in carbonatites, and in his review Heinrich (1967) reports 157 minerals in carbonatites, part of which may be considered as typical of these rocks. But it is very doubtful if the unique occurrence of graphite in a carbonate-quartz vein (Lake Nemegosenda) correlates it genetically with carbonatite. Similarly graphite (Heinrich, 1967), believed to occur in the Goryachegorsky massif (Kuznetzky-Ala-Tau), cannot be considered as a characteristic mineral of these formations. In this massif and in several other nepheline-syenite massifs of Eastern Sayan and Tuva graphite is related to the assimilation of marbles. A whole series of minerals constituting a large number of sulfides in the Palabora massif (Forster, 1958) were not characteristic at all. The presence of some rare metals in most of the carbonatites is not confirmed by their mineral assemblages, as minerals like digenite, linnaeite, bravoite, etc. require definite identification. Probably the occurrence of minerals like beryl, topaz, thorogummite, britholite, and chevkinite in carbonatites may in some cases be considered as relics. The occurrence of epidote and cassiterite in the weathered carbonatites of Mrima Hill (Coetzee and Edwards, 1959) probably indicates regional intermingling of the weathered centers with these minerals or mixed rocks. In the Canadian massifs scapolite occurs in phlogopitic rocks of metasomatic origin (Slaudiansky and Aldan type—Korzhinskii, 1953) instead of in carbonatites. Probably goyazite and gorceixite that occur at the core of weathered carbonatites are hypergene in origin.

Thus minerals of doubtful nature are placed alongside minerals associated with carbonatites. The principal minerals of carbonatites that occur in several massifs are listed below. These minerals are of endogenetic origin and are closely associated with other typomorphic minerals of carbonatites. Minerals of singular occurrence or minerals of doubtful origin (topaz, beryl, chevkinite, astrophyllite, ludwigite, epidote, cassiterite, linnaeite, bravoite, digenite, etc.) were not considered. Here the emphasis is on the rare-earth minerals (all rare-earth minerals of carbonatites in this book are considered as accessory minerals—author). These minerals are grouped and classified according to their chemical composition into native elements, fluorides, sulfides, oxides, and silicates. In each case, except for the silicates, first the rock-forming minerals and then the rare-earth minerals are discussed. Grouping of minerals and their description in relation to their distribution in different types of carbonatites were possible because the principal mineral constituents of carbonatites change from massif to massif.

Mineral Assemblages in Carbonatites

Native elements	—gold, silver
Carbides	—moissanite
Fluorides	—fluorite, sellaite
Sulfides and Sulfosalts	—pyrrhotite, pentlandite, molybdenite, chalcopyrite, pyrite, marcasite, sphalerite, millerite, covellite, chalcosine, bornite, galena, tetrahedrite, bournonite, jamesonite, boulangerite, valleriite
Oxides	—magnetite, spinel, hematite, quartz, brucite, cerianite, pyrochlore, columbite, fersmite, natroniobite, fergusonite, aeschynite, rutile, anatase, brookite, ilmenite,

	perovskite, lueshite, calzirtite, zirconolite, baddeleyite, thorianite
Carbonates	—calcite, dolomite, ankerite, magnesite, siderite, breunnerite, rhodochrosite, strontianite, alstonite, barite, norsethite, burbankite, carbocernaite, natrofairchildite, sahamalite, parisite, bastnaesite, synchysite, cordylite, huanghoite, ancylite, calkinsite, lanthanite, manasseite, hydrotalcite
Phosphates	—apatite, isokite, monazite, rhabdophane, crandallite, goyazite, florencite, gorceixite, svanbergite, vivianite, bobierrite, collinsite
Sulfates	—barite, celestine, anglesite, anhydrite
Silicates	—garnet, forsterite, monticellite, clinohumite, zircon, sphene, thorite, cerite, ramsayite, melilite, orthite, niocalite, lavenite, lamprophyllite, labunsovite, vinogradovite, wollastonite, pectolite, schizolite, amphibole, mica, chlorite, serpentine, talc, nepheline, cancrinite, microcline, orthoclase, albite, natrolite, chabazite

CLASS I: NATIVE ELEMENTS AND CARBIDES

Forster (1958) and Heinrich (1967) mentioned gold and silver from this class associated with sulfides. But the diagnostic features of these minerals are absent. Silicon carbide (moissanite) is well known from different massifs and placed under this class.

Moissanite (SiC). This is considered as a rare mineral. It occurs in carbonatized magnetite-olivinitic breccias of the Arbarastakski massif (Glushikna et al., 1963) in close proximity to the picritic porphyry. It is fine-grained, intergrown with magnetite, and occurs in very minute amounts. It is golden in color and flattened, $n_g > 2.67$. It also occurs in kimberlites (Marshintsev et al., 1966).

CLASS II: HALOGENIDES (FLUORIDES)

From this class only fluorite is widely distributed in carbonatites. But occurrences of sellaite, cryolite, pachnolite, gearksutite, prosopite, ralstonite, and weberite (Heinrich and Quon, 1963) are also known. The relation of the last six minerals with carbonatites is not known and therefore these are not discussed below.

Fluorite (CaF_2). This is a mineral typical of pneumatohydrothermal veins, forms at a wide range of temperatures in many hydrothermal deposits and is genetically associated with acid and alkaline rocks. Fluorite is rare in hypabyssal carbonate massifs but is widely distributed in volcanic veins of Africa. A few of these occurrences are in Turi Mis, Vuoriyarvi, Mbeya, Alnö, Fen, Toror, Chilwa, Ngualla, Sengeri Hill, Okoruzu in Bolshetagninskii massifs (Frolov and Bagdasarov, 1967), Amba Dongar (Sukheshwala and Udas, 1963), and within veins of Fremont County (Heinrich and Anderson, 1965) and Mac Mountain (Heinrich and Quon, 1963).

Fluorite is uniformly disseminated in carbonatites and forms veinlets of several generations. Different colored veinlets that intersect each other indicate their different origin. Fluorites are violet, green or colorless. Their properties are normal and they contain TR_2O_3* = 0.02–0.34% (in the massifs of Eastern Sayan and Vuoriyarvi), Sr = 0.38–0.56%, and Ba = 0.01–0.10% (analyst: M.V. Kukharenko and E.A. Fabrikova).

This is a typical mineral of ankeritic veins. It is associated with TR-bearing fluor-carbonates, hematite, and sometimes with quartz. It is formed as veins in Fe-Mg carbonates. The central part of the carbonatite body of Tuva with fluorite-hematite mass is very near to carbonatite in composition.

Sellaite (MgF_2). Rare fluorides of magnesium were mentioned by Reeve and Deans (1954) from barite-sideritic carbonatite massif of Nkombwa, where its volcanic equivalent together with chlorite, alkaline amphibole and minerals of Sr and Ba are developed around siderites. It is white, uniaxial (+ve) $n_e = 1.390$ and $n_o = 1.378$; tetragonal in symmetry. Sellaite is formed in the last phase of late carbonatite formation.

CLASS III: SULFIDES AND SULFOSALTS

Sulfides are always present in carbonatites (Forster and Heinrich, 1967; Kapustin, 1965a), but their exact paragenesis and distinct interrelation with other minerals in carbonatites are not certain. These minerals are therefore mainly described from the published literature.

In early carbonatites sulfides (relics from mixed rocks) are either absent or are replaced by magnetite. Occurrence of sulfides in significant amounts in all phases is related to the process of dolomitization-amphibolitization and the formation of late carbonatites. Sulfide mineralization is abundant in late carbonatites and its proportion varies in different massifs. In the Kola Penin-

*TR—Rare earths.

sula the massif-like Vuoriyarvi is quite rich in sulfide minerals which are, however, negligible in Sallanlatva and Sebl-Yavr massifs. In the veins of Namo-Vara and Kovdor the sulfide content is not high. In carbonatites of Eastern Sayan and Eastern Siberia pyrrhotite, pyrite and other minerals of this group are always found, and in the Maimecha-Kotui Province the admixture of sulfides is quite prominent. Concentration of sulfides occurs in carbonatites of Palabora (Russel et al., 1954; Forster, 1958), in late veins of massifs like Alnö (Eckermann, 1948a), Fen (Brögger, 1921), Fremont County, Ravalli County, and Lemhi County (Heinrich, 1967). Only the more widespread and well studied minerals of this group are considered below. The cubanite, linnaeite, digenite, antimony, bravoite, and arsenopyrite reported from African carbonatites (Higasy, 1954; Forster, 1958) cannot be considered as characteristic. Hence these minerals are not considered.

Pyrrhotite (Fe_nS_{n+1}). This is the most widespread of the sulfides in complex massifs (Kapustin, 1965) and occurs as disseminations in stable, primary ijolites and melanocratic fenites (Vuoriyarvi, Afrikanda, Kovdor, East Sayan massifs). It is found in carbonatites in all locations (Eastern Siberia—Gaidukova et al., 1962; Pozharitzkaya, 1966; Iron Hill—Larsen, 1942; Magnet Cove—Erickson and Blade, 1963; Fen—Brögger, 1921; Alnö—Eckermann, 1948a; Palabora—Forster, 1958), and is of several generations.

In the stable early carbonatites pyrrhotite is rare and is confined to the marginal or central parts of the veins or zones of dolomitization. It is associated with tetraferriphlogopite, richterite, and other minerals. It is usually preceded by dolomite and often disseminated in weakly cataclastic rocks. In leucocratic parts of the rocks the pyrrhotite content is not so high (up to 15%) but it increases in the melanocratic parts (principally the parts rich in magnetite). In Vuoriyarvi veinlets and veins of pyrrhotite (with the admixture of carbonates) occur along the contacts of carbonatite with pyroxenite or distinctly in pyroxenite rich in primary magnetite. In Kovdor on the eastern flank of the Pilkoma-Selga Mountain (east of Jeleznoi Mountain), individual veins of pyrrhotite-biotite-apatite 2 m thick were observed within the melanocratic fenites. These veins occur along pinched out carbonatite veins. The pyrrhotites in these veins are of earlier generation (lst generation) and form disseminated small (up to 1–5 mm) individual hexagonal dipyramidal crystals elongated along the *z* axis. The dipyramidal (2021) and (1011) and basal pinacoid (0001) grains are rare and thin grains of hexagonal prism (1010) are developed.

Pyrrhotite of the 2nd generation spontaneously acquires prismatic crystals of pyrrhotite of the 1st generation or forms independent flattened crystals principally of basal pinacoids. It is also associated with richterite, dolomite, and tetraferriphlogopite.

Pyrrhotite of the 3rd generation occurs in late calcitic veins with burbankite, showing massive accumulation or veins of dendritic crystals with branching toward the center of the calcite veins.

Pyrrhotite of the 4th generation is formed by spontaneous recrystallization of the early generation engulfed by ankeritic veins in which it is stable at the first phase and forms a fine-grained accumulation.

Pyrrhotites of the 1st, 2nd, and 3rd generations are bronze-yellow in color; 4th generation pyrrhotite is quite lustrous. Similarly the magnetic properties of pyrrhotite also differ, 1st and 2nd generation pyrrhotite is strongly magnetic, the 3rd weakly magnetic, and the 4th nonmagnetic. A special study of pyrrhotite (Graboreki and Zerdenko, 1965) showed constant development of domain structures, while pyrrhotites of the 1st and 2nd generations are more inclined to the antiferromagnetic and ferromagnetic phases characteristic of high-temperature pyrrhotite (higher than 320°C). The prismatic-pyramidal variety of magmatic pyrrhotite usually shows an affinity to the high-temperature minerals of hydrothermal sulfide deposits (Betekhtin, 1953) and the flattened ones (similar to troilites) to low-temperature minerals. In pyrrhotite there is the constant presence of Ni (Table 4).

Table 4. Ni-content in pyrrhotite (in wt.%) (Analyst—V.M. Vasilev)

Generation	Massif		
	Vuoriyarvi	Kovdor	Sayan
1	0.20–0.28	0.24–0.20	0.34
2	0.22–0.20	0.19–0.15	0.17
3	0.08–0.14	—	—
4	0–0.04	—	—

Pyrrhotite has a relatively short stability range; in late ankerite-dolomitic veins it is replaced by pyrite or marcasite (Kapustin, 1965; Fick and Van der Heyde, 1959), which forms rhythmic-zonal veins around it. In hypergene conditions pyrrhotite is unstable and is replaced by marcasite or limonite.

Pentlandite (Fe, Ni)S. This is a characteristic mineral of rocks of gabbronoritic composition. It occurs in the massifs of Palabora (Forster, 1958), Vuoriyarvi, and in Kovdor (Kapustin, 1965a), where it is associated with pyrrhotite, forming small (0.1–1.0 mm) tabular grains therein. Pentlandite shows two sets of cleavages; sp. gr. 4.8[1]. In polished section the mineral is isotropic; reflectivity is quite high, higher than pyrrhotite; X-ray pattern is similar to the standard. Chemical analysis is as follows: Fe 33.31%, Ni 34.12% (Vuoriyarvi). Spectral analysis indicates the presence of Co, Mg, V, Ti, Cr, and Mn. Pentlandite is rare in carbonatites and forms at the beginning of the process of dolomitization together with early pyrrhotite and tetraferriphlogopite. In

[1]Here and afterward sp. gr. has been determined by G.G. Prokhorova in the laboratory of IMGRÉ.

late carbonatites it is totally leached out and replaced with druses of millerite and pyrite crystals.

Molybdenite (MoS_2). This occurs frequently in carbonatites in minor amounts. It occurs in Iron Hill (Larsen, 1942; Heinrich, 1967), Magnet Cove (Erickson and Blade, 1963), Mrima Hill (Coetzee and Edwards, 1959), Ravalli and Fremont County (Heinrich and Levinson, 1961; Heinrich and Anderson, 1965), in the massifs of Siberia and the Kola Peninsula (Sallanlatva, Vuoriyarvi, Kovdor, Turi Mis—Kukharenko et al., 1965). Molybdenite occurs only in late ankeritic-dolomitic veins and in ankeritized parts of mixed rocks. It accompanies carbonate, barite, quartz, pyrite, strontianite, and anatase. It comes in two morphological varieties; flattened crystals and thin lepidodendritic aggregates and veinlets. The latter variety is placed in the monoclinic system (Sominoi, 1966). The properties of molybdenite are normal. It forms in the early phase of the hydrothermal process, earlier than the principal mass of sulfides (except pyrrhotite).

Chalcopyrite ($CuFeS_2$). This occurs in all the massifs, constantly accompanies pyrrhotite but forms later than it and develops along the fractures of the pyrrhotite mass. Usually it is present in significant amounts. Near the Palabora massif it forms small deposits (Russel et al., 1954; Forster, 1958). Chalcopyrite is formed in the last stage of the process of dolomitization together with richterite and dolomite. Sometimes rims and veins of bornite are formed along with it. Under hypergene condition it is easily dissociated and replaced by malachite.

Pyrite (FeS_2). This is a typical mineral for ankeritic-dolomitic veins and also for other varieties of carbonatites that cannot be definitely classified. It is widely distributed in the massifs of the Kola Peninsula (Kapustin, 1964, 1965a; Kukharenko et al., 1965), the USA (Larsen, 1942; Olson et al., 1954; Heinrich, 1967), Scandinavia (Brögger, 1921; Eckermann, 1948a; Saether, 1948), and Siberia.

Rare disseminated pyrite occurs at the contact zone of early carbonatite bodies of one of the massifs of Sayan and also in the massifs of Lueshe (Meyer and Bethune, 1960), Mrima Hill (Coetzee and Edwards, 1959a), and Tundulu (Dixey et al., 1955). In the Sayan massif pyrite is probably derived from the mixed rock (pyrite-bearing gneisses) and is replaced by magnetite on the periphery. In African massifs it is accompanied by minerals of Sr, Ba and TR—typical of late carbonatites. The pyrite content of ankeritic veins is not below 15% and increases sharply in veins around melanocratic ferruginous rocks (Vuoriyarvi, Sebl-Yavr, East Sayan massifs). It decreases in veins intersected by leucocratic fenites, gneisses, and early carbonatites (Vuoriyarvi, Petyaian-Vara, Namo-Vara; Southern Siberia, Gulinskii, Sallanlatva). Pyrite is associated with chlorite, anatase, marmatite, carbocernaite, orthoclase, quartz, replacing earlier ferruginous silicates, magnetite, and especially pyrrhotite. Pyrite forms colloform banding with chlorite (Fig. 22, *a*). In ankeritic carbonatites well-developed cubic or octahedral crystals of pyrite are formed.

The properties of pyrite are normal; sp. gr. 4.54–4.57. Spectral analysis indicates the presence of Ni, Co, Mn, Ti (analyst: I.P. Toyushev in the laboratory of IMGRÉ). Formation of pyrite after pyrrhotite and magnetite shows the relative potentiality of growth of sulfur in ankeritic carbonatites, while most of the iron is extracted from the surrounding rocks. In hypergenic conditions pyrite easily decomposes and is replaced by melanterite and limonite.

Marcasite (FeS_2). This is rare in carbonatites, sometimes forms fine-crystalline encrustations on pyrrhotite or on a mass of veins. Thin needle-shaped crystals of marcasite occur on the crystals of podolite in association with crystals of barite, chlorite, and ancylite. Marcasite is formed by the dissolution and decomposition of early pyrrhotite.

Sphalerite (ZnS). This is a typical mineral for late ankeritic veins which occur in several massifs in Africa (Nkombwa—Phillips, 1955; Mrima—Coetzee and Edwards, 1959; Mbeya—James and McKie, 1958; Palabora—Forster, 1958), the USA (Ravalli and Fremont County—Heinrich, 1967), Siberia (Gaidukova et al., 1962) and the Kola Peninsula (Kapustin, 1964, 1965a), Scandinavia (Alnö—Eckermann, 1958). Sphalerite occurs in the massifs of Sallanlatva and Vuoriyarvi and in one of the Siberian massijs (Frolov, 1960). We divided sphalerites into two generations: marmatite (early) and cleiophane (late). Marmatite is relatively equally developed in ankeritic carbonatites, forming independent monocrystalline grains of tetrahedral crystals in the rock cavities, and is associated with pyrite, anatase, carbocernaite, and monazite. Cleiophane often forms monomineralic veins and zones in the central parts of the ankeritic body accompanying galena, strontiatine, barite, ancylite, or fluor-carbonates containing TR elements. Zoned crystals of sphalerite with marmatite at the nucleus and periphery are found in Vuoriyarvi.

Marmatite is black; cleiophane is green or yellow, or often colorless; sp. gr. (both varieties) 3.89 and 4.08 respectively; hardness normal. Chemical composition (analyst: N.G. Raginoi) of marmatite from Vuoriyarvi is as follows: Zn = 52.06%, Fe = 13.29%. The sample from Kovdor gave 49.64% Zn and 15.17% Fe. Spectral analysis of marmatite indicates the presence of Bi, Sb, Cd, Mn and that of cleiophane, Sb, Cd, Cu, and Ag. Under hypergenic conditions smithsonite is formed after sphalerite.

Millerite (NiS). This is a characteristic mineral of hydrothermal nickel-

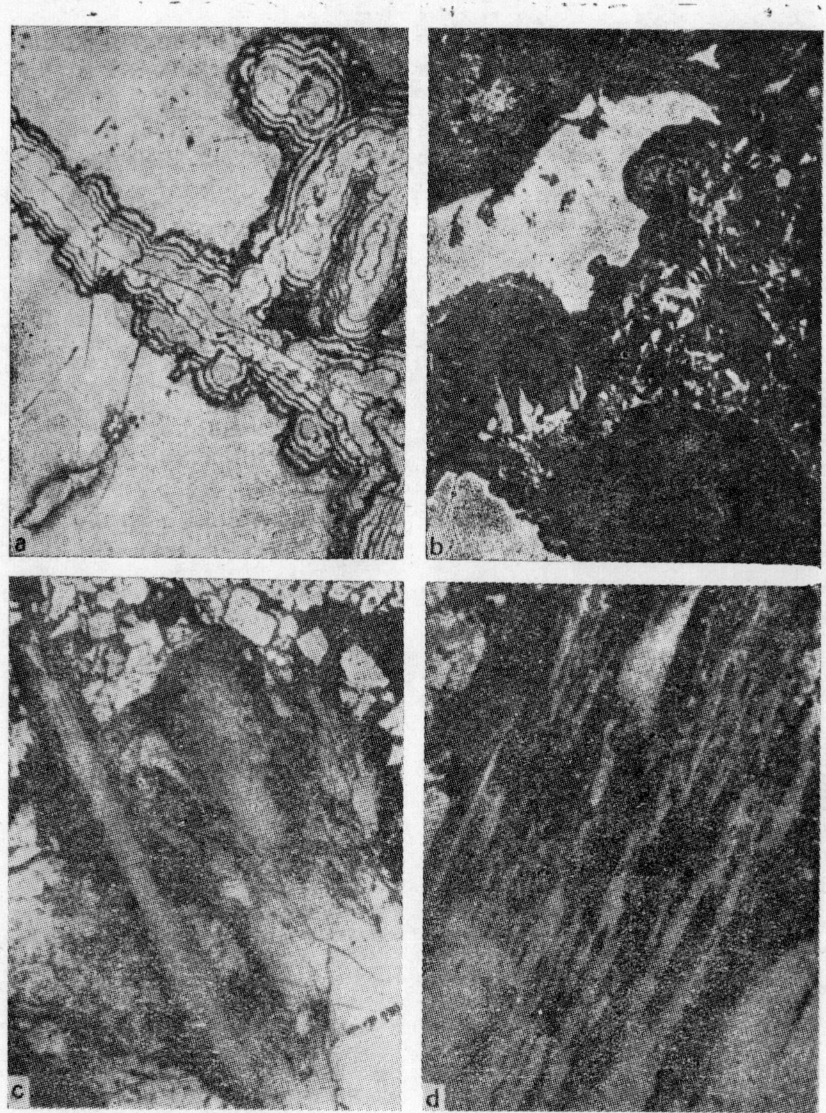

Fig. 22. Interrelation of sulfides in late carbonatites.

a—Colloform veinlets of fine-grained pyrite in pyrrhotite; b—Hexagonal crystals of millerite intergrowing with podolite (brown) in place of dissolution of pyrrhotite crystals (bright) and pentlandite; c—Hexagonal form of bournonite (bright-pyrite); d—Hexagonal aggregate of jamesonite in ankerite, Vuoriyarvi massifs. Under crossed nicol, mag. ×48.

Table 5. Interplaner distance of sulfosalts and millerite

Boulangerite				Jamesonite				Bournonite				Millerite			
1		2		3		4		5		6		7		8	
I	*d*, Å	*I*	*d*, Å	*I*	*d*, Å	*I*	*d*, Å	*I*	*d*, Å	*I*	*d*, Å	*I*	*d*, Å	*I*	*d*, Å
1	2	3	4	5	6	7	8	9	10	11	12	13	14	15	16
20	3.98	1	3.90		—	5	6.03	2	5.5	1	5.29	2	5.01	4	4.836
100	3.72	10	3.68		—	5	5.10	2	4.70		—	6	2.95	4	2.970
10	3.44	1	3.50	2	4.21	30	4.10	4	4.32	3	4.27	10	2.81	9	2.792
20	3.30	1	3.22	5	3.92	40	3.87	4	4.09	2	4.12	4	2.51	5	2.514
40	3.21	2	3.15	1	3.70	20	3.72	8	3.86	10	3.94		—	2	2.417
40	3.01	3	3.08	2	3.56	30	3.59	6	3.68	4	3.71	5	2.25	5	2.242
90	2.81	10	2.83	10	3.45	100	3.44	2	3.25		—	10	1.881	10	1.876
30	2.68	2	2.71	1	3.30	10	3.34	8	2.96	10	2.95	8	1.820	7	1.821
5	2.59		—	4	3.21	50	3.18	6	2.89	5	2.87	1	1.784		—
5	2.51	1	2.50	6	3.12	50	3.09	8	2.81	9	2.82	8	1.730	7	1.730
20	2.33	3	2.32	1	2.96	20	2.95	10	2.73	10	2.72	1	1.650	3	1.642
30	2.14	2	2.10	10	2.85	90	2.84	8	2.67	8	2.68	8	1.611	7	1.609
10	2.05		—	7	2.74	80	2.75	8	2.58	8	2.58	1	1.576		—
10	1.937	1	1.96	1	2.61	10	2.63	2	2.47		—	5	1.535	6	1.536
30	1.910	2	1.911	1	2.40	10	2.36	4	2.37	2	2.44		—	1	1.457
80	1.859	9	1.861	1	2.28	30	2.30	2	2.29	1	2.30		—	1	1.414
50	1.752	4	1.760	2	2.23	40	2.24	2	2.22	1	2.22	1	1.342	2	1.340

1	2	3	4	5	6	7	8	9	10	11	12	13	14	15	16
20	1.716	1	1.715	1	2.16	10	2.16	4	2.09	2	2.02	2	1.312	4	1.309
10	1.647		—		—	5	2.11	8	1.980	9	1.97	5	1.261	7	1.260
10	1.583	1	1.580	4	2.08	50	2.06	8	1.945	9	1.95	1	1.215	4	1.206
5	1.520		—	4	2.01	40	2.02	8	1.845	8	1.840	1	1.920		—
20	1.463	2	1.462	1	1.970	10	1.965	8	1.763	7	1.770	2	1.188	4	1.183
20	1.404	1	1.410	1	1.902	10	1.907	2	1.723	1	1.716	3	1.151	6	1.146
10	1.375	1	1.374		—	10	1.866	6	1.660	6	1.667	10	1.121	8	1.117
10	1.293		—	2	1.838	30	1.837	6	1.625	5	1.625	5	1.102	6	1.107
10	1.236		—	1	1.801	10	1.797	2	1.588		—	1	1.184		—
5	1.209		—	1	1.770	10	1.768	6	1.555	4	1.549	1	1.109		—

Explanation: 1, 4—after ASTM Bulletin, 1943; 5, 8—after Mikheev, 1957; 2, 3, 6, 7—after author (Vuoriyarvi massif). The Vuoriyarvi sample was X-rayed in RKD diffractometer with Cu-Ni radiation, $2R=57.3$, $2r=0.6$ mm (analyst: R.A. Alexandrova).

bearing veins. In carbonatites it is rare, but it occurs in the massifs of Palabora (Forster, 1958) and Vuoriyarvi (Kapustin, 1965a). Here it forms druses of needle-shaped crystals (up to 5 mm in length) in the cavities in ankeritic veins containing a corroded variety of pyrrhotite with relics of primary pentlandite. Fragments of needle-shaped millerite crystals enclose the pentlandite grains within ankerite (Fig. 22, *b*). Millerite is associated with pyrite, sphalerite, podolite, and strontiobarite. It is bronze-colored with a tarnishing character. Hardness 3.5; spectral analyses indicate the presence of more than 1% admixture of Cu, Mn, Sb, Ni, Fe, and Co. X-ray analysis of millerite is given in Table 5. Millerite is formed by the decomposition of primary nickel-rich minerals.

Covellite (CuS). This mineral occurs in the carbonatites of the Palabora massif (Forster, 1958) and the massifs of Vuoriyarvi and Kovdor, and was also found as a thin incrustation on chalcopyrite. In the last two massifs the chalcopyrite is sometimes completely replaced by covellite and bornite (anomalous zone) in the zone of weak ankeritization, staffelitization, and dolomitized carbonatites. Covellite is associated with galena, bornite, and tetrahedrite and is formed in the late phase of the process of ankeritic vein formation, replacing chalcopyrite.

Chalkosine (Cu_2S). This was reported by Heinrich (1967). We observed it in cavities in ankeritic carbonatites in Kovdor in the form of small individual grains (1–2 mm) associated with chalcopyrite. Its properties are normal. X-ray pattern is similar to the standard.

Bornite (Cu_5FeS_4). This forms a thin incrustation around chalcopyrite (massifs of Eastern Sayan, Kovdor, Vuoriyarvi, Sebl-Yavr, Turi Mis) and occurs along with galena, tetrahedrite, and cleiophane in association with ankeritized pyrrhotite in carbonatites, which always contain chalcopyrite. Bornite is formed after chalcopyrite. Under the microscope in reflected light bornite is pink to grayish in color, isotropic. Spectral analysis of bornite from Vuoriyarvi and Kovdor shows $>1\%$ (Cu+Fe) and traces of Ni, Pb, Zn and Sb.

Galena (PbS). This is a typical mineral of hydrothermal veins of late ankeritic-dolomitic carbonatites. It is widely distributed in the massifs of Vuoriyarvi and Sallanlatva and in several massifs of Siberia, and is also sometimes found in the massifs of Africa and North Siberia. Galena is intimately associated with ancylite, cleiophane, barite, and strontianite, and forms in the late phase of ankeritic veins (Kapustin, 1965a). The close association of galena with orange-colored barite and siderite is conspicuous in baritic veins rich in galena (Sallanlatva, Vuoriyarvi, Namo-Vara), and an analogous association of galena with siderite-barite in hydrothermal vein (Betekhtin, 1953). Galena forms rounded mono-crystalline grains up to 2 cm in size or veins in the ankeritic mass. Octahedral crystals of galena with rounded grains occur in cavities. Here ancylite and strontianite crystals are also formed.

The properties of galena are normal; sp. gr. 7.53 (Eastern Sayan). Chemical composition (analyst: K.I. Isaeva) of galena is as follows: Bi=0.75%, Ag=0.029% (Vuoriyarvi), Bi=0.335%, Ag=0.01% (Sallanlatva). Spectral analysis of galena indicates constant presence of Ba, Zn, Fe, Sb, and Mg. In samples collected from a depth greater than 70 m (Vuoriyarvi), galena is replaced by a crystalline mass of anglesite in which needle-shaped crystals of strontianite, hematite, and quartz are sometimes formed. Possibly the formation of anglesite took place in the late hydrothermal phase. In hypergene conditions galena is covered by cerussite crusts.

Tetrahedrite ($Cu_{12}Sb_4S_{13}$). This mineral occurs in ankeritic-dolomitic veins in the massifs of Vuoriyarvi and Sallnalatva (Kapustin, 1965a), as small (0.1–1 m) tetrahedral crystals associated with galena, ancylite, barite, and strontianite, and in the form of thin encrustations on pyrite crystals. It is black in color with sub-metallic luster; sp. gr. 4.8 (determined by micromethod). X-ray data are similar to the standard. Chemical analysis (analyst: A.N. Laryukova) is as follows: Sb=27.32%, As=1.03%—indicating pure tetrahedrite. Spectral analysis indicated the presence of Cu, Fe, Sb, As, Pb, Zn, Bi, Co, and Ag.

Bournonite ($PbCuSbS_3$). This is a rare sulfantimonite, known to occur near hydrothermal deposits (Nagelni Ridge and others), and is observed in ankeritic veins of Vuoriyarvi (Kapustin, 1965a), where small (0.1–0.15 mm) hexagonal grains of bournonite were formed (Fig. 22, *c*) penetrating ankerite. It is sometimes intimately intergrown with pyrite and galena; sp. gr. 5.8 (determined by micromethod); X-ray data similar to the standard (Table 5). Under the microscope, in reflected light, the mineral is white in color and anisotropic. Spectral analysis indicates the following: Pb, Cu, and Sb>10%; As and Zn>1%; Ag, Bi, Ga, Cd, and Mg—traces. Bournonite is possibly formed along with galena in the late phase of the development of ankeritic vein.

Jamesonite ($Pb_4FeSb_6S_{14}$). This mineral occurs in mesothermal sulfide veins of many deposits (Neptune ore-deposits). It is located in ankeritic-dolomitic veins of Vuoriyarvi (Kapustin, 1965a), where fibrous or radiate masses of jamesonite are formed on the upper surface of the fragmented relics of pyrrhotite mixed with pyrite. Needle-shaped crystals of jamesanite (up to 3 mm in length) are formed or pyrite crystals and columnar masses penetrate ankerite (Fig. 22, *d*). Jamesonite is steel-gray in color with sub-metallic luster;

cleavage is prominent in the direction of elongation; hardness 2.5; X-ray data similar to the standard (Table 5); sp. gr. 5.62. In reflected light jamesonite is white in color, strongly anisotropic, and reflectivity is similar to or less than galena. Twinning is prominent in all jamesonite crystals parallel to the direction of elongation.

Chemical analysis (analyst: N.G. Kurbanov) of jamesonite shows 9.85% Pb and 3.02% Fe. Spectral analysis indicates As, Sb, and Bi > 1% and Ag, Ni and Co—traces. Possibly jamesonite is an early sulfosalt in carbonatite and is formed from surplus Fe (before galena and sulfantimonite). In the last phase aggregates of boulangerite, galena, and pyrite are formed around jamesonite.

Boulangerite ($Pb_5Sb_4S_{11}$). Like bournotite, boulangerite occurs in mesothermal sulfide deposits (Nagelni Ridge). In carbonatites it is rarely found, but it occurs in ankeritic veins together with bournotite and cleiophane (Vuoriyarvi-Kapustin, 1965a), where thin (< 0.01 mm) needle-shaped crystals up to 5 mm in length and columnar masses of boulangerite penetrate ankerite. Although several sulfide minerals are formed along with boulangerite its exact relation with other sulfides is not clear. Boulangerite is lead-gray in color and easily tarnishes. X-ray analysis is given in Table 5. Under reflected light (oil immersion) it is white in color and strongly anisotropic; reflectivity is similar to galena. Spectral analysis indicates Pb, Sb, and Cu > 1%; Zn, Bi, Ag, Fe—traces. Chemical analysis (analyst: A.N. Laryukova) shows 0.81% As and 26.32% Sb.

Valleriite ($Cu_3Fe_4S_7$). This is reported by Higasy (1954) from the ankeritic carbonatite of Lolekek in association with pyrrhotite and pentlandite. Valleriite forms later than pyrrhotite and occurs in small amounts. Its composition was not studied. Higasy observed 0.005% Ni in it.

CLASS IV: OXIDES

Oxide minerals (principally rare metals) are widely distributed in carbonatites. Most important among them are magnetite and pyrochlore, which are typical of carbonatites of the 2nd stage. Other minerals also often occur but not in sufficient amounts to be of industrial interest.

Magnetite (Fe_3O_4). This is the typical mineral of all complex rocks (except alkaline) and is characteristic of ultrabasites (hypabyssal facies) of all regions. It is formed in the zone of impregnation as thick schlieren (Derby, 1891) and in veins (Vuoriyarvi, Kovdor, Gulinskii, Jacupiranga, Palabora). A high concentration of magnetite is typical of magnetite-forsterite rocks.

Magnetite is characteristic of early carbonatites of hypabyssal and

Table 6. Chemical composition of magnetite (in wt. %)

Components	Olivinites		Pyroxenites	Melteigites	Magnetite-forsteritic rocks		Carbonatite of 2nd stage							
	Lesnaya Varaka	Afrikanda		Ozernaya Varaka	Kovdor	Vuoriyarvi		Kovdor	Siberia	Gulinskii	Kaiserstühl	Oka	Magnet Cove	Alnö
TiO_2	13.60	7.31	10.40	8.85	0.77	0.74	0.64	0.79	0.92	1.18	2.53	1.80	3.14	1.36
Al_2O_3	0.76	1.40	1.85	0.75	3.27	3.15	2.36	1.75	1.92	1.08	5.99	2.18	1.25	1.67
Fe_2O_3	49.10	57.00	53.94	54.58	67.03	67.24	67.33	67.05	66.54	67.97	63.42	68.05	64.19	66.56
V_2O_3	—	0.04	0.08	0.01	0.10	0.08	0.04	0.07	0.01	0.03	—	0.02	0.02	—
FeO	25.05	29.46	29.60	34.42	21.95	20.31	21.18	26.12	21.40	22.67	19.72	20.76	19.38	20.32
MnO	0.28	0.70	0.60	0.41	0.54	0.47	—	0.42	0.38	0.51	2.35	0.85	0.56	—
MgO	11.18	4.09	3.53	0.96	6.28	8.01	7.45	3.72	5.03	6.19	5.99	5.89	8.37	5.43
ZnO	About 0.09	—	—	—	0.06	—	—	0.03	—	—	—	—	—	—
Total	100.06	100.00	100.00	100.00	100.00	100.00	100.00	100.00	96.20	97.63	100.00	98.55	96.91	95.31
No. of samples analyzed	1	3	8	4	13	3	4	3	1	1	3	1	1	1
Analyst	V.A. Klassen					V.A. Klassen			M.V. Kukharchik, A.E. Hovorossova				M.V. Kukharchik, V.N. Arkhengalkaya	
Author			A.A. Kukharenko et al., 1965					A.A. Kukharenko et al., 1965			W. Wimmenauer, 1963			

volcanic facies. It is disseminated in the carbonatic lavas of Oldoino Lengan. In carbonatite of the 1st stage magnetite occurs in significant amounts as corroded, shapeless relics and as thin needle-shaped inclusions in calcite (Kovdor, Mogo-Vidi, Vuoriyarvi, Tuxta-Vara, Ozernaya Varaka, Siberian massifs). In rocks of the 2nd stage the proportion of magnetite increases sharply and the individual veins are rimmed by magnetite crystals along the contacts (Fig. 15, *d*). In carbonatites magnetite shows an antipathetic relation with biotite and is usually absent from biotite carbonatite (Ozernaya Varaka, Kovdor, Pilkoma-Selga, South Siberian massif). However, it forms profuse impregnations in carbonatites with magnesium and ferruginous phlogopite (Vuoriyarvi, Kovdor, Sallanlatva, Siberian massifs, Magnet Cove, Palabora).

The distribution of magnetite in carbonatite is not uniform. Even within a single body the magnetite content varies from 5 to 50%, depending primarily on the presence of relics of magnetite-bearing rocks. In the absence of such relics magnetite is locally concentrated (schlieren) in the thick and weathered parts of the bodies. The portions rich in magnetite as a rule show a flow-bedded structure in which it is associated with phlogopite, apatite, and forsterite. Magnetite-rich early carbonatites are intimately associated with brecciated magnetite-forsterite rocks in Kovdor and Vuoriyarvi massifs, where the magnetite content in some place rises to 60%. For a significant part of the carbonatite body a considerable amount of magnetite is derived from mixed rocks (magnetite-forsterite and ultrabasite), where independent magnetites are constantly present with affinity to carbonatitic features that occur around various rocks (Gulinskii, Mrima Hill, Hudini, Oldoino Dili, Kruidfontein and other massifs, occurring around gneisses, schists, and other rocks poor in magnetite). The magnetite content of carbonatite usually does not exceed 20%.

The property of early-generation magnetite, as in ultrabasite, changes in the late-generation mineral occurring in carbonatite. In magnetite from ultrabasites the TiO_2 content rises to 14%, whereas magnetite from carbonatite does not contain more than 1–2% TiO_2 (Table 6). Magnetite in carbonatites is an intermediate variety between pure magnetite and magnesioferrite (Mg : Fe = 1 : 5 to 1 : 1.2), with more affinity to magnesioferrite (Knop, 1892; Wimmenauer, 1963). Impurities of rare elements in magnetite are constant but probably most of them are due to mechanical inclusions. In magnetite from carbonatite of the Kola Peninsula and Eastern Sayan the compositional range of rare elements is constantly as follows:

Nb_2O_5	0.001–0.005%
Ta_2O_5	0–0.0003%
ZrO_2	0.01–0.05%

An admixture of pyrochlore and baddeleyite is also found in this magnetite. Attempts to separate the admixtures showed that the Nb and *Zr* content in magnetite decreases with any decrease in the size of the fractions from which the materials are derived.

The variation of $ZrO_2\%$ with the variation in size fractions of magnetite from the Kovdor massif is given below (determined in the laboratory of IMGRÉ).

Size (mm)	$ZrO_2\%$	$Nb_2O_5\%$
0.5–0.25	0.12	0.03
0.25–0.1	0.06	0.010
<0.1	0.02	0.007

This indicates the difficulty of separating magnetite from the admixture and therefore the selected grains, which are usually few in number, remain full of these admixtures.

Spinel (Mg, Fe) Al_2O_4. This occurs in the rocks of the massifs studied, in spinel-almanditic rocks (apariesites) (Strauss and Trula, 1951b) of the Magnet Heitz intrusive. Spinel is constantly found as an accessory mineral and very minute impregnations in magnetite in all the rocks of these massifs and in magnetite from carbonatite (Rimskaya-Korsakova, 1950). It is sky-blue to green in color; sp. gr. 4.24–4.32; isotropic, $n = 1.76$–1.79. Hovorossovi found 5.22% FeO, 3.78% Fe_2O_3, and 1.82% ZnO in spinel of Vuoriyarvi. Composition of spinel from Kovdor (Kukharenko et al., 1965) is as follows: SiO_2 0.12, TiO_2 0.17, Al_2O_3 64.33, Fe_2O_3 4.58, FeO 5.23, MnO 0.15, MgO 23.32, ZnO 1.63, H_2O 0.12, loss on ignition 0.03, total 99.68 (in weight %, analyst: M. Pukha); the chemical formula of this spinel is $Mg_{0.88}Fe_{0.12}(Al_{1.40}Fe_{0.60})O_4$. In carbonatites spinel is not stable and is replaced by green phlogopite.

Hematite (Fe_2O_3). This occurs only in late ankerite-dolomitic veins. It is found in fair quantities in the carbonatite massif of Fen (Brögger, 1921). It occurs in veins of almost all the massifs of the Kola Peninsula and South Siberia. It is also found in the massifs of Africa (Smith, 1953; Coetzee and Edwards, 1959) and the USA (Heinrich, 1967). A large carbonate body showing hematitization occurs in Tuva, but its relation with carbonatite is not clear. Hematite is formed under hypabyssal and volcanic conditions (in the form of phenocrysts). The characteristic color produced by hematitization of the mixed rocks often accompanies the fluoritic veins of Siberia. Massive hematitization occurs in the Bolshetagninskii massif (Frolov and Bagdasarov, 1967), in the massifs of Fen (Brögger, 1921; Saether, 1948), and Zangu (Tuttle et al., 1967). A linear zone of magnetitization up to 100 m thick is found within the gneisses to the east of Ozernaya Varaka massif.

In carbonatites hematite together with calcite replaces ferruginous carbonates, sometimes forming continuous porous, foliated lepidodendritic masses and their dispersed phenocrysts. Hematite is associated with calcite, quartz, fibrous aegirine (Siberia), fluorite, albite and fluor-carbonate containing TR. Hematites show normal properties. Spectral analysis indicates the presence of Ti, Nb, Mn, V, Zn, and Zr.

Quartz (SiO_2). This is more widely distributed in carbonatites than was earlier thought. It occurs in fair quantities in the massifs of Nkombwa (Reeve and Deans, 1954; Deans and McConnel, 1955), Alnö (Eckermann, 1963), Lesnaya and Ozernaya Varaka, Vuoriyarvi, and Sebl-Yavr. Quartzose carbonatites occur in the Gulinskii (Epshtein, 1959). In the Bolshetagninskii massif quartz occurs as phenocrysts in carbonatites. In the veins of Turi-Mis the quartz content rises to 30%. In pure carbonatites quartz is rare. It occurs only in the zones of carbonatized gneisses and in independent carbonatized veins (relic-like) in Ozernaya Varaka. Quartz is the typical mineral of late ankeritic-dolomitic veins and occurs in Fremont County (Heinrich and Shapirio, 1966) and Namo-Vara, in veins that are most common in all types of rocks. But in veins intersected by fenites, principally in gneisses rich in silica, the amount of quartz increases hundreds of times, forming thick quartzose zones. Formation of a thick aureole of porous quartzitic rocks around late carbonatites in Namo-Vara is due to leaching of all components (except silica) from gneisses and accumulation of quartz under metasomatic carbonatization of the gneisses. Near the carbonatite veins the quartzose mass recrystallizes and the cavities are filled with druses of bipyramidal crystals of black quartz (zones of quartz vugs, the dimension of the individual vug being up to 30 cm, are formed) at the intersection of quartzose veins and nucleii of ancient pegmatites around carbonate-podolite veinlets (Namo-Vara).

In mixed rocks and ankeritic veins, besides the black bipyramidal quartz, late redeposited colorless or amethystic quartz is also formed. Crystals of this colorless or amethystic quartz grow on the crystals of carbonate or replace carbonatites at the center of the veins. Radiated chalcedony is often associated with quartz (Fig. 21, *c*).

Quartz is associated with chlorite, orthoclase, albite, hematite, barite, monazite, and strontianite. It shows normal properties.

Brucite [$Mg(OH)_2$]. This is rare in carbonatites. It occurs in the Arbarastachsky massif (Glagolev, 1962), Vuoriyarvi, and in veins of early carbonatites with forsterite undergoing fenitization and richteritization. Brucite forms fibrous aggregates (nemalite) intimately intergrown with dolomite and replacing forsterite (sometimes together with serpentine and talc). Brucite is white in color; X-ray analysis similar to the standard; biaxial, –ve; $n_g = 1.580$, $n_p = 1.559$. We observed brucite replaced by serpentine.

Hypogene cerianite (CeO_2). This occurs in calcitic veins intersecting nepheline syenites (Canada—Graham, 1955). It is assoicated with tremolite and forms greenish-yellow idiomorphic octahedral crystals. Isotropic, $n>2$; sp. gr. 7.19. Its composition is similar to the theoretical composition. The composition of the analyzed mineral is as follows (wt. %): CeO_2 80%, (La, Yb, $Y)_2O_3$ 4.5%, ThO_2 5.1%, ZrO_2 0.6%, Nb_2O_5 1.8%, Ta_2O_5 0.6%, the interrelation between the rare-earth elements in cerianite is: $La_6Ce_{91}Pr_{0.9}Nb_{2.1}$. The genetic relation of carbonatite veins with cerianite has not been well established. Possibly cerianite forms along with richeterite with the decomposition of rare-earth pyrochlore.

Pyrochlore $(Na, Ca, TR, U, Th, Zr)_2 (Nb, Ta, Ti)_2 O_6 (F, OH)$. This does not occur in ultrabasites and alkaline rocks, but only as an accessory mineral in early carbonatites of the 2nd stage. It occurs in almost all the massifs of Siberia, the Kola Peninsula (Borodin and Nazarenko, 1957; Gaidukova et al., 1962; Kapustin, 1964; Kukharenko et al., 1965). Scandinavia (Fen—Brögger, 1921; Björlykke, 1934, 1955; Sorum, 1955; Alnö—Holmquist, 1893; Eckermann, 1948a), Africa (Fawley and James, 1955; James and McKie, 1958; Jäger et al., 1959; Meyer and Bethune, 1958, 1960; Van der Veen, 1963), the USA (Larsen, 1942; Grogan, 1960), Canada (Maurice, 1957; Rowe, 1958; Perrault, 1959; Hogarth, 1961), and Brazil (Leonardos, 1956a; Guimaraes, 1957, 1958). Four generations of pyrochlore differing in composition are postulated in carbonatites: (i) blackish-brown, (ii) reddish-brown, (iii) dark brown, and (iv) cream-colored or red (Gaidukova et al., 1962; Kapustin, 1964).

Accessory hatchettolite (black uranium-tantalum pyrochlore) is formed somewhat early. It occurs in very small quantities. In the massifs of Siberia and the Kola Peninsula hatchettolite is formed in carbonatites, phlogopite-forsteritic and aegirinitic facies but it shows an antipathetic relation to biotite. This mineral occurs in the marginal and central parts of carbonatite bodies along the zones of albitization, fenitization, and apatitization, often forming thin impregnations at the contact of these reaction zones. Toward the center and in the deeper part of carbonatite bodies hatchettolite is replaced by pyrochlore (reddish-brown). Hatchettolite is associated with magnetite, phlogopite, forsterite, baddeleyite, aegirine, and principally with apatite, in which accessory hatchettolite is often concentrated (in several cases we have established a linear correlation between these two minerals). Hatchettolite forms idiomorphic octahedra within silicate crystals and often contains inclusions of apatite prisms. It is uniformly intergrown with baddeleyite (Evzikova, 1960). It is often replaced by reddish-brown or dark brown pyrochlore on the periphery.

Reddish-brown pyrochlore is the typical accessory mineral of early carbonatite of the 2nd stage, and most pyrochlore is found in this variety of carbonatite. It is intimately associated with magnetite, apatite, phlogopite, and pyroxene, and is randomly distributed in carbonatites occurring within different rocks. Reddish-brown pyrochlore is also found in the marginal and central part of carbonatite bodies within an apatite aggregate. But this is not always the case, as with hatchettolite.

Idiomorphic octahedral reddish-brown pyrochlore grows on the crystals of opaque minerals and contains inclusions of apatite prisms. Often these crystals form alternate zones with or without a hatchettolite nucleus, the zones being parallel with elongation of the octahedral grains (Fig. 23).

In carbonatites pyrochlore forms simultaneously with the formation of silicate, magnetite, and apatite, with which the octahedral pyrochlore is constantly associated. But often it crystallizes later in some parts, and in a carbonatite mass individual zones (normally in conformity with the general structure of stocks) contain pyrochlore and apatite.

In carbonatites showing fenitization and amphibolitization hatchettolite and reddish-brown pyrochlore crystals are broken, dispersed, and corroded along the peripheries, and are replaced by dark brown pyrochlore almost without Ta, Th and U. Crystals of this variety are usually full of richterite inclusions and carbonates and take the form of cubic-octahedral (sometimes rhombohedral) grains.

Reddish or greenish (cream color) pyrochlore is relatively rare and occurs in lesser quantities. It is found in late veins and is associated with early-

Fig. 23. Zoned crystals of hatchettolite in apatite mass, Vuoriyarvi. Under crossed nicol, mag. ×48.

generation pyrochlore, rarely with columbite (Vuoriyarvi—Kapustin, 1964; Siberia—Gaidukova et al., 1962; Gaidukova, 1966) in regions of ankeritization of early pyrochlore-bearing carbonatite. This mineral is rich in Sr, Ba, TR, and Ti (Sr-pyrochlore and pandaite—Harris, 1965).

The physical properties of all the varieties of pyrochlore are similar (Table 7). The first two generations are metamict while the last two are crystalline. The structure of the metamict samples is restored above a temperature of 550–600°C, shown by the exothermic peaks of the curves of the minerals (Fig. 24, *1–5*). Similarly for 3rd generation pyrochlore, indicating the presence of a metamict phase. Dehydration in these minerals takes place at an interval of 200°C. The general properties of pyrochlore vary little. Sp. gr. increases with the increase of Ta and decreases (also the R.I.) with dehydration and transformation to the metamict state (Table 7).

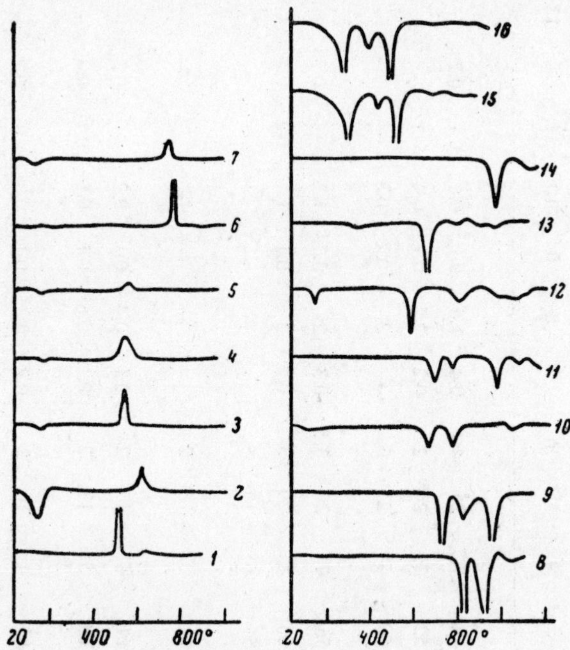

Fig. 24. Thermal curves of minerals.

1—Hatchettolite; 2—Hydrated hatchettolite; 3—Reddish-brown pyrochlore; 4—Bright-brown pyrochlore; 5—Bright pyrochlore (4th generation); 6—Aeschynite; 7—Niobium-zirconolite; 8—Dolomite; 9—Ankerite; 10—Burbankite; 11—Carbocernaite; 12—Ancylite; 13—Lanthanite; 14—Strontianite; 15—Manasseite; 16—Hydrotalcite.

The chemical composition of pyrochlore was studied in detail (Borodin and Nazarenko, 1957a; Perrault, 1959; Gaidukova et al., 1962; Van der Veen,

Table 8. Composition of rare elements ($TR_2O_3 = 100\%$) in minerals from early carbonatites

Mineral	La	Ce	Pr	Nd	Sm	Eu	Gd	Tb	Dy	Ho	Er	Tu	Yb	Lu	Y	Massifs
1	2	3	4	5	6	7	8	9	10	11	12	13	14	15	16	17
Pyrochlore, 1st generation	11.2	49	7.7	25	4.1	0.4	1.5	0.1	0.6	0.1	0.2	—	0.1	—	—	Siberia
Do	12	52	7	24	2	0.2	2.2	0.1	0.4	0.1	—	—	—	—	Not det.	Vuoriyarvi
Do	11	50	7	25	3	—	3	0.2	0.8	—	—	—	—	—	,,	Kovdor
Pyrochlore, 2nd generation	9	56	7	20	3.5	0.3	2	0.7	1.2	—	0.3	—	—	—	,,	Vuoriyarvi
Do	10	55	8	20	3	0.2	2	0.1	1	0.2	0.5	—	—	—	,,	Sebl-Yavr
Do	15	57	6	17	5	—	—	—	—	—	—	—	—	—	,,	Sayan
Pyrochlore, 3rd generation	14	61	5	18	2	—	—	—	—	—	—	—	—	—	,,	Lesnaya Varaka
Do	14	61	5	17	2	0.1	0.4	0.1	0.2	—	0.2	—	—	—	,,	Sebl-Yavr
Do	15	58	5	18	2	0.1	0.6	0.1	0.5	0.1	0.4	—	0.2	—	,,	Sayan
Pyrochlore, 4th generation	13	63	4	16	2	0.2	0.3	0.1	0.2	—	0.2	—	—	—	,,	Vuoriyarvi
Aeschynite	15	51	7	20	3	0.7	1	0.4	1.2	0.2	0.3	—	0.2	—	,,	,,
Dysanalite	18	60	4	15	2	0.2	0.4	—	0.1	—	0.1	—	0.2	—	,,	Kovdor

1	2	3	4	5	6	7	8	9	10	11	12	13	14	15	16	17
Dysanalite	16	59	6	16	1	0.1	1	—	0.5	—	0.2	—	0.2	—	Not det.	Gulinskii
Do	16	47.5	9.5	25	2	—	—	—	—	—	—	—	—	—	,,	Arbarasf
Do	11.5	49	7.7	25	4.1	0.4	1.5	0.1	0.6	0.1	0.2	—	0.1	—	,,	Aldan
Niobozirconolite	4	31	9	23	7	0.7	4.5	0.5	4	—	0.9	—	0.4	—	15	Vuoriyarvi
Do	5	35	10	30	5	1	3.2	0.8	2	0.2	0.4	—	0.4	—	17	Kovdor
Baddeleyite	18	48	7	23	2	0.4	1	0.1	0.4	—	0.1	—	—	—	Not det.	,,
Do	18	50	6	24	1	—	1	—	—	—	—	—	—	—	,,	Vuoriyarvi
Do	16	46	6	19	3	0.4	3	0.3	2	0.1	0.5	—	0.4	—	3.3	Gulinskii
Thorianite	8	52	8	23	4	—	4	0.7	0.1	0.2	—	—	—	—	Not det.	Kola
Do	9	52	7	24	4	—	4	—	—	—	—	—	—	—	,,	Siberia
Schorlomite	7	24	7	35	6	2	10	0.2	1.8	—	1.4	—	1.6	—	5	Gulinskii
Sphene	16	46	8	23	3	0.3	2	0.3	1	0.1	0.2	—	0.1	—	Not det.	Kovdor
Eudialite	18	50	7	19	2	0.4	2	0.2	1.8	—	0.4	—	0.2	—	,,	,,

1963; Kukharenko et al., 1965). Analyses (Table 7) yielded the crystallochemical formula $A_2B_2O_6F$ (Borodin and Nazarenko, 1957a), where A—Na, Ca, Sr, Ba, TR, U, Th, Fe^{2+}, Zr; B—Nb, Ta, Ti, Fe^{3+}.

'A' is constantly less than 2 and this deficiency in cations of group A is closely related to the dehydration and partly to the introduction of Ca and Na together with high-valency cations like U, Th, TR. Cations escaped from some parts. Attempts to place H_3O^+ in group A to compensate the deficit (Sergeev, 1961; Kukharenko et al., 1965) are not justified, as the structure of metamict pyrochlore is not established and its crystal structure is restored only after ignition, when there is complete dehydration. The increase in the cell size of pyrochlore with the entrance of hydroxyl (Kukharenko et al., 1965) is also not clear, as most of the cells were measured after dehydrating the mineral at higher temperatures. In calculating the formula this fact was not taken into account, so that the multi-valency cations primarily took the position of the low-valency state (in unchanged hatchettolite and pyrochlore U^4 and Fe^{2+} persist, whereas in the changed condition U^6 and Fe^{3+} persist). In oxide form they constitute another group (group B together with A).

For pyrochlore visual typomorphism may be ascertained, as each variety of it is characterized by definite stages of the process of formation. Hatchettolites are rich in Ta, U, Zr, Th, and Ti, and reddish-brown pyrochlore in Th. Late-stage red pyrochlores are rich in Sr and Ba. Dark brownish pyrochlore has the theoretical composition $CaNaNb_2O_6$. In the minerals of this group isomorphism is widespread (Borodin and Nazarenko, 1957a; Ginsburg et al., 1958). Besides isovalency isomorphism, namely Ca→Sr, Ca→Ba, Nb→Ta, and Ca→Fe^{2+}, there is the possibility of heterovalency isomorphism such as CaNb→$TRFe^{3+}$; NaCaNb→U^4Ti; CaNb→U^4Fe^{3+}; 2Ca→(U^4, Th); 2Ca→Zr; NaNb→$TRFe^{3+}$; NaCaNb→ZrTi.

There is the probability of formation of a stable variety of pyrochlore rich in Zr, Ta, Ti, and U (high content of ZrO_2, up to 12%, is found only in pyrochlore of carbonatites) with regular arrangement in the crystal lattice of the mineral. The composition of rare-earth elements in pyrochlore is shown in Table 8.

In late carbonatites pyrochlore is unstable and is replaced by marginal rims (Fig. 25) of fersmite and columbite aggregates (massifs of Siberia, Africa, and Fen). Columbitization of pyrochlore outstrips ankeritization of calcite. In hypergene conditions pyrochlore shows bleaching and dehydration, as a result of which the crystals show a secondary zonal structure with a dark nucleus enclosed by a bright margin of more hydrous pyrochlore. In the center of the crystal the water content is about 5% while at the periphery it is about 11%. Primary and hydrated pyrochlores are easily differentiated by their thermal curves: for the hydrous variety sharp endothermic peaks between 120 and 180°C are characteristic (Fig. 24, *2*). During the weathering of carbonatites pyrochlore is concentrated in alluvium and talus deposits (Araxa and

Tapira in Brazil—Leonardos, 1956a, b; Guimaraes, 1957, 1958) and in smaller proportions in the placer deposits occurring not far from the source carbonatites. Being very brittle, pyrochlore is easily broken and is quickly dispersed in the placers, where there is frequent deposition of columbitized pyrochlore and columbite, which are mechanically more stable.

Columbite (Fe, Mn) Nb_2O_6. This occurs as a rare accessory mineral in carbonatites (Fen—Sörum, 1955; Saether, 1958; Mbeya—Fawley and James, 1955; Ngualla—James and McKie, 1958; Ravalli County—Hess and Trumpour, 1959). As an independent mineral it is rare, but it often replaces pyrochlore in ankeritized early (pyrochloritized) carbonatites. Columbite along with fersmite forms rims around the pyrochlore crystals, veinlets in the pyrochlore mass, and octahedral pseudomorphs after pyrochlore (Fig. 25). The process of columbitization of pyrochlore is widespread and is possibly characteristic for late carbonatites (Gaidukova, 1960a, b; Zhabin and Gaidukova, 1961; Björlykke, 1955; Fawley and James, 1955; Van der Veen, 1963). Sometimes columbite is recrystallized in ankeritic veins and forms individual (Vuoriyarvi) rhombic prism-shaped crystals (130) with the development of pinacoidal (010) grains and rhombic pyramids (131). It is black in color, sp. gr. 5.54; X-ray analysis is similar to the standard. The chemical composition

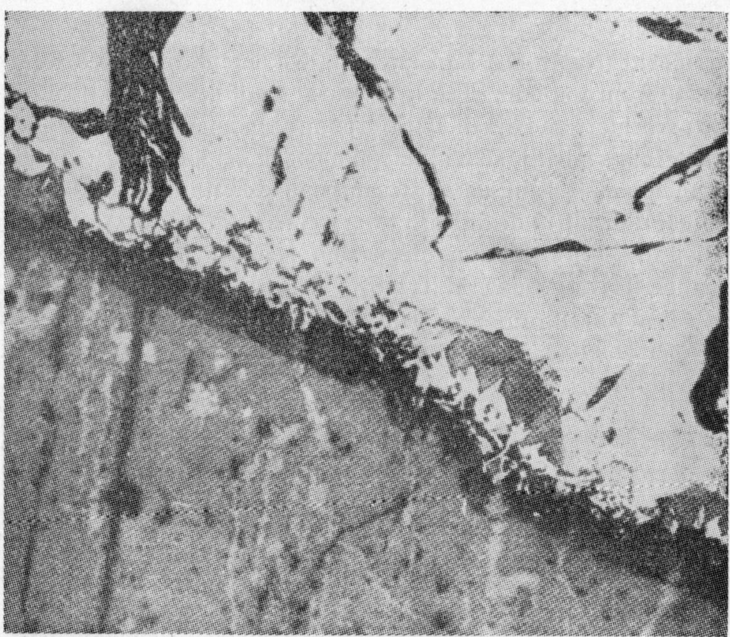

Fig. 25. Replacement of needle-shaped columbite by pyrochlore (gray). Dark-gray carbonate, Siberia. In polarized light, crossed nicol, ×48.

(analyst: A.N. Manuchov) of columbite is as follows (wt. %): Nb_2O_5 76.15, Ta_2O_5 2.81, FeO 18.40, MnO 3.31, total 100.67%. The crystal-chemical formula of the sample analyzed is as follows: $Fe_{0.93}Mn_{0.07}Nb_2O_6$. Columbite is formed from pyrochlore in the zones of ankeritized early pyrochloritized carbonatite. Under hypergene conditions it is deposited in the placers.

Fersmite ($CaNb_2O_6$). This mineral occurs in the massifs of Fen (Sörum, 1955) Ngualla (James and McKie, 1958), Lueshe (Wambeke, 1965), Mbeya (Fawley and James, 1955), Ravalli County (Hess and Trumpour, 1959), Siberia (Zhabin and Gaidukova, 1961), and other places (Van der Veen, 1963). Fersmite is not formed as an individual mineral but is intimately associated with columbite, replacing pyrochlore in ankeritized parts of early carbonatites. Aggregates of small needle-shaped fersmite crystals are found around pyrochlore crystals intersecting columbite. Sometimes fersmite forms independent pseudomorphs after pyrochlore. It is often accompanied by barite, chlorite, alkali amphibole, and podolite.

Sp. gr. of fersmite was not determined due to its intimate intergrowth with columbite. Other properties are normal; X-ray analysis is similar to the standard. Spectral analysis of fersmite (with columbite inclusion) indicates the following: Nb, Ca, Fe, Ti, Ce, Mn. Composition of fersmite is given in Table 9.

Natroniobite ($NaNb_2O_6$). Kukharenko (Kukharenko et al., 1965) reported this mineral from dolomitized early carbonatites of Lesnaya Varaka, where it replaced pyrochlore and dysanalyte, forming pseudomorphs after them. The X-ray pattern is similar to that of fersmite but in composition it is similar to lueshite and possibly represents a structural modification thereof. It is brown in color but difficult to distinguish (even crystals) in microcrystalline aggregates. Biaxial, −ve, with strong dispersion, negative elongation, z: $N_p = 15°$ (other properties are shown in Table 9). The crystal-chemical formula is $(Na_{0.93}Ca_{0.12}TR_{0.06})_{1.11}(Nb_{1.76}Ti_{0.22}Fe_{0.06}Mg_{0.02}Ta_{0.01})_{2.07}O_{5.24}(OH)_{0.76}$. Probably natroniobite is a variety of fersmite forming under increasing concentration of Na.

Aeschynite ($CeTiNbO_6$). This is a typical mineral for pegmatites and alkaline and nepheline syenites of the miascite series (Bonshtedt-Kupletskaya, 1951; Dana et al., 1951). In carbonatites aeschynite is rare. It occurs in Siberia (Gaidukova, 1966), Ravalli County (Heinrich and Levinson, 1961), and as an accessory in late dolomitized veins occurring within nepheline-bearing fenites (Kola Peninsula). Aeschynite is intimately associated with pyrite, strontiobarite, orthoclase, chlorite, and quartz, forming small (0.2–1.0 mm) flattened crystals with uneven distorted grains full of inclusions of orthoclase and pyrite. In aeschynite crystals thin grains of rhombic prisms (110)

Table 9. Chemical composition (in wt. %) and physical properties of fersmite group of minerals

Components	Fersmite				Natroniobite
	Siberia	Montana	Ural		Kola Peninsula
Nb_2O_5	66.92	74.44	71.17	70.02	74.06
Ta_2O_5	—	—	0.44	—	0.83
TiO_2	2.63	2.01	4.43	3.21	5.56
SiO_2	2.41	0.32	1.20	0.75	0.97
ThO_2	—	0.10	1.02	—	0.56
TR_2O_3	4.00	6.36	5.70	4.79	3.25
Al_2O_3	4.43	0.10	0.44	1.28	0.20
Fe_2O_3+FeO	2.55	0.34	1.44	1.71	1.35
MgO	1.07	—	0.08	0.98	0.35
CaO	14.56	15.02	12.76	14.49	2.24
$(Na, K)_2O$	0.25	—	0.27	0.46	9.08
H_2O	0.56	0.18	0.92	0.72	1.83
F	0.56	—	—	1.87	—
Others	—	0.19	—	0.48	0.05
$-O=F_2$	0.22	—	—	0.79	—
Total	99.72	99.06	99.87	100.07	100.33
Analyst			M.E. Kazakova	T.A. Burova	Yu.N. Kuipovitch
Author	V.S. Gaidukova el al., 1962		A.G. Zabin et al., 1961	E.M. Bonshtedt-Kupletskaya, T.A. Burova, 1946	A.A. Kukharenko et al., 1965
Sp. gr.	4.12	4.79	4.38	4.69	4.40
n_g	2.13	2.19			2.21–2.24
n_m	2.04	2.08			2.19–2.21
n_p	1.98	2.07			2.10–2.13
$2V^o$		20–25			10–35

and often (120) are developed, but the majority are usually pinacoids (010) formed by the flattening of the crystals. Cone-shaped grains are usually absent. Aeschynite is brownish-red in color and is crystalline, but under the microscope it is cryptocrystalline in nature, while the individual anisotropic parts (with increasing R.I.) are confined to the metamict mass (similar configurations are found in other metamict minerals). Biaxial, +ve; pleochroism is weak in shades of brown, the scheme being $N_g > N_p$. The X-ray pattern of the nonignited material is similar to that of ignited material (up to 1,100°C) and to the aeschynite standard. Thermal curves of aeschynite show exothermic peaks (Fig. 24, *6*).

Table 10. Chemical composition (in wt. %) and physical properties of aeschynite

Components	Aeschynite		Lyndochite	Aeschynite		
	Kola	Siberia	Canada	Korea	Vishnevo-Gorsky	Ravalli County
Nb_2O_5	24.05	35.73	41.43	35.90	29.60	49.4
Ta_2O_5	1.45	—	3.84	—	1.93	—
TiO_2	28.12	39.06	16.39	17.10	23.18	15.7
SiO_2	Net	6.00	0.07	3.84	0.18	—
ThO_2	6.20	0.05	4.95	3.75	12.35	3.3
TR_2O_3	36.00	2.17	22.56	27.03	28.91	25.4
Al_2O_3	Net	0.21	0.13	3.80	0.10	—
Fe_2O_3	0.90	2.51	1.32	1.28	1.05	2.0
CaO	1.44	13.49	4.86	5.35	1.77	4.2
H_2O	1.86	0.51	1.36	0.97	1.00	—
Others	—	0.51	2.73	2.027	—	—
Total	100.02	100.24	99.64	101.047	100.07	100.0
Analyst	A.V. Bykova	T.I. Stolyarova			A.V. Bykova	
Author		V.S. Gaidukova, 1966	D. Dana et al., 1951	V.S. Gaidukova, 1966	A.G. Zabin et al., 1962	Heinrich, Levinson, 1961
Sp. gr.	5.16	3.94	4.909	4.92	4.98	4.20
n_g	2.36					2.20
n_p	2.25					
a_0, Å		5.44				
b_0, Å		10.90				
c_0, Å		7.49				

The chemical composition (Table 10) of the mineral from the Kola Peninsula is similar to that from Vishnevik Mountain. The crystal-chemical formula is as follows: $(TR_{0.83}Ca_{0.09}Th_{0.08})_{1.00}$ $(Nb_{0.67}Ti_{1.29}Fe_{3.004})_{2.00}O_{5.81}$, which is very close to that of the theoretical formula TR $(Ti, Nb)_2O_6$. Aeschynite from Ravalli County resembles niobo-aeschynite (sample 6 in Table 10), while aeschynite from Siberia (sample 2 in Table 10) with formula $(Ca_{0.63}TR_{0.03})_{0.66}$ $(Nb_{0.70}$ $Ti_{1.22}$ $Fe^{3+}_{0.08})_{2.00}$ $O_{4.985}$ sharply differs from normal aeschynite of high Ca content and from lyndochite, placed by Gaidukova with aeschynite, by the smaller content of TR. The dull and opaque characters of this mineral are to be carefully considered in distinguishing this mineral. Composition of TR from aeschynite is shown in Table 8.

Aeschynite is formed in the first stage of the formation of ankerite-dolomitic carbonatites together with anatase, pyrite, and quartz, it is formed in part from Nb and Ti derived from mixed rocks.

Rutile (TiO_2). This group of minerals is typical for Alpine vein or syenitic pegmatites (Ilmensky and Vishnevik Mountain, Ural). In carbonatites these are relatively rare and occur only in late dolomite-ankeritic veins (Vuoriyarvi—Kozireva and Ilinsky, 1959; Kapustin, 1964; Siberia-Tuchkova, 1959; Gaidukova, 1966; Lemhi County—Anderson, 1960, 1961; Ravalli County—Heinrich, 1967; Iron Hill—Larsen, 1942; Chilwa-Garson, 1959; Mbeya—Van der Veen, 1963). Accumulation of rutile is well known in the zone of carbonatization of mixed rock, particularly on the margin of the Magnet Cove massif (Fryklund et al., 1954; Erickson and Blade, 1963). In all these massifs rutile is rich in niobium and is similar to ilmenorutile. It is associated with barite, chlorite, quartz, and pyrite, and forms fine irregular or tetragonal bipyramidal crystals (up to 5 mm) with lenticular grains. It is black in color with distinct (110) cleavage and strong pearly luster. X-ray pattern similar to the standard; uniaxial, +ve, yellowish-brown in color with distinct pleochroism in shades of brown ($N_e > N_0$). The chemical composition of this mineral (Table 11) varies, and Nb_2O_5 content varies from 1 to 19% with constant presence of minor Ta_2O_5 (<0.3%). Ilmenorutile from Siberia (Table 11, sample No. 7) is rich in vanadium. The composition of this mineral is similar to niobium-rich rutile—more precisely lying intermediate between rutile and ilmenorutile. Nb and Ta are usually in the heterovalence isomorphic state in the following scheme: $3Ti \rightarrow Fe_2Nb_2$. Ilmenorutile often occurs in the peripheral zones of the carbonatite body. Toward the center it is replaced by anatase and brookite, making it stable under varying conditions.

Anatase (TiO_2). To date this has been found chiefly in Alpine veins. It is the typical mineral of late dolomite-ankerite veins, widely distributed in carbonatites. It occurs in the massifs of Chilwa (Garson, 1955, 1959), Mrima Hill (Coetzee and Edwards, 1959), Iron Hill (Larsen, 1942), Magnet Cove (Erickson and Blade, 1963), Kola Peninsula (Kapustin, 1964), and is also found in Bolshetagninskii and in one of the Siberian massifs. Anatase is one of the minerals of later veins. It is formed chiefly in the peripheral parts of the veins intersecting ultrabasites rich in perovskite (Vuoriyarvi, Kovdor, Sebl-Yavr), and is associated with pyrite, strontianite, quartz, chlorite, brookite, and ancylite. Gneisses and schists in carbonatites are poor in Ti (Namo Vara, Siberian massif) and anatase is rare.

Anatase forms well-developed tetrahedral bipyramidal crystals (1–5 mm), with rare development of tetrahedral prisms and pinacoids (001) (Fig. 26, *1a*, *b*). Anatase is dark blue in color with a strong adamantine luster and twinning along (001); sp. gr. 3.86–3.89; X-ray pattern is similar to the standard; uniaxial, −ve; and strongly pleochroic in blue shades ($N_e > N_0$); $n_e = 2.51$, $n_0 = 2.60$ (Vuoriyarvi). Chemical analysis (M.V. Kukharchik) indicates 0.45–1.04% Nb_2O_5. Spectral analysis shows the presence of V, Mg and Zr. The blue color of anatase probably indicates the presence of Ti^{3+} (Chesnikov,

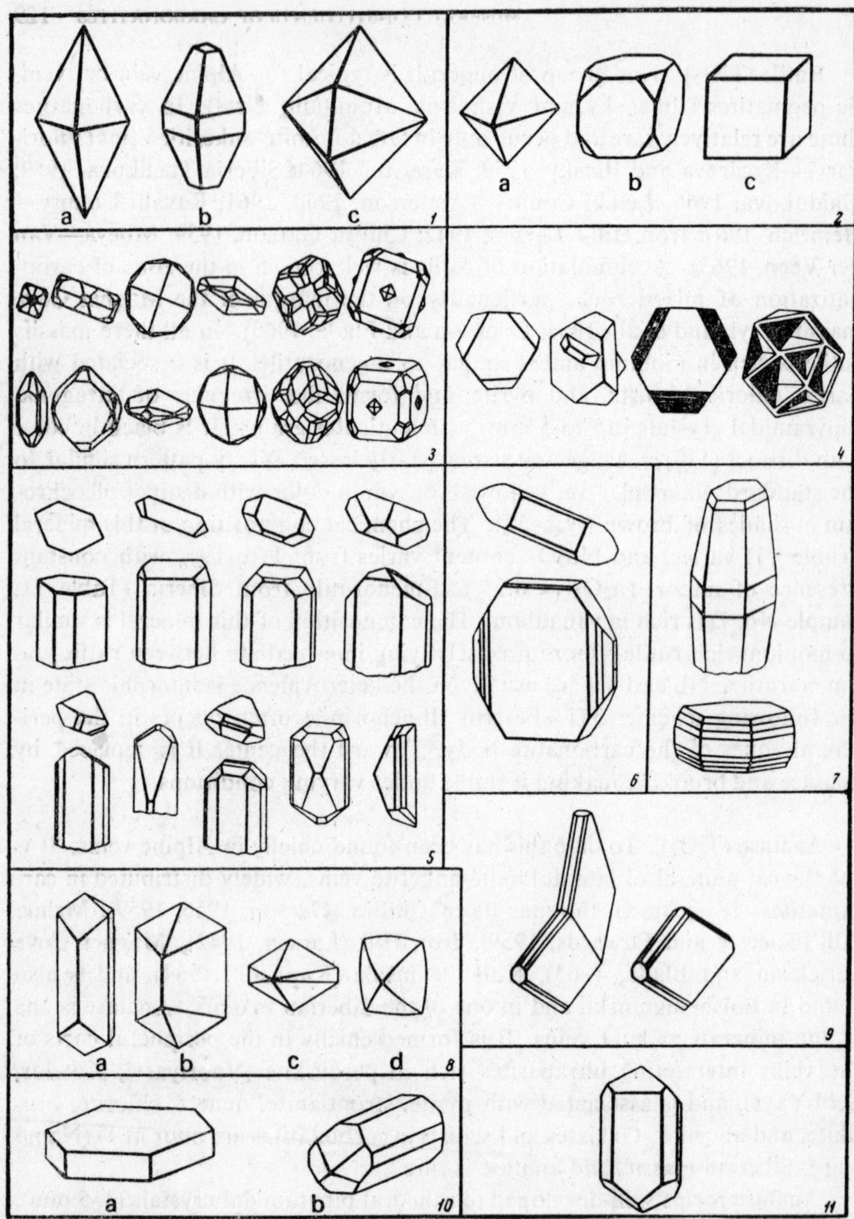

Fig. 26. Characteristic forms of crystals.

1, a, b—Anatase; 1, c—Brucite; 2—Perovskite (a—from ultrabasites; b, c—from carbonatites); 3—Calzirtite (Bulakh, Shavaleevsky, 1962); 4—Niobium-zirconolite (Bulakh et al., 1960); 5—Baddeleyite (Rimskaya-Korsakova, Dinaburg, 1964); 6—Carbocernaite (Bulakh et al., 1961); 7—Parisite; 8—Ancylite (a, d—after author; b, c—Dana et al., 1952); 9—Calkinsite (Pecora and Kerr, 1953); 10—Barite (a—Colorless; b—Yellowish); 11—Monazite.

1959). Anatase is stable under hypergene conditions. It is concentrated in alluvium and talus deposits and may (in complex massifs with other minerals) act as an index mineral in late carbonatites.

Table 11. Chemical composition (in wt. %) and physical properties of rutile and ilmenorutile

Components	Vuoriyarvi		Changit	Vishnevogorsky	Magnet Cove	Siberia	
	1	2	3	4	5	6	7
Nb_2O_5	8.80	9.20	5.74	14.91	2.45	1.09	19.16
Ta_2O_5	—	—	—	0.16	2.06	—	—
TiO_2	85.18	82.33	87.50	68.62	95.65	92.32	69.62
V_2O_5	—	—	—	—	0.26	1.06	5.51
SiO_2	—	—	—	0.66	0.02	—	2.21
Fe_2O_3	—	—	—	1.56	0.02	2.10	1.99
FeO	5.42	6.78	—	12.44	1.38	0.94	Net
Others	—	—	—	1.93	0.029	1.32	1.79
Total	99.40	98.31	93.24	100.28	99.869	98.83	100.28
Analyst	G.P. Ovsyaninkova			V.A. Oshman		T.I. Stolyarova	
Author			T.I. Tuchkova, 1959	E.M. Boushtodf-kuplets-koya, 1951	E.W. Heinrich, 1967	V.S. Gaidukova	
Sp. gr.	4.34	4.37	4.38	4.88	4.281	3.60–3.94	
a_0, Å		4.62	4.64			4.585–4.582	
b_0, Å		2.96	2.98			2.958–2.962	
n_e	2.8	2.8					
n_0	2.65	2.60					

Formula of samples analyzed:
1. $(Ti_{0.89}Nb_{0.05}Fe_{0.06})_{1.00}O_{1.995}$;
2. $(Ti_{0.86}Nb_{0.06}Fe_{0.08})_{1.00}O_{1.99}$.

Brookite (TiO_2). This is a relatively rare mineral typical for ankerite-dolomite veins. It occurs in almost all the massifs of the Kola Peninsula and South Siberia (Kapustin, 1964). It is also found in Vuoriyarvi (Kozireva and Ilinski, 1959; Kukharenko et al., 1965) and in Magnet Cove (Holbrook, 1947; Ericklund et al., 1954). Brookite is intimately associated with pyrite, quartz, anatase, barite, and chlorite, forming pseudohexagonal (arkansite), black crystals (up to 3 mm) and shows well-developed granular habit (Fig. 26, *1c*); sp. gr. 3.94–3.95; X-ray pattern similar to the standard; pleochroic in pale shades of brown ($N_g > N_p$), biaxial, +ve; $2V = 30°$, dispersion strong ($r > v$), $n_p = 2.59$, $n_g = 2.8$. Spectral analysis indicates the presence of Ti, U, Nb, Mg, Fe, and Y.

Brookite from Magnet Cove contains 0.8 to 9.6% Nb_2O_5 (Dana et al., 1951). Like anatase, brookite also occurs chiefly in veins that intersect the titanium-rich ultrabasites.

Ilmenite ($FeTiO_3$). This is often found in carbonatites, but in small quantities. Early carbonatite does not contain ilmenite and even in the magnetite (which is derived from ultrabasites) present in it the TiO_2 content decreases by 0.8 to 1%. Ilmenite is a typical byproduct of the process of amphibolitization-dolomitization. It is intimately associated with pyrrhotite and tetraferriphlogopite. In the zones of amphibolotization primary sphene, perovskite, and titanomagnetite present in intrusive ijolites, pyroxenites or olivinites (Vuoriyarvi, Sebl-Yavr, Lesnaya Varaka) are replaced by aggregates of ilmenite and calcite with the formation of skeletal pseudomorphs (Fig. 27). A small amount of ilmenite occurs in late ankeritic veins (Kovdor, Vuoriyarvi, Sallanlatva), but this is replaced on the periphery by anatase.

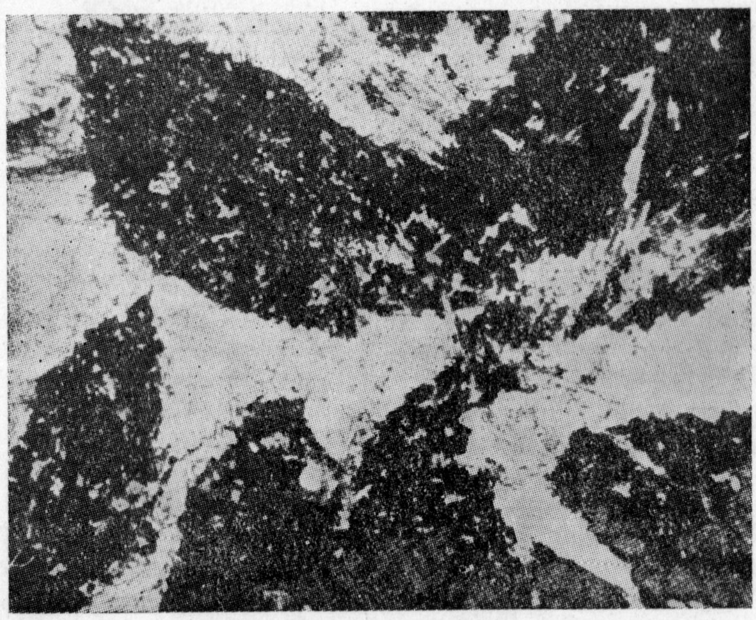

Fig. 27. Pseudomorphism of ilmenite (with inclusions of richterite and calcite) after sphene, Vuoriyarvi massif. Under crossed nicol, mag. ×24.

Ilmenite forms black flattened crystals (up to 2 cm) and often shows intergrowths with pyrrhotite. Sp. gr. 4.54–4.57; X-ray pattern similar to the standard. Chemical composition of ilmenite (analyst: A.P. Manukhov) gives the following result: MnO 1.35%, Nb_2O_5 0.62–0.71%, Ta_2O_5 0.02%.

Perovskite (Ca, TR, Sr) (Ti, Nb, Fe^{3+}) O_3. This is typical for rocks rich in Ca and Ti but poor in SiO_2 (gabbroids and agpaitic nepheline syenite). Accessory perovskite forms impregnations in olivinites and pyroxenites of complex massifs. In ultrabasites independent veins containing aggregates of perovskite and titanomagnetite occur (Borodin, 1959, 1960, 1963a; Kukharenko et al., 1965). Perovskite is the typical accessory mineral of early carbonatites of Kovdor, Sebl-Yavr, Oldoino Lengan, Mrima Hill, Kruidfontein. It is associated with pyroxene, mica, schorlomite, calcite, and apatite, forming disseminated cubic granules (Fig. 26, *2*). The composition and properties of perovskite vary (Table 12). In ultrabasites perovskite is practically devoid of inclusions and shows the theoretical formula $CaTiO_3$. In alkaline rocks it is rich in TR, Sr, and Nb. In carbonatites of Kaiserstühl it always contains 4 to 12% Nb_2O_5, and in Oka up to 42% of Nb_2O_5 (dysanalyte and latrappite). With any change in chemical composition (Table 12) the properties of perovskite also change (Kukharenko and Bagdasarov, 1961); with an increase in Nb and TR sp. gr. increases and R.I. decreases. Isomorphism in perovskite is found to occur accordingly: CaTi→NaNb; Ca→Sr; 2Ca→NaCe; 2Ti→ Fe^{3+} Nb. A continuous series is possible between perovskite and dysanalyte (without Ti) Ca (Fe^3 Nb) O_3. There is probably a similar series between perovskite and lueshite. Compositions of rare-earth elements in perovskite sharply differ (?) (Borodin and Barinskii, 1962, Table 8).

Perovskite is unstable. In carbonatite of the 2nd stage it is replaced by pyrochlore (Pozharitzkaya and Epshtein, 1963; Kukharenko et al., 1965), but when amphibolitization takes place it is replaced by ilmenite and in late carbonatites by anatase. In hypergene conditions perovskite is well preserved in alluvium and placers.

The dysanalyte content in carbonatite is related to the general Ti content of the massifs—increasing in massifs rich in this element (Vuoriyarvi, Sebl-Yavr) and decreasing in massifs poor in it (Sallanlatva, Siberian massifs). Dysanalyte is absent from carbonatites associated with massifs containing Ti-free ultrabasites (Siberian massifs—Frolov et al., 1967, 1969).

Lueshite (Na, Ca, TR) (Nb, Ti) O_3. This mineral occurs in carbonatites of Lueshe (Safiannikoff, 1959), Kovdor (Rimski et al., 1963; Lapin and Kazakoʌ, 1966), Sallanlatva (Orlova et al., 1963), Vuoriyarvi and Sebl-Yavr and also in Siberia (Bagdasarov et al., 1962). It also occurs in small amounts as impregnations along the marginal zones of early carbonatite bodies of the 2nd stage and also at the contact of alkaline rocks. It is associated with biotite, pyrrhotite, apatite, pyroxene, magnetite, and dolomite (Vuoriyarvi, Kovdor, Siberian massifs), forming cubic and octahedral crystals (0.1–5 mm) sometimes twinned according to the twin law of fluorites. Lueshite is dark yellow to black in color. Its composition and other properties change very little. Ca, TR, and Ti are always found in it, principally in lueshite from syenitic dikes (Lapin, 1966).

Table 12. Chemical composition (in wt. %) and physical properties of perovskite group of minerals

Components	Perovskite								Dysanalyte	
	Olivinites		Pyroxenites			Ijolites			Carbonatites	
	Lesnaya Varaka	Sebl-Yavr	Afrikanda		Sebl-Yavr	Ozernaya Varaka	Kovdor	Afrikanda	Siberia	Aldanski
Nb_2O_5	0.34	0.17	0.35	1.24	0.24	0.81	1.23	2.50	9.04	5.72
Ta_2O_5	0.07	0.05	0.07	—	0.06	0.10	0.10	Traces	—	0.95
SiO_2	0.18	0.35	0.84	0.40	0.16	0.46	0.31	1.93	—	1.46
TiO_2	54.08	55.17	55.30	54.48	57.10	53.00	51.14	51.47	50.04	47.94
ThO_2	0.18	0.04	0.13	0.01	0.04	0.11	0.83	—	0.02	0.69
TR_2O_3	4.13	2.17	2.18	3.00	2.53	5.20	4.06	10.70	3.18	7.13
Al_2O_3	—	—	Traces	0.40	—	Traces	0.22	1.30	0.10	—
Fe_2O_3	1.58	1.47	1.68	1.40	1.18	Traces	1.42	0.43	2.02	2.19
CaO	36.66	37.61	36.46	39.00	34.34	34.20	37.32	26.35	34.89	31.19
(Sr, Ba)O	0.94	1.24	Traces	Nil	2.62	1.25	0.28	1.65	0.15	0.61
Na_2O	0.96	0.83	0.46	0.30	1.00	0.76	2.82	1.10	0.57	1.89
K_2O	0.56	0.50	0.44	0.10	0.52	0.48	0.36	Traces	—	0.13
Others	0.82	0.93	1.89	—	0.95	3.68	0.34	2.64	0.74	0.49
Total	100.50	100.53	99.80	100.33	100.74	100.05	100.43	100.07	100.75	100.39
Analyst	E.N. Baranova		K.A. Baklanova	V.S. Bykova	E.N. Baranova		T.A. Burova	K.A. Baklanova	E.A. Dorofeeva	
Author	A.A. Kukharenko et al., 1965								V.S. Gaidukova et al., 1962	
Sp. gr.	4.06	4.08	4.03	4.06	4.08			4.19		

Components	Dysanalyte							Lueshite			
	Carbonatites										
	Kovdor	Vuoriyarvi	Magnet Cove	Sri Lanka	Oka		Kaiserstühl	Kovdor		Siberia	Luesha
Nb_2O_5	3.95	5.70	4.38	22.32	15.80	27.60	49.0	65.20	49.74	67.95	79.74
Ta_2O_5	0.29	0.50	5.08	Traces	1.32	2.79	—	0.55	2.76	0.36	Traces
SiO_2	0.80	0.72	0.08	Traces	0.48	Nil	—	1.47	Nil	2.23	0.73
TiO_2	53.04	45.20	44.12	39.90	38.63	25.00	12.3	4.90	17.47	6.35	3.62
ThO_2	—	—	—	—	—	0.04	0.27	3.19	3.27	—	—
TR_2O_3	4.76	6.11	5.52	8.80	0.26	3.28	3.4	—	3.61	1.48	—
Al_2O_3	0.93	1.15	—	—	0.36	—	—	0.79	0.92	—	—
Fe_2O_3	0.95	5.20	5.66	4.76	7.45	6.38	6.3	0.63	0.63	1.38	1.27
CaO	32.40	33.10	33.22	21.69	33.16	28.70	12.3	4.37	6.67	4.19	0.76
(Sr, Ba)O	—	—	—	—	—	0.65	1.3	0.18	0.22	—	—
Na_2O	2.30	2.50	—	Traces	1.22	3.75	—	14.30	10.60	14.90	12.23
K_2O	—	—	—	—	—	0.22	—	1.81	2.15	0.49	Traces
Others	0.66	0.58	1.47	1.81	1.18	0.90	6.13	2.90	1.71	0.95	1.11
Total	100.08	100.76	99.53	99.28	99.86	100.31	91.00	100.29	99.75	100.28	99.46
Analyst	A.V. Bykova							T.A. Burova	M.E. Kazakova	N.N. Kuznetzova	Hein Kopott
Author	Yu.L. Kapustin, 1964		D. Dana et al., 1951		G. Perrault, 1959		W. Wimmenauer, 1963	A.A. Kukharenko et al., 1965	A.V. Lapin, and M.E. Kazakova, 1966	B.S. Gaidukova et al., 1962	A. Safiannikoff, 1959
Sp. gr.	4.48	4.49						4.45			

Probably there exists an isomorphous series between perovskite and lueshite (Table 12). Although the X-ray pattern of lueshite is similar to that of perovskite its cell size is larger. Biaxial, +ve; often metamict.

Calzirtite ($CaZr_3TiO_9$). This mineral occurs in Siberian carbonatites (Zdorik et al., 1961), Sebl-Yavr (Bulakh and Shevaleevski, 1962), Gulinskii (Zhabin et al., 1962), and similarly in Brazil (Tapira—Van der Veen, 1965a). It is typical for early carbonatites of the 1st stage and is associated with them in the zones of calcitized ijolites. It is associated with dysanalyte, phlogopite, apatite, and pyroxene, forming intergrowths with apatite or independently forming well-developed granular crystals showing polysynthetic twinning (Fig. 26, *3*) according to the tetragonal prismatic habit. Calzirtite is brown in color, uniaxial, +ve, tetragonal, with space lattice 4/mmm. Its structure (determined from the structural type of fluorite) (Pyatenko and Pudovkina, 1961) indicates a_0 along the triparameters and c_0 along biparameters. Composition (Table 13) resembles the chemical formula $CaZr_3TiO_9$ or the structural formula $Ca\,(Ca, Zr)_2\,Zr_4\,(Fe, Ti)_2\,O_{16}$.

Calzirtite is the early zirconized mineral in carbonatite of the 1st stage. In late stages it is more unstable and is replaced by aggregates of sphene and zircon or zircon and ilmenite.

Zirconolite-Zirkelite $CaZr\,(Ti, NbFe)_2\,O_7$. This was first reported from the fenitized (micatized) melteigitic massifs of Jacupiranga (Hussak and Prior, 1895). It is morphologically similar to the placer minerals of Sri Lanka but differs from them chemically (Blake and Smith, 1913). Borodin (Borodin et al., 1956) first mentioned the new mineral zirconolite and afterward referred to its niobium variant as niobozirconolite (Borodin et al., 1960). Bulakh (Bulakh et al., 1960) also referred to a mineral similar in composition to zirkelite. It is also mentioned under the same name, zirkelite, in Siberia (Gaidukova et al., 1962; Pozharitzkaya et al., 1966a).

Zirkelite occurs in amphibolitized and fenitized pyroxenites (Afrikanda, Aldan). Niobozirkonolite is the typical mineral of the process of amphibolitization-dolomitization confined to carbonatite (Sebl-Yavr, Vuoriyarvi, Kovdor, Siberia) and zones of carbonatization (Kovdor). It is intimately associated with apatite, clinohumite, tetraferriphologopite, pyrrhotite, and richterite, forming impregnated, independent, small (0.01–1 mm) flattened crystals (Fig. 28, *a*) in apatitized veins or replacing pyrochlore of the 2nd generation and baddeleyite, relics of which are often seen at the center of a zirkelite aggregate (Fig. 28, *b*). Zirconolite develops irregular forms, while niobozirconolite gives rise to well-developed granular flattened crystals or cube-like polycrystalline growths (Fig. 26, *4*), retaining their own complex twinning (angle between independent lamella is about 70°). The flattened surfaces of the crystals are very smooth. The tapered grains are striated parallel to the thin edges, striation resulting from twinning along the basal pinacoid. The mineral is usually metamict, but the finer crystals of the mineral show crystalline forms or are anisotropic in parts (Kapustin, 1964). Metamict zirconolites are recrystallized at a temperature of 760°C, developing cubes of the pyrochlore type, and into new phase at 1100°C with systematic distribution of the components. The structure of zirconolite is probably monoclinic, similar to the structure of CaF_2, but retaining its own hexagonal characteristic (Pyatenko and Pudovkina, 1964).

Table 13. Chemical composition (in wt.%) and physical properties of calzirtite

Components	Aldan			Siberia	Gulinskii	Sebl-Yavr	Bukusu
Nb_2O_5	—	0.10	3.41	2.52	3.64	0.2	—
TiO_2	11.49	16.04	15.80	14.35	14.40	15.3	18.1
ZrO_2	75.68	70.56	61.63	63.15	68.44	71.0	66.2
HfO_2	—	—	0.44	—	—	1.3	—
SiO_2	0.29	0.41	2.93	2.83	—	—	0.8
Fe_2O_3	1.05	1.64	1.39	1.22	1.52	—	0.4
CaO	11.17	11.26	12.62	14.08	11.30	10.5	13.3
Others	—	0.17	0.55	1.44	0.68	1.86	0.7
Total	99.68	100.18	98.77	99.59	99.98	100.46	99.5
Analyst				A.V. Bykova			
Author	T.B. Zdorik et al., 1961			Yu.A. Bagdasarov and A.A. Frolov, 1963	A.G. Zabin et al., 1962	A.G. Bulakh and I.D. Shivabevski, 1962	I.W. Baldock, 1968
Sp. gr.		4.90			5.01	5.09	
n_e		2.33			a_0=15.30 Å	2.25	
n_0		2.19			c_0=10.20 Å	2.20	

The composition of zirconolite varies (Table 14). Besides its niobium variant other varieties, rich in U, Th, and TR (Sri Lanka and Norway, Table 14), are also well known. Isomorphism in zirconolite occurs in the following order: $CaTi \rightarrow TRFe^{3+}$; $2Ti \rightarrow Fe^{3+}Nb$; $5Ti \rightarrow 4Nb$; $Ca \rightarrow (Sr, Ba)$. The physical properties of zirconolite change with change in composition (Table 14). Its sp. gr. and R.I. increase with increasing Nb and decrease with the hydration of the mineral and its transition to the metamict condition.

The interrelation of rare-earth elements in zirconolite is somewhat related to the richness of yttrium in comparison to other elements of carbonatites and alkaline rocks (Table 8). In zirconolite about 2–3% water probably constitutes one of the principal components (hydroxyl? Fig. 24, 7) and evaporates completely at 760°C.

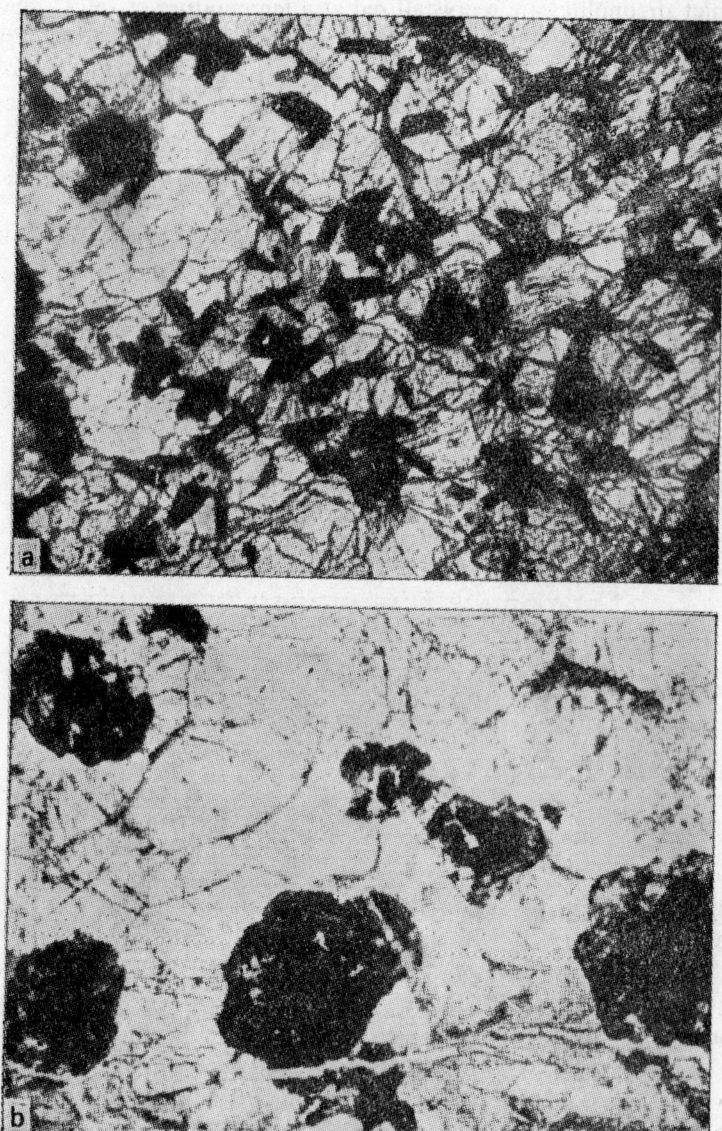

Fig. 28. Niobium-zirconolite (zirkelite).

a—Accumulation in apatite; b—Replacing hatchellolite (black at center). Vuoriyarvi massif. Under crossed nicol, mag. ×64.

Zirconolite is formed with the transformation of pyroxenites, while niobozirconolite is formed with dolomitization and amphibolitization of the carbonatites, replacing baddeleyite and pyrochlore. At the last stage of the process it replaces pyrochlore of the 3rd generation (rarely) or zircon and ilmenite aggregates. Due to weathering of carbonatites niobozirconolites are deposited as placers.

Baddeleyite (ZrO_2). Although this is one of the rarer minerals it occurs in several carbonatite massifs (Siberia—Gaidukova et al., 1962; Pozharitzkaya, 1966; Kola Peninsula—Kapustin, 1964; Kukharenko et al., 1965; Rimskaya-Korsakova and Dinaburg; 1964; Africa—Hiemstra, 1955; Fawley and James, 1955; Forster, 1958; Heinrich, 1967; Brazil—Hussak, 1895; USA—Dana et al., 1953). Concentration of this mineral has taken place in carbonatites and apatitized magnetite-forsterite rocks, where it is ultimately associated with apatite and accessory hatchettolite. Baddeleyite is the typical accessory mineral of early carbonatites of the 2nd stage. We did not find it in carbonatites of the 1st stage, although Pozharitzkaya (1966) mentioned the presence of this mineral in such rocks. In magnetite-forsterite rocks baddeleyite is fine-grained (0.1–1 mm) but in their carbonatized parts and in carbonates it is recrystallized as coarser granules (2–8 mm). It is intimately associated with apatite and accessories like hatchettolite, pyrochlore, and thorianite. In the Gulinskii and Kovdor massifs (Ezikova, 1960; Krasnova et al., 1967) and Vuoriyarvi massifs these minerals form oriented growths in which the axis of the baddeleyite crystal is oriented perpendicular to the cubic grain of thorianitite or parallel to the octahedral crystals of pyrochlore.

The crystallography of baddeleyite was studied in detail by Rimskaya-Korsakova and Dinaburg (1964). The crystals are hexagonal, flattened, extended along the *z* axis and often twinning (Fig. 26. *5*). The physical properties and composition of baddeleyite (Table 15) are more or less constant. Biaxial, –ve; pleochroic in brown ($N_g > N_m > N_p$); $z : N_p = 10–13°$. It is monoclinic and has fluorite-type structure; structural class $2/m - P2_1/c$; cell-sizes: $a_0 = 5.21$, $b_0 = 5.26$, $c_0 = 5.37$ Å; $\beta = 99°28'$. Minerals of SiO_2, Fe_2O_3, Nb, and Ta are present as inclusions in baddeleyite. These are, probably, mechanically included. Significant isomorphous inclusions in baddeleyite are Hf and TR. The formulas of this mineral calculated from different published chemical analyses are as follows:

1. $(Zr_{0.99}Hf_{0.01})_{1.00}O_2$; 2. $(Zr_{0.99}Hf_{0.01})_{1.00}O_2$;
3. $(Zr_{0.99}Hf_{0.01})_{1.00}O_2$; 4. $(Zr_{0.98}Hf_{0.02})_{1.00}O_2$;
5. $(Zr_{0.99}Hf_{0.01})_{1.00}O_2$; 6. $(Zr_{0.99}Hf_{0.01})_{1.00}O_2$.

In the late stages of the process baddeleyite recrystallizes and dissolves. It forms a higher proportion on the periphery than in the central parts of the veins. Concentration significantly increases in the zone of apatitized

Table 15. Chemical composition (in wt. %) and physical properties of baddeleyite

Components	Vuoriyarvi		Kovdor		Sallanlatva	Siberia	Palabora	Pakos Di Kaldas		Sri Lanka	
$(Nb, Ta)_2O_5$	0.60	0.84	0.48	0.21	0.25	0.31	—	—	—	—	—
ZrO_2	97.22	96.28	97.01	95.10	97.16	97.47	95.20	96.52	97.19	98.90	97.22
HfO_2	2.2	2.4	1.10	2.2	1.8	1.20	—	—	—	—	—
TiO_2	—	—	Traces	—	0.15	0.21	1.65	—	—	—	—
Fe_2O_3	—	—	0.17	—	—	—	2.10	0.41	0.92	0.82	0.34
TR_2O_3	—	0.28	0.10	0.27	0.12	0.24	—	—	—	—	—
CaO	—	—	0.37	—	—	—	0.80	0.55	—	0.06	0.24
Others	—	—	0.73	—	—	—	0.60	2.04	1.76	0.47	1.40
Total	100.02	99.80	99.96	97.78	99.48	99.43	100.35	99.52	99.87	100.25	99.20
Analyst	M.V. Kukharchik		E.A. Isaeva	M.V. Kukharchik and V.N. Arkhangelskaya							
Author			A.A. Kukharenko et al., 1965				S.A. Hiemstra, 1955	D. Dana et al., 1951			
Color	Gray	Black	Gray	Dark gray		Dark brown			Brown		
Sp. gr.	5.48	5.62	5.50	5.68	5.52	5.56	5.025		5.538	5.72	
$2V°$	27	31	30	31	27		30	30			
n_g	2.28	2.41	2.30	2.44	2.35	2.40	2.243	2.20			
n_m	2.21	2.38					2.236	2.19			
n_p	2.14	2.21	2.15	2.22	2.19	2.20	2.136	2.13			

magnetite-forsterite rocks. It is replaced by niobozirconolite and zircon due to the processes of amphibolitization and ankeritization, respectively. Under hypergene conditions baddeleyite is stable and is deposited in the alluvium as placers, and may serve as an indicator for carbonatites.

Thorianite (ThO_2). This is a rare mineral in carbonatite. It occurs at Palabora (Russell et al., 1954), Siberia (Gaidukov et al., 1962) and the Kola Peninsula (Kapustin, 1964; Krasnova et al., 1967), where it is accompanied by magnetite, apatite, phlogopite, pyrochlore, and baddeleyite. Thorlanite occurs in carbonatite of the 2nd stage and in the zone of carbonatization. It forms idiomorphic cubic crystals of dark brown color (sometimes black) with shining grains. Sometimes it shows characteristic intergrowths with baddeleyite (Krasnova et al., 1967). Sp. gr. 8.89; highly radioactive; X-ray pattern similar to the standard and obtained by primary heating. Isotropic, $n=2.20$. Chemical composition simple (Table 16). Significant among the inclusions are U and U_3O_8, which vary between 0.5 and 25% (uranium-thorianite). Pb (probably radiogenic) and TR (the interpreted composition of TR in thorianite is given in Table 8) are constantly present in thorianite.

Table 16. Chemical composition of thorianite (in wt. %)

Components	Palabora		Siberia	Kola	
$(Nb, Ta)_2O_5$	—	—	0.04	—	—
TiO_2	—	—	0.03	—	—
ZrO_2	—	—	0.70	—	2.35
ThO_2	59.90	51.80	92.44	94.85	93.65
U_3O_8	—	24.73	3.46	2.12	0.48
UO_2	15.97	—	—	—	—
TR_2O_3	4.60	3.82	1.55	1.66	0.48
PbO	9.61	12.43	0.26	—	0.08
Others	—	—	1.35	1.20	2.80
Total	90.08	92.78	99.83	99.83	99.84
Analyst				A.V. Bykova	V.V. Firulina
Author	H.D. Russell et al., 1954		V.S. Gaidukova et al., 1962		N.I. Krasnova et al., 1967

Due to the rare occurrence of thorianite it is very difficult to evaluate the condition of formation. Probably it is formed by recrystallization and decomposition of thorium-rich pyrochlore during the process of amphibolitization-dolomitization. Under this condition pyrochlore (3rd generation) is practically free of Th.

The formula of thorianite from the sample analyzed (author) is: $(Th_{0.96} TR_{0.03} U_{0.01})_{1.00}O_{1.985}$.

Thorianite is relatively stable and is deposited in the alluvium. Only in one case was red ferrithorianite reported.

CLASS V: OXYGEN-CONTAINING SALTS

Carbonates

Carbonates are the principal rock-forming minerals of the carbonatites, constituting about 40 to 90% of them and controlling their structure. The most important is calcite. Magnesium-ferruginous carbonates are also important.

Rock-Forming Carbonates

Calcite ($CaCO_3$). This is widely distributed in rocks of the massifs studied and occurs in olivinites, pyroxenites, and often in turjaite and ijolite; rarely in nepheline syenites. It constitutes the main body of both stages of carbonatites and occurs in small quantities in late veins. In the process of carbonatization calcite may be differentiated into several generations. Calcite of the 1st generation occurs in early carbonatites of the 1st stage, while the 2nd generation occurs with carbonatites of the 2nd stage, accompanying different groups of minerals (Table 3). The characteristic structure of the calcitic aggregates in these rocks was shown earlier. Individual grains of calcite in early carbonatites are fresh and transparent. Even the gaseous and liquid inclusions are few. Twinning is less developed in calcites occurring in veins that are not subjected to cataclasism. The composition and properties of calcite are quite persistent and are normal. An admixture of Mg and Fe is reported, but we observed neither of these elements in any calcite (primary) intergrown with dolomite (Van der Veen, 1965; Heinrich, 1967; Kononova and Tarashan, 1968) with a much larger increase (to 800) than assumed by these authors. Occurrence of dolomite in all cases is accompanied by richterite, pyrrhotite, or tetraferriphlogopite, often with massive cataclasis. Dolomite is usually formed along the periphery of calcite veins and is later in origin.

In early carbonatites calcite is associated with pyroxene, forsterite, mica, apatite, and magnetite, but occasionally some minerals not usually associated with these early carbonatites also occur as inclusions. The pink calcite occurring in the central part of the carbonatized bodies of one of the Siberian massifs contains inclusions of thin flattened laminated hematite (identified by X-ray). The hematite cannot be detected under the microscope. The evaporation of a dilute HC1-solution of calcite leaves a residue of thin flakes of hematite. In early carbonatites (black) containing dysanalytes from Vuoriyarvi, Kovdor, and Siberia the calcite grains show intergrowths with thin needles of magnetite (Fig. 13, *a*). Possibly magnetite and hematite are separated with the decomposition of ferruginous calcites in the central part of the carbonatite bodies and recrystallize with falling temperature. A significant quantity of Fe and Mg always occurs in the calcite of early carbonatites.

For calcite of early carbonatites the presence of an appreciable quantity of Sr, Ba, and TR is important. The presence of these elements (and the characteristic interrelations between them) significantly distinguishes calcite occurring in carbonatites from those occurring in other genetical types (Higasy, 1954). The early generation of calcite (Kononova and Tarashan, 1968) shows a consistent, extraordinarily intense thermoluminescence—more than 100 times more intensive than calcite from other sources (from nepheline syenite). The present author's suggestion that the primary carbonates should be placed in a separate group is justified inasmuch as there is nothing comparable to such carbonatites in respect of thermoluminescence. Calcite is characteristic for carbonatites of all the deep-seated facies but in recent carbonate lavas it occurs as alkaline-calcitic carbonate. With the beginning of the process of amphibolitization and the formation of late carbonatites calcite is replaced by dolomite (and ankerite).

Calcites of the 3rd and 4th generations constitute early (with burbankite or barite–calcite) and late (with hematite and zeolite) veins in late carbonatites, accompanied by different minerals (Table 3). Calcite of both generations forms massive aggregates, often large poikiloblastic crystals with inclusions of other minerals. Calcite of the 4th generation, however, sometimes forms druses of crystals of individual crystals in the rock cavities. Calcite of the 3rd generation is associated with burbankite. In Vuoriyarvi and South Siberia it is rich in Sr and Ba (Table 17).

Bright orange-colored calcites belonging to the 5th generation form independent monomineralic veins 0.8 m thick (around fenites—Kovdor and Vuoriyarvi) or massive or vug structures with druses of hexagonal-prismatic crystals within the rock cavities. Hypergene calcites belong to the 6th generation. In all places these show surface weathering. They often form small veinlets and veins (up to 0.3 m thick) around oxidized and weathered carbonates, and usually contain pigmented inclusions like limonite, montmorillonite, and oxides of manganese. Calcites of the 4th, 5th, and 6th generations are practically free of such elements as Sr, Ba, and TR, which are negligible in amount: 0.1 to (0.002–0.01) %.

Alkali elements do not occur in calcites. Occurrences of Sr, Ba, and TR in calcites of early generation are quite constant, irrespective of the composition of the mixed rocks or the region of occurrence, and thus signal the presence of carbonatites. The Sr/Ba ratio in carbonatites is 8–10, while the composition of TR constantly varies with the prevalence of Ce, La, Nd, particularly with the presence of La and Y (Table 18).

At high temperatures (910–940°C) calcites of different generations are

Table 17. Chemical composition (in wt. %) and physical properties of carbonates

Components	Calcite									
	Early carbonatites									
	1st stage					2nd stage				
	Vuori-yarvi	Ozernaya Varaka	Gulinskii	Sayan	Magnet Cove	Vuori-yarvi	Kovdor	Sebl-Yavr	Siberia	Gulinskii
	1	2	3	4	5	6	7	8	9	10
Fe_2O_3	0.07	0.08	0.20	0.16	0.20	0.13	0.15	0.13	0.14	0.14
FeO	0.19	0.18	0.23	0.32	—	0.37	0.42	0.37	0.43	—
MnO	0.15	—	—	0.19	—	0.17	0.07	0.09	—	—
MgO	0.16	0.09	0.17	0.15	0.21	0.20	0.22	0.07	0.17	0.15
CaO	53.71	54.00	54.16	53.70	52.80	53.60	54.47	54.12	53.30	54.05
SrO	0.42	0.44	0.48	0.52	1.05	0.68	0.60	0.68	0.54	0.56
BaO	0.04	0.05	0.04	0.06	0.10	0.06	0.07	0.10	0.05	0.04
Na_2O	0.19	0.21	0.17	0.18	0.16	0.14	0.29	0.19	0.21	0.19
Ignition loss	45.8	43.4	43.2	45.8	42.5	41.5	43.4	42.0	44.7	42.5
Total	100.73	98.45	98.65	101.08	97.02	96.85	99.69	97.75	99.54	97.63
Sp. gr.	2.79	2.72	2.72	2.72		2.72	2.62		2.71	
n_o	1.678	1.676	1.675	1.675	1.674	1.672	1.672	1.674	1.673	1.674
n_e	1.472	1.480	1.470	1.470	1.470	1.472	1.472	1.470	1.470	1.471
Analyst	A.N. Makukhoga, L.I. Baum, V.V. Zamotina and N.S. Gorokhova									
Author										

Components	Calcite	Dolomite					Paraankreite-ankerite			Breunnerite
	Early carbonatites, 2nd stage			Late carbonatites						
	Oka	Lesnaya Varaka	Vuoriyarvi		Siberia			Sebl-Yavr	Sallanlatva	
	11	12	13	14	15	16	17	18	19	20
Fe_2O_3	0.19	0.07	0.02	0.01	0.05	0.07	0.09	—	0.09	0.18
FeO	—	2.12	1.18	1.93	1.31	1.31	8.75	5.57	8.35	31.40
MnO	—	—	—	—	0.61	0.78	2.24	1.50	1.14	2.20
MgO	0.15	20.04	17.75	23.42	19.30	19.22	14.76	15.23	16.24	15.20
CaO	53.09	28.98	30.81	30.78	31.26	31.26	27.95	31.37	28.33	3.70
SrO	1.05	0.08	0.09	0.14	0.11	—	0.56	0.40	0.37	0.30
BaO	0.08	0.01	0.01	0.02	0.01	—	—	0.10	—	—
Na_2O	0.20	0.02	0.01	—	—	About 0.56	0.54	—	0.12	6.36
Ignition loss	45.3	45.9	49.8	41.3	46.9	46.94	45.20	46.19	46.52	40.60
Total	100.06	97.22	99.67	97.60	99.55	100.14	100.09	100.36	100.26	99.94
Sp. gr.		2.97	2.90	2.91						
n_0	1.672	1.683	1.680	1.680	1.681			1.700	1.709	
n_e	1.470	1.475	1.472	1.470	1.472			1.500	1.512	
Analyst	A.N. Makukhoga, L.I. Baum, V.V. Zamotina and N.S. Gorokhova									
Author					V.S. Gaidukova et al., 1962			A.A. Kukharenko et al., 1965		

Table 18. Composition of rare-earth elements ($\Sigma TR_2O_3 = 100\%$) in carbonates

Mineral	La	Ce	Pr	Nd	Sm	Eu	Gd	Tb	Dy	Ho	Er	Tu	Yb	Y	Number of samples	Massifs
Calcite of 1st generation	20	49	5	18	3	0.2	3	0.3	1	0.1	0.2	—	0.2	Not det.	3	Vuoriyarvi
Do	22	49	5	17	3	0.2	2	0.2	0.7	0.3	0.3	—	0.3	Do	2	Kovdor
Do	22	48	5	18	2	0.3	2	0.3	0.7	0.2	0.3	—	0.2	Do	2	Sallanlatva
Do	21	46	5	17	2	0.2	2.1	0.2	1	0.1	0.2	—	0.2	4	2	Siberia
Do	20	46	6	16	2	0.1	2	0.2	1	0.2	0.2	—	0.3	7	7	Do
Calcite of 2nd generation	24	47	5	17	3	0.5	1.4	0.3	0.8	0.2	0.4	—	0.4	Not det.	4	Vuoriyarvi
Do	21	45	5	16	3	0.3	2	0.2	1	0.1	0.2	—	0.2	6	2	Kovdor
Do	26	46	5	18	3	0.1	1.4	0.1	0.2	0.1	0.1	—	—	Not det.	1	Gulinskii
Do	23	44	5	16	2	0.3	2	0.2	0.3	0.1	0.2	—	0.2	6.7	2	Siberia
Do	22	45	5	15	1.4	0.2	2	0.2	0.5	0.1	0.2	—	0.4	8	1	Do
Calcite of 4th generation	29	49	5	14	1.3	0.1	1	0.1	0.3	0.1	0.1	—	—	Not det.	2	Vuoriyarvi
Calcite of 5th generation	29	50	5	13	1.2	0.1	1	0.1	0.6	—	—	—	—	Do	2	Namo-Vara
Dolomite of 1st generation	27	48	4	17	3	—	0.6	—	0.2	—	0.2	—	—	Do	2	Siberia
Dolomite of 2nd generation	29	49	2	18	2	—	—	—	—	—	—	—	—	Do	2	Sallanlatva
Ankerite	27	49	5	17	1	—	—	0.8	—	0.2	—	—	—	Do	2	Vuoriyarvi
Ankerite	28	49	4	18	0.2	0.2	0.4	—	0.2	—	0.1	—	—	Do	1	Sallanlatva
Burbankite	33	52	3.5	11	0.4	—	0.1	—	—	—	—	—	—	Do	1	Kola
Carbocernaite	34	54	2.6	9	0.4	—	—	—	—	—	—	—	—	Do	1	Kola
Bastnaesite	23	46	5	25	1	—	—	—	—	—	—	—	—	Do	1	Kola
Ancylite	35	50	4	9	1	—	0.3	0.1	0.2	—	0.2	—	0.2	Do	2	Kola
Parisite	35	51	3	10	1	—	—	—	—	—	—	—	—	Do	2	Siberia
Huanghoite	20	53	7	17	2	—	1	—	—	—	—	—	—	Do	1	Siberia
Calkinsite	32	50.2	4	12	0.5	—	0.2	0.1	0.2	—	0.2	—	0.6	Do	1	Kola
Lanthanite	33	50	6	10	1	—	—	—	—	—	—	—	—	Do	1	Kola
Zircon	14	25	5	12	1	0.2	2	0.3	1.6	0.3	0.7	0.1	1.8	36	1	Kola

dissociated. But the temperature-dependence of dissociation is not so prominent, although earlier generations (1st–3rd) decompose at lower temperatures (910–925°C).

In early carbonatites calcite is replaced by dolomite and ankerite. Under hypergene conditions it is readily dissolved.

Dolomite $CaMg(CO_3)_2$. This occurs in carbonatites in lesser quantities than calcite, but is widely distributed and occurs in almost all the massifs where thick bodies of carbonatite are developed (Gulinskii, Lueshe, Kruidfontein, Mbeya, Kangankunde, Fen). Kapustin (1960, 1961, 1964, 1966b) showed that in carbonatites dolomites are essentially of two generations, each having different complex minerals (Tables 2 and 3). This is controlled by different types of geological structure and different phases of intrusions of damkjernite dikes and late calcitic veins with burbankite.

Dolomite of the 1st generation is formed in the central and peripheral parts of early carbonatite bodies and in zones of cataclasis and schistosity. Dolomitization is prevalent in Vuoriyarvi and Sebl-Yavr along the zone of cataclasis, where richterite and dolomite occur in most of the carbonate veins. MgO content of these veins varies from 0.4 to 10%, while in cataclastic veins it rises to 15%. Dolomite forms microveins between the calcite grains or intersects them (often along the cleavage and twinning planes, Fig. 18). The dolomite is fine-grained, the individual grains being either rounded or rhombic in shape. Within the fine-grained dolomite rare but large (1–2 cm) relics of primary calcite are found, and the rock body acquires a pseudoporphyritic texture. Dolomite is always associated with richterite, pyrrhotite, and tetraferriphlogopite, and also with corroded primary minerals of early carbonatites (see above). The absence of dolomite from stable early carbonatites, its consistent development after calcite, its occurrence with other late minerals and its corrosion of primary minerals of early rocks all indicate its secondary origin.

The early carbonatites within ultrabasites rich in Mg (Vuoriyarvi, Sebl-Yavr, Lesnaya Varaka) are subjected to maximum dolomitization. The carbonatites with minimum dolomitization occur within leucocratic schists, gneisses, and syenites practically devoid of Mg (massifs of Siberia, Sallanlatva, Fen, Turi Mis, Kovdor, Pilkoma-Selga, and Votzu-Vara).

Dolomite of the 2nd generation is formed together with ankerite in late carbonatites. The veinlets of 2nd generation dolomite intersect early carbonatite containing richterite and dolomite of the 1st generation. In late carbonatites it is associated with ankerite, pyrite, marmatite, carbocernaite, strontianite, and anatase (with other minerals), and forms aggregates of rounded grains and often druses of rhombohedral crystals (with characteristic deformed grains) within the rock cavities. The intimate association of dolomite with ankerite give rise to the formation of aggregates of zoned crystals in which iron-bearing zones show alternation. The thermal curves of dolomite of the two generations are normal and differ little (Fig. 24, *8*). The composition and properties of dolomite are quite persistent. In dolomite of the 1st generation FeO is less than 2.5%, admixture of Fe is quite common and reaches 2%, while in the 2nd generation it shows an increase (to the transition to parankerite—2.5 to 8% FeO, Table 20). The Sr, Ba, and TR contents of dolomite are very small (Table 17).

Both generations of dolomite in carbonatites everywhere show a reaction relation with calcite and replace it. Often the common occurrence of both carbonates makes it difficult to determine their paragenesis. For determination of their interrelation it is essential to make a detailed study of their textures, both in thin sections and in hand specimens, and also to analyze the mutual relations of each with the associated minerals and the interrelation of the latter with other minerals.

Magnesian-ferroan carbonates-ankerite and parankerite Ca (Mg, Fe) $(CO_3)_2$. These are principal rock-forming minerals of late carbonatite, widely distributed and occur in all the massifs of Siberia (Epshtein, 1959; Gaidukova et al., 1962; Frolov, 1960; Frolov and Bagdasarov, 1967; Frolov et al., 1969), the Kola Peninsula (Kukharenko et al., 1965; Kapustin, 1964), Scandinavia (Brögger, 1921; Eckermann, 1948a), Africa (Garson, 1953; Tuttle et al., 1967), Canada and the USA (Heinrich, 1967). Thick bodies of ankeritic carbonatites occur in hypabyssal massifs (Siberia, Europe) and in volcanic veins (Nkombwa, Kangankunde, Mbeya, Chilwa). In deeper massifs these minerals are of secondary importance and form individual veins, metasomatic zones (Siberia), or independent veined zones that run for a few kilometers (Namo-Vara, Ravalli County, Siberian massifs). In late veins ankerite and parankerite constituting about 20 to 90%, particularly in veins and stocks that occur within the ultrabasites, give rise to dolomites in veins that are formed after early carbonatites or quartz and podolite, and intersect fenites. The more ferruginous carbonatites are formed later than dolomite, and these are well seen in the Kola Peninsula, Eastern Sayan, and in the African massifs (Nkombwa, Kangankunde-Reeve and Deans, 1954; Deans and McConnell, 1955; McKie, 1962). Sometimes ankerite and siderite form veinlets that penetrate the dolomite masses or zoned crystals of dolomite, the inner parts of which are more ferruginous in composition. Compositions and properties of magnesian-ferroan carbonates are given in Table 17. Compositions of the rare-earth elements are normal (Table 18). Thermographs of these minerals are similar to the standard ones (Fig. 24). Under hypergene conditions all the magnesian-ferroan carbonates easily decompose and limonitic ochers are formed.

Magnesite ($MgCO_3$). This mineral is rare in carbonatites, but occurs in significant amounts in Sallanlatva, where it is found in the fine-grained carbonatite with siderite and barite. In Kovdor the core of the prismatic magnesite crystals shows intergrowth with ankerite in the cavities. Magnesite is associated with barite, chlorite, sphalerite, podolite, and in Kovdor with collinsite and hydrocarbonates of Ca and Mg. Properties and composition of magnesite are normal (Table 17). Thermal curves are also close to the standard ones (Fig. 24).

Siderite ($FeCO_3$). This occurs in almost all the massifs in very small amounts. In the veins of Nkombwa, Kangankunde, and Lake Chilwa it forms a thick nucleus at the center of the carbonatite mass. A significant amount of siderite occurs in Sallanlatva and in the massif of Yenisei Ridge. Siderite replaces early carbonates, forming metasomatic veins in the ankerite mass, and is intimately associated with barite, galena, TR-bearing fluor-carbonate, and quartz. The properties of the mineral are normal. At the late stage it is replaced by chlorite or hematite. Under hypergene condition siderite easily decomposes and is replaced by limonite.

Breunnerite (Mg, Fe) CO_3. This is found in late dolomitic veins in the massifs of Vuoriyarvi and Sallanlatva (Kukharenko et al., 1965), as flattened masses; independent rhombohedral crystals associated with galena and ancylite are present in cavities. The composition and properties of breunnerite are normal (Table 17). Under hypergene condition it is replaced by limonite.

Rhodochrosite ($MnCO_3$). This mineral occurs frequently in carbonatites in significant amounts. It is found in Vuoriyarvi (Neske-Vara and Namo-Vara), Kovdor, Sallanlatva (Orlov et al., 1963), Eastern Sayan and Eastern Siberia (Zdorik, 1966). It is formed in the 1st stage of the formation of ankeritic veins, together with cleiophane, chlorite, quartz microveins, spherulites, druses and crusts of needle-shaped crystals in the rock cavities. Rhodochrosite is widely distributed in the superficial zones of the massifs (Nkombwa, Kangankunde, Chilwa-Reeve and Deans, 1954; Phillips, 1955; Garson, 1959; McKie, 1962). Under hypergene conditions rhodochrosite easily decomposes and is replaced by Mn-hydroxides, which are widely developed at the center of weathering in most massifs. Properties and composition of rhodocrosite are normal; sp. gr. 2.98.

Aragonite ($CaCO_3$). This is rare in carbonatites. It occurs as crusts on the surface and in veins of weathered carbonatites (hypergene), or as needle-shaped crystals in the cavity of ankeritic veins (late-hydrothermal). Aragonite is white or colorless, biaxial, $-$ve, $n_p = 1.512$, $n_g = 1.660$; the X-ray pattern is close to standard. Spectral analysis indicates the presence of Ca (more than 5%) and traces of Mg, Fe, Yb, Mn, Zn, Al, and Sr.

Raremetal Carbonates

Strontianite ($SrCO_3$). This mineral is relatively rare. However, it is widely distributed in carbonatites (Reeve and Deans, 1954; Garson, 1959; McKie, 1962; Heinrich, 1967; Tuttle et al., 1967; Bulakh, 1961; Zdorik, 1966; Kapustin, 1964, 1965c) and occurs in several massifs (Alnö, Nkombwa, Kangankunde, Namo-Vara, Sebl-Yavr, Kovdor, Sallanlatva, Vuoriyarvi, and the Siberian massifs). Strontianite is the typical mineral of ankerite-dolomitic veins and is associated with barite, anatase, quartz, and sulfides. It forms a radiate mass 5 × 7 × 10 cm in size, individual prismatic crystals and spherulite in carbonate mass, and druses of needle-shaped crystals within rock cavities. In weathered carbonatites of Sallanlatva and Siberia powdery strontianite replaces ancylite and strontiobarite. The needle-shaped crystals of strontianite are of rhombic (110) habit, while the crystals of other shapes do not show any definite crystal habit. Strontianite is either colorless or white or red (due to the presence of Fe and TR). It is biaxial, –ve. X-ray pattern is similar to the standard; monoclinic. The chemical composition of strontianite from carbonatites of the Kola Peninsula (Table 19) differs appreciably from the standard samples of Strontian (England), in which Sr shows isomorphous replacement by Ba. Possibly this is reflected in the increase of sp. gr. and R.I. in samples from carbonatites. Strontianite of the Kola Peninsula containing 3.27% BaO differs from the veined strontianite of Namo-Vara and, together with Mg-Fe-carbonatite, form podolite and quartz. Composition of strontianite is shown in Table 19; its formula is close to the theoretical.

Table 19. Chemical composition (in wt. %) and physical properties of strontianite

Components	Kovdor	Namo-Vara	Vuoriyarvi	Sallanlatva	Siberia	Strontian
CaO	0.83	1.04	0.31	0.15	0.49	4.05
SrO	67.10	66.58	66.48	68.36	66.74	65.01
BaO	1.75	3.27	0.52	0.33	1.15	—
CO_2 loss on ignition	29.82	29.91	29.7	30.0	28.2	30.84
Others	—	—	—	—	—	0.06
Total	99.50	100.80	97.01	98.84	96.58	99.96
Analyst	E.A. Fabrikova, N.S. Gorokhova					
Author	Yu.L. Kapustin, 1964					D. Dana et al., 1953
Sp. gr.	3.68	3.81	3.68	3.65		3.69
n_g	1.681	1.690	1.680	1.680		1.680
n_m		1.686		1.675		
n_p	1.521	1.525	1.520	1.522		1.520
$2V^0$	6	8		6		

Thermal curves of strontianite (Fig. 24, *14*) show endothermic peaks due to the transition of the mineral into hexagonal modification (Tzvetkov, 1964) without decomposition. On cooling they revert to the original shape.

For the formation of strontianite the Sr is probably in part derived from the mixed rocks (principally from early carbonatites), but in veins that intersect gneisses and fenites Sr is derived, although in very minor quantity, from the surrounding rocks.

Alstonite CaBa $(CO_3)_2$. This is a rare mineral occurring in low-temperature hydrothermal Pb-Zn deposits (Brownley Hill, Fallow Field, England—Dana et al., 1953). Alstonite in carbonatite is reported from Vuoriyarvi (Kozireva and Ilinsky, 1959) a porous mass and also as independent crystals within calcite. We observed alstonite in the same massif in burbankite-calcitic veins and mangano-calcitic veins (Kapustin, 1964), marmatite, and norse-

Table 20. X-ray data of Ca, Ba, Mg carbonates

Alstonite				Barytocalcite				Norsethite			
I	*d*, Å	*I*	*d*, Å	*I*	*d*, Å	*I*	*d*, Å	*I*	*d*, Å	*I*	*d*, Å
1	4.40	7	4.51	1	7.5	8	7.8	2.5	4.33		
3	3.90	25	3.93	1	6.0	6	5.74	2	4.01		
10	3.70	100	3.68	2	4.20	25	4.345	3.5	3.82	35	3.860
5	3.05	62	3.12	3	4.02	40	4.018	10	3.08	100	3.015
2	2.60	31	2.60	1	3.85	18	3.864	4	2.60	35	2.656
1	2.52	10	2.54	1	3.83	16	3.827	2.5	2.51	35	2.512
	—	4	2.27	1	3.22	14	3.238	1	2.38		—
3	2.11	37	2.13	9	3.12	90	3.140	2.5	2.15	35	2.104
1	2.00	17	2.00	10	3.10	100	3.125	1	2.10		—
3	1.918	31	1.92		—	4	2.673	1	2.01		—
	—	2	1.84	1	2.61	12	2.612	3	1.931	35	1.931
1	1.642	12	1.64	1	2.50	20	2.512	2	1.870	35	1.864
1	1.528	7	1.56		—	4	2.479	1	1.682		
1	1.502	5	1.49	1	2.375	20	2.379	1	1.639		
	—	2	1.46		—	6	2.348	1.5	1.593		
1	2.355	5	1.36	2	2.156	25	2.157	2	1.542		
1	1.308	7	1.38	1	2.100	8	2.106	1	1.486		
	—	2	1.27	1	2.030	12	2.039	1	1.465		
	—	5	1.22	2	2.00	20	2.009	1	1.294		
1	1.012			1	1.962	14	1.962	1.5	1.259		
1	0.985			1.5	1.950	8	1.948	1	1.119		
				1	1.910	10	1.908	1	1.059		
				1	1.889	10	1.888	1	1.009		
						6	19.682	1	0.941		
				1	1.640	6	1.642				

Explanation: 1, 3, 5—after author (Vuoriyarvi massif), 2, 4—according to ASTM Bulletin, 1963, 6—after Ch. Milton and others, 1969 X-ray analysis of Vuoriyarvi sample was taken in RKD diffractometer with $2R=54.7$ mm, $2r=0.6$ mm and Fe–Ni radiation—analyst: R.A. Alexandrova.

thite. Alstonite forms fine-grained masses, veins in masses of calcite, and druses of small (< 1 mm) prismatic white crystals showing vitreous luster. Biaxial, −ve; X-ray pattern (Table 20) similar to standard. Alstonite is orthorhombic; $a_0=4.99$, $b_0=8.77$, $c_0=6.11$ Å; space group $2/m2/m2/m$; $z=2$; dimorphous with barite-calcites.

The formula of alstonite from Vuoriyarvi is as follows: $Ca_{1.00}\,Sr_{0.10}\,Ba_{0.90}(CO_3)_{2.00}$; this is close to the theoretical formula $Ca\,Ba\,(CO_3)_2$. Spectral analysis indicates the presence of Mn, Fe, Mg, Y, La, and Zn. It is formed at the last stage of formation of hydrothermal burbankite-calcite veins together with other minerals of Sr and Ba.

Barytocalcite $CaBa\,(CO_3)_2$. This is relatively rare in occurrence. It was first reported from Alston Moor (England) in hydrothermal sulfide veins together with barite, galena, and strontianite. We observed barytocalcite in Vuoriyarvi (Kapustin, 1964), and Frolov (1960) and Pozharitzkaya (1960) observed it in one of the Siberian massifs.

In Vuoriyarvi barytocalcite forms either fine-grained veins or poorly developed prismatic crystals (up to 1–2 cm) in a calcite groundmass accompanied by norsethite, alstonite, marmatite, and pyrrhotite. In the massifs of Eastern Siberia prismatic crystals (1–2 mm) of barytocalcite together with rounded and fused grains form on the walls of the cavities of ankeritic carbonatites. Here it is associated with quartz, strontianite, carbonate, and marmatite. In the veins of Namo-Vara flattened crystals (up to 6×4 cm) of barytocalcite are formed in the ankerite mass and also in quartz. Only in one instance was barite found to occur with barytocalcite.

Barytocalcite is bright green in color with one prominent cleavage; biaxial, −ve; X-ray pattern is close to standard (Table 20); symmetry group $2/m-P2_1$; $z=2$. The chemical composition of the mineral from Vuoriyarvi is given in Table 21. Its crystal-chemical formula is $Ca_{1.03}\,Sr_{0.08}\,Ba_{0.92}\,Mg_{0.03}(CO_3)_{2.00}$.

Barytocalcite is the typical mineral of late calcite veins (with burbankite), but it is formed at the initial stage of crystallization of ankeritic veins. It is later replaced by fine-grained aggregates of barite and quartz, forming pseudomorphs after it (Namo-Vara).

Norsethite $BaMg(CO_3)_2$. This rare mineral was first described (Milton et al., 1959) from the effusive and sedimentary rocks of the Green River formation (USA) and from the carbonatite massifs of Vuoriyarvi (Kapustin, 1964). Norsethite is also found in late burbankite-calcite veins occurring around pyroxenites. It forms anhedral grains, individual rounded grains, or poorly developed minute flattened crystals with trigonal pyramids. In hand specimen it hardly differs from calcite except that it is greenish in color (the mineral from the USA). Sometimes it shows color banding, the intensity of the color decreasing toward the periphery of the grains. The mineral has rhombohedral cleavage and vitreous luster; hardness 3.5; uniaxial, –ve; X-ray pattern of the mineral from Vuoriyarvimass if is similar to that from America (Table 20). Chemical composition (Table 21) is simple and is represented by the formula $BaMg(CO_3)_2$, with minor amounts of Ca and Sr replacing Ba. The yellowish-green color of the mineral is indicative of the presence of Fe or TR. With rising temperature the mineral dissociates into MgO and $BaCO_3$.

Table 21. Chemical composition (in wt. %) and physical properties of Ca, Ba, and Mg carbonates

Components	Alstonite		Barytocalcite		Norsethite	
	Vuoriyarvi	Alston Moor, England	Vuoriyarvi	Sayan	Vuoriyarvi	Green River
MgO	—	—	0.50	—	14.43	13.9
CaO	18.30	17.60	18.75	18.67	0.49	0.5
SrO	3.15	4.25	1.81	1.54	1.54	—
BaO	48.67	48.54	48.92	49.33	51.25	52.9
CO_2	23.39	29.41	29.95	30.0	32.31	31.2
Others	—	—	—	—	—	0.8
Total	99.51	99.80	99.93	99.54	100.02	99.3
Analyst	L.S. Baum		A.V. Bykova	L.S. Baum	A.V. Bykova	C. Milton et al., 1959
Author		D. Dana et al., 1953				
Sp. gr.	3.72		3.54	3.53	3.74	3.837
n_g	1.676	1.672	1.682	1.684	1.687	1.685
n_m	1.674	1.671	1.680	1.682		
n_p	1.525	1.526	1.528	1.524	1.517	1.515
a_0, Å		4.99			5.00	5.02
b_0, Å		8.77			16.66	16.75
c_0, Å		6.11			6.26	6.29
α_{rh}			12		47°02′	47°02′
$2V^0$			12			

For solubility in acid norsethite is closer to calcite than to dolomite. It is soluble in cold dilute HC1 with slower effervescence than calcite. It belongs to the trigonal system with D_3^7–R 32 space group. Under hypergene conditions this mineral is relatively stable.

Burbankite $(Na, Ca)_6 (Ca, Sr, Ba, TR)_6 (CO_3)_{10}$. This mineral is rare in occurrence. It occurs in carbonatites of Bearpaw Mountain (Pecora and Kerr,

1953), Vuoriyarvi (Borodin and Kapustin, 1962), Siberia (Zdorik, 1966), and in fenites and metasomatites (Tichonenkova and Kazakova, 1964; Efimov et al., 1969). It is typical for late calcitic veins but also occurs in the primary stage of crystallization of ankerite-dolomitic veins. Relics of recrystallized and corroded calcite intersected by microveins of burbankite occur within the burbankites along the central part of large veins. In Siberia (Zdorik, 1966) burbankite occurs only in ankeritic carbonatites in the form of large (up to 10 cm), poorly developed hexagonal-prismatic crystals, replaced by strontianite, barite, carbocernaite, and orthite aggregates.

Burbankite is yellow or greenish in color, transparent with conchoidal fracture; hardness 3.5; X-ray pattern close to standard; hexagonal in symmetry; uniaxial, –ve; symmetry group *P63mc*. Properties and composition are variable (Table 22). According to Voronkov (Voronkov et al., 1967) the crystal-chemical formula of burbankite is (Na, Ca)$_6$ (Ca, Sr, Ba, TR)$_6$ $(CO_3)_{10}$.

Table 22. Chemical composition (in wt. %) and physical properties of burbankite

Components	Vuoriyarvi		Siberia	Bearpaw Mountain	Lovozero	Ural	Vuoriyarvi
TR_2O_3	16.22	15.12	20.00	9.48	18.95	14.81	23.00
Fe_2O_3	0.10	0.48	0.24	0.03	—	0.19	0.22
MgO	Net	0.35	0.14	0.14	—	0.32	Net
CaO	9.81	10.86	12.38	13.46	7.09	6.76	12.85
SrO	9.96	12.86	16.60	19.42	26.35	18.45	6.17
BaO	14.60	11.62	5.49	13.56	2.33	9.97	7.14
Na_2O	12.19	11.44	11.62	9.69	14.52	9.81	13.67
K_2O	0.74	0.99	0.03	0.15	—	2.35	0.22
CO_2	32.14	34.30	32.40	32.55	30.77	32.55	35.97
H_2O	2.60	0.97	0.02	0.18	—	3.94	0.25
Others	0.06	1.24	0.57	0.89	—	0.87	0.13
Total	98.42	100.23	99.49	99.55	100.01	100.02	99.62
Analyst	M.E. Kazakova	T.A. Kapito-nova	K.A. Doro-feeva		M.E. Kazakova	Z.T. Kataeva	E.N. Baranova
Author	L.S. Borodin and Yu.L. Kapustin, 1962		T.B. Zdorik, 1966	W.T. Pecora and J.G. Kerr, 1953	R.P. Tikhonen-kova, 1964	A.F. Etimob et al., 1969	A.A. Kukharenko and others, 1965
Sp. gr.	3.58	3.54	3.59	3.50	3.50	3.50	3.48
n_0	1.635	1.632	1.629	1.627	1.618	1.629	1.629
n_e	1.623	1.620	1.617	1.615	1.606	1.621	1.622
a_0, Å	10.52	10.41	10.43	10.53			10.49
c_0, Å	6.51	6.48	6.38	6.50			6.42

Burbankite, a double-salt compound, decomposes into two phases at 670°C and at 730°C (Fig. 24, *10*) in association with the oxides of Ca, Ba, Sr, and Na_2CO_3. The composition of TR in burbankite is highly variable (Table 18). It is not a stable mineral and easily decomposes in successive stages. It is replaced by carbocernaite most often by the aggregates of barite, strontianite, and ancylite. The gaps remaining in place of these crystals are filled by other crystals. During weathering it disintegrates with the release of TR ochre.

Carbocernaite (Na, Ca) (Ca, Sr, Ba, TR) $(CO_3)_2$. This rare mineral occurs in Vuoriyarvi (Bulakh et al., 1961) and in several carbonatite massifs of Siberia (Zdorik, 1966) and Vietnam (Bulakh and Uzok, 1967). It is found in dolomitized burbankite-calcite veins together with chlorite, pyrite, marmatite, anatase, and quartz in the form of druses of small (0.1–5 mm) crystals that form incrustations on chlorites. The crystals are rhombic in habit (Fig. 26, *6*) and bright yellow in color; biaxial, –ve; stable (Table 23). The crystal-chemi-

Table 23. Chemical composition (in wt. %) and physical properties of carbocernaite

Components	Vuoriyarvi		Fan Si Pan, Vietnam	Siberia
TR_2O_3	25.52	26.10	24.61	17.06
Fe_2O_3	0.52	1.50	3.12	0.49
MgO	0.34	—	0.28	4.29
CaO	15.31	15.10	19.76	19.27
SrO	13.89	12.43	5.58	16.33
BaO	3.37	3.20	5.96	2.50
Na_2O	6.12	5.11	3.92	2.43
K_2O	—	—	1.24	0.20
H_2O	0.15	2.40	0.93	0.50
CO_2	34.00	31.82	33.69	36.82
Others	—	1.70	0.92	0.35
Total	99.22	99.36	100.01	100.24
Analyst	M.E. Kazakova	E.N. Baranova		T.I. Ukhina
Author	Yu.L. Kapustin, 1964	A.G. Bulakh et al., 1961	A.G. Bulakh and E.P. Izokh, 1967	T.B. Zdorik, 1966
Sp. gr.	3.50	3.53	3.656	3.4
n_g	1.700	1.708	1.708	
n_m	—	1.679	1.679	
n_p	1.570	1.569	1.566	
$2V^0$	54	52	56	
a_0, Å	6.34	6.39	6.241	
b_0, Å	7.25	7.27	7.30	
c_0, Å	5.62	6.21	5.23	

cal formula of carbocernaite is as follows: (Na, Ca) (Ca, Sr, Ba, TR) $(CO_3)_2$ (Voronkov and Pyatenko, 1966); symmetry group *Pb2m*. With rising temperature it decomposes into two phases (Fig. 24, *11*), similar to burbankite, at 615 and 930°C.

Carbocernaite is formed by hydrothermal action on burbankite. It has a narrow stability range and is replaced constantly by aggregates of barite, ancylite, and strontianite, but under hypergene conditions it is more stable than burbankite and decomposes very slowly.

Fairchildite $K_2Ca(CO_3)_2$. This rare carbonate of K and Ca occurs in slags that remain after the fusion of wood ash resulting from forest fires (Dana et al., 1953). We observed the sodium-rich variety of fair-childite which may be called sodium-fairchildite.

Sodium-Fairchildite. This occurs in late burbankite-calcite veins in Vuoriyarvi and forms individual flattened crystals (size 1–2 mm) or fan-shaped aggregates in the calcite mass. It is white in color with basal-pinacoid (?) cleavage and shows vitreous luster; hardness 2.5. In ultraviolet light the mioeral is weakly fluorescent, orange; uniaxial; – ve; sometimes shows weak birefringence; $n_e = 1.459$, $n_0 = 1.525$. Under the microscope it shows polysynthetic twinning along the (001) cleavage. X-ray analysis is similar to that from the USA (Table 24).

The composition of fairchildite from Vuoriyarvi differs from that of other fairchildites in the presence of Na together with K and an insignificant amount of Sr and Ba. Calculation of the crystal-chemical formula of this mineral (Vuoriyarvi), viz., $Na_{2.00}Ca_{0.99}(CO_3)_{2.00}$, conforms with the sodium-

Table 24. X-ray data on natrofairchildite and fairchildite

1		2		1		2		1		2	
I	*d*, Å	*I*	*d*, Å	*I*	*d*, Å	*I*	*d*, Å	*I*	*d*, Å	*I*	*d*, Å
6	6.71	50	6.64	1	2.77	20	2.78	2	1.493	20	1.49
3	4.50	30	4.59	6	2.20	50	2.21		—	20	1.41
1	4.40	—	—	5	2.10	50	2.15	1	1.323	20	1.32
2	4.30	20	4.31	1	2.02	30	2.03	1	1.271	20	1.28
2	3.89	—	—	6	1.891	50	1.88	1	1.218	—	1.21
3	3.28	20	3.33	—	—	10	1.75	1	1.136	—	—
10	3.18	100	3.19	1	1.713	10	1.71	1	1.011	—	—
4	2.67	30	2.69		—	30	1.70	1	0.933	—	—
9	2.64	80	2.64	1	1.681	10	1.66	1	0.844	—	—
				1	1.618	20	1.61	1	0.741	—	—

Note: 1—communication to author (Vuoriyarvi massif); 2—after ASTM Bulletin, 1943 in RKD diffractometer with Cu–Ni radiation, $2R = 57.3$ mm, $2r = 0.6$ mm. Analyst: R.A. Alexandrova.

analog of fairchildite, namely, $Na_2Ca(CO_3)_2$. Spectral analysis indicates the presence of Mg, Fe, Mn, La, and Y.

The presence of sodium-fairchildite in Vuoriyarvi was first observed in complex alkaline carbonates of hypogene origin. One of the principal rock-forming carbonate lavas of Oldoino Lengai is composed of Ca and alkaline components (Du Bois et al., 1963). It forms aggregates of stretched idiomorphic flakes often showing polysynthetic twinning. Uniaxial, –ve. The chemical compositions of two varieties of lavas similar in composition to this mineral are given (Table 25). In both cases A1 was apparently in excess because S, C1, SiO_2, and SO_3 were neglected in the calculation. The ratios of Na, Ca, and CO_2 are 3 : 1 : 2, and this is very close to that in the usual sodium-fairchildite, $(Na, K)_2$ Ca $(CO_3)_2$, which is reflected in the analysis of these lavas. Probably other, similar carbonates (for example, dehydrated and also hydrated) occur in these rocks.

Table 25. Chemical composition of natrofairchildite and Oldoino Lengai lava

Components	Vuoriyarvi		Theoretical composition	Oldoino Lengai	
	Wt. %	Atomic	Wt. %	Wt. %	
CaO	25.61	0.4573	27.18	19.09	17.52
SrO	0.85	0.0080	—	0.89	0.85
BaO	0.44	0.0028	—	1.05	1.02
Na_2O	29.46	0.9500	30.12	29.00	30.00
K_2O	1.35	0.0287	—	6.90	7.50
H_2O	—		—	1.81	1.91
CO_2	41.93	0.9530	42.70	31.98	30.73
Cl	—	—	—	2.07	3.03
Others	—	—	—	7.12	8.18
$-O=Cl_2$	—	—	—	0.57	0.75
Total	99.64		100.00	99.34	99.99
Analyst	A.V. Bykova and L.I. Baum				
Author				Du Bois et al., 1963	

Sodium-fairchildite is not a stable mineral and is easily transformed into aggregates of very fine-grained calcite. We found sodium-fairchildite only in samples at depths greater than 70 m. Slightly weathered carbonate lavas are always found to occur in Oldoino Lengai (Du Bois et al., 1963).

Sahamalite $TR_2Mg(CO_3)_4$. This mineral is found in dolomitic carbonates of Mountain Pass (Jaffe et al., 1953) and in siderite-dolomite carbonatite veins of Kangankunde (Garson, 1955), where it is associated with synchysite monazite, puartz, and strontianite. It occurs as small colorless monoclinic crystals; sp. gr. 4.30; biaxial, −ve; $n_p = 1.679$, $n_m = 1.776$, $n_p = 1.887$; $2V = 57°$.

The composition of sahamalite from Mountain Pass is as follows (wt. %): CeO_2 31.4, La_2O_3 27.8, MgO 6.1, FeO 2.0, CO_2 31.7, insoluble 0.5, total 99.5 (Jaffe et al., 1953). Crystal-chemical formula is $TR_2Mg(CO_3)_4$. Sahamalite is rare and is formed in late carbonatites that are rich in TR and Fe.

Parisite $CaCe_2(CO_3)_3F_2$. This is a typical accessory mineral of late dolomitic-ankeritic carbonatites. It is found in the Kola Peninsula (Kapustin, 1964), Siberia (Gaidukova et al., 1962; Zdorik et al., 1967), and Africa (Tundulu, Kangankunde—Garson, 1955), where it accompanies accessory bastnaesite (Mountain Pass, Karonge). Parisite accompanies chlorite, quartz, fluorite, sphalerite, pyrite, and hematite. It occurs as incrustations on rocks and often as druses of small flattened crystals in open spaces formed by earlier minerals of the TR group. In Siberia accessory parisite occurs replacing burbankite. Parisite crystals occur as sharp hexagonal-platy forms with weakly developed prismatic grains (Fig. 26, *7*). X-ray analysis similar to the standard; uniaxial, +ve. Composition and properties are given in Table 26.

Bastnaesite ($CeCO_3F$). This mineral occurs rarely in carbonatites of hypabyssal facies (massifs of Siberia and the Kola Peninsula), but even here it is in accessory amounts. It is often found on the surface of subvolcanic carbonatites stocks (Tundulu, Chilwa, Kangankunde) and in independent veins of late carbonatites (Karonge, Mountain Pass—Garson, 1957–1958, 1959, 1961–1962; Pray and Sharp, 1951; Olson et al., 1954; Thoreau et al., 1958; Heinrich, 1967). It is usually found in ankerite-dolomite veins together with fluorite, parisite, quartz, thorite, and monazite, and forms aggregates of individual crystals or microveinlets within the rock mass. In hematitized parts (sometimes with needle-shaped aegirine) bastnaesite recrystallizes and forms large flattened crystals. It is dark yellow in color; X-ray pattern similar to the standard; biaxial, +ve. Chemical composition and properties are more or less constant. In Vuoriyarvi (Kukharenko et al., 1965) independent hydroxyl-bastnaesite with low F and higher R.I. occurs (Table 26). The composition of TR in basnaesite is normal (Table 18). Thermal curves of different varieties of bastnaesite are more or less similar, but the endothermic peaks of the variety low in F and rich in water interfere in the region of lower temperatures.

Fluor-carbonate of TR occurs in fluorite-bearing carbonatites; in late carbonatites it is associated with minerals formed later than burbankite.

Synchysite $CaCe(CO_3)_2F$. This occurs in negligible quantities with fluor-carbonates of TR in carbonatite veins of South Siberia and Mountain Pass. In typical carbonatites this mineral is very rare, but it is found in ankerite carbonatites of Chilwa, Songwe, and Nkombwa (Pecora, 1956; Dixey et al.,

Table 26. Chemical composition (in wt. %) and physical properties of fluor-carbonate TR

Components	Siberian				Kola Peninsula	Mountain Pass	Karonge		
	Parisite				Bastnaesite				
ThO_2	—	5.36	5.36	—	0.50	—	—	—	0.02
TR_2O_3	62.00	63.70	63.70	75.81	70.85	69.17	70.50	70.76	69.43
CaO	10.25	1.00	2.47	0.55	0.40	0.70	—	—	0.78
SrO	—	—	—	—	0.70	2.20	—	—	0.04
H_2O	0.30	2.54	2.54	—	5.07	0.22	—	—	—
CO_2	22.87	20.40	20.40	18.92	19.70	18.31	16.56	18.06	14.62
F	8.29	0.98	0.98	8.90	1.15	6.88	3.75	1.50	6.26
Others	0.31	—	3.33	—	2.49	5.50	—	5.25	6.26
$-O{=}F_2$	4.80	0.41	0.40	3.74	0.50	2.90	1.57	0.63	2.63
Total	99.22	93.57	99.48	100.44	100.36	100.08	89.24	94.92	94.78
Analyst	V.N. Lure	T.I. Stolyarova			K.A. Baklanova				
Author	V.S. Gaidukova and others, 1962			T.B. Zdorik, 1966	A.A. Kukharenko and others, 1965	J.C. Olson et al., 1954	J. Thoreau et al., 1958		
Sp. gr.	4.16		4.50	4.90	4.745	4.94			
n_e	1.780	1.800		1.825	1.86	1.821			
n_0	1.678	1.740		1.723	1.760	1.728			
a_0, Å	7.10			7.16		7.23			
c_0, Å	9.88			9.79		9.98			

1955; Garson, 1963). We observed accessory synchysite in talc-dolomite-ankerite carbonatites in one of the massifs of Siberia together with pyrite, molybdenite, sphalerite, parisite, and quartz. It forms hexagonal-prismatic pink crystals (up to 2 mm in length) with rounded margins on the crystals of carbonates and quartz within the geodes. Uniaxial, +ve; $n_e = 1.769$, $n_0 = 1.673$; X-ray pattern is similar to parisite with a slight difference in interplaner spacing. Spectral analysis shows the presence of Ca, La, Ce, Sr, Ba, Yb, Y, Mn, Fe, and Zn.

Cordylite $BaCe_2(CO_3)_3F_2$. This is the rare fluor-carbonate of TR and Ba. So far it has been reported from alkaline pegmatites of Narsarsuk (Greenland). This mineral was studied by Kukharenko (Kukharenko et al., 1965) from quartzose-dolomitic carbonatites of Lesnaya Varaka massif, where it occurs as yellowish hexagonal tabular forms. Hexagonal in symmetry, crystal spacing D_{6h}^4 (Donnay and Donnay, 1953) with $a_0 = 5.10$ Å, $c_0 = 23.09$ Å; $z = 6$;

sp. gr. 4.31; uniaxial, –ve; $n_e=1.577$, $n_0=1.764$. The composition of the mineral from Greenland is as follows (wt. %): TR_2O_3 49.39, ThO_2 0.30, CaO 1.91, BaO 17.30, FeO 1.43, CO_2 23.47, H_2O 0.80, F 4.87, insoluble 2.58; $(-O=F_2)=2.05$, total 100.00 (Flink, 1901).

Huanghoite $BaCe(CO_3)_2F$. This mineral was first reported from hydrothermal carbonatite veins in a deposit of the Korean Republic (Semenov, 1963). We found it in ankerite-dolomite carbonatites from a Siberian massif. In the latter case hunghoite occurs in vugs along with pyrite, sphalerite, barite, strontianite, quartz, fluorite, and relics of corroded monazite. Huanghoite forms flattened crystals (up to 0.3 mm) or radiating aggregates on quartz crystals. Sometimes a granular mass of huanghoite is also found, filling the interstices of quartz crystals of thin fractures of fluorites. Huanghoite crystals are thin hexagonal prisms, terminated by basal pinacoids (0001). Grains are unequal, show steplike forms and are covered with dendrites or coated with small grains of pyrite, chlorite, and hematite crystals.

Huanghoite is yellowish in color with distinct pinacoid cleavage. Under the microscope a dust of hematitic accumulation is seen in huanghoite from some places. Hardness 5.5; X-ray pattern close to standard (Table 27); uniaxial, –ve. Its composition and properties (Table 28) are similar to the identical mineral from China. Hexagonal in symmetry; $a_0=5.1$, $c_0=19.6$ Å; $z=6$. Composition of TR is strongly ceritic (Table 18). Formula of this mineral from Siberia is as follows: $Ba_{1.05}\ Ca_{0.04}\ TR_{1.02}\ (CO_3)_2\ F_{1.04}$. The presence of Fe^{3+} indicates the occurrence of hematite but in the calculation of the formula of huanghoite this was ignored.

Table 27. X-ray data of huanghoite

1		2		1		2		1		2	
I	*d*, Å	*I*	*d*, Å	*I*	*d*, Å	*I*	*d*, Å	*I*	*d*, Å	*I*	*d*, Å
7	4.04	1	3.91	3	1.642	7	1.616	3	1.202	3	1.201
10	3.26	10	3.21	3	1.574	7	1.557	3	1.184	5	1.176
7	2.55	7	2.50	4	1.371	7	1.355	3	1.157	3	1.157
6	2.15	5	2.10	1	1.336	7	1.335	2	1.091	6	1.083
7	2.11	9	2.09	6	1.325	6	1.325	1	0.989		
9	1.997	10	1.973	2	1.275	1	1.305	2	0.921		
3	1.769	4	1.759	2	1.267	5	1.252	2	0.780		

Explanation: 1—after author (condition of X-ray analysis: Diffractometer RKD with Cu–Ni, $2R=57.3$ mm, $2r=0.6$ mm, analyst: R.A. Alexandrova); 2—after E.I. Semenov (1963).

Ancylite $SrCe(CO_3)_2(OH)H_2O$. This is a rare mineral, first reported from pegmatites of Narsarsuk, Chibina and Lovozero massifs (Böggild, 1901; Semenov and Kazakova, 1953). It is the typical mineral of late ankerite-dolomite carbonatites. It occurs in almost all the massifs of the Kola

Table 28. Chemical composition and physical properties of huanghoite

Components	Siberia		Korean Republic		
	Wt. %	Atomic		Wt. %	
TR_2O_3	37.90	0.2297	38.40	37.35	38.25
Fe_2O_3	1.91	—	—	—	0.10
(Ca, Sr)O	0.66	0.0127	—	—	0.54
BaO	36.15	0.2363	36.46	36.14	39.35
CO_2	19.20	0.4363	20.90	18.90	19.38
H_2O	0.80	—	0.93	—	0.05
F	4.40	0.2315	4.00	3.45	1.65
Others	0.72	—	—	—	0.80
$-O=F_2$	1.85	—	1.68	—	0.69
Total	99.89	—	99.01	95.84	99.43
Analyst	A.V. Bykova		V.N. Klitina	A.V. Bykova	Chazan Cin
Author			E.I. Semenov, 1963		
Sp. gr.	4.58		4.51		4.67
n_o	1.766		1.76		
n_e	1.588		1.602		

Peninsula (Kozireva and Ilinsky, 1959; Bulakh, 1961; Orlova et al., 1963; Kapustin, 1964), Siberia (Frolov et al., 1969; Motichko 1959), and in veins of Ravalli County (Heinrich and Levinson, 1961; Heinrich, 1967). Accessory ancylite is typical for carbonatites poor in F, and appears later than burbankite and carbocernaite. It forms spontaneously along with burbankite and carbocernaite but shows a strongly antipathic relation with TR-bearing fluorcarbonates. It is associated with barite, strontianite, chlorite, galena, and thorite in the form of aggregates of small crystals or druses of prismatic crystals (up to 2 mm, Fig. 26, *8*) within the geodes. Rhombic; X-ray pattern similar from different places; symmetry class $2/m2/m2/m$: preliminary cell-dimension data are as follows: $a_0=5.00$, $b_0=8.48$, $c_0=7.01$ Å. Ca and Ba are constantly present in ancylite and in sample No. 2 (Table 29) show the following ratio: Ca : Sr : Ba = 1 : 1 : 1. The composition of TR in ancylite is highly variable (Table 18). The thermal curves of ancylite indicate its complex nature (Fig. 24, *12*).

Calkinsite $TR_2(CO_3)_3 \cdot 4H_2O$. This is also a rare mineral. It occurs in calcitic veins in the massifs of Bearpaw Mountain (Pecora and Kerr, 1953) in association with minerals like burbankite, sulfides, and phlogopite that are in the process of transformation. It occurs (our observation) in burbankite-calcitic veins in the Vuoriyarvi massifs, where it forms thin flattened crystals (up to 1 × 1 mm) on the surface of burbankite. It is associated and shows a sympathetic relation with barite, strontianite, and pyrite. It is bright yellow in color, transparent with distinct cleavage parallel to its elongation, and brittle. The X-ray pattern as well as other properties are identical to the same mineral from the USA (Tables 30, 31). Under the microscope it is colorless with

Table 29. Chemical composition (in wt. %) and physical properties of ancylite

Components	Vuoriyarvi*		Kovdor	Sallanlatva		Chibina	Narsarsuk (Greenland)
	1	2	3	4	5	6	7
Ce_2O_3	44.37 (Ce_2O_3 + La_2O_3)	43.12 (Ce_2O_3 + La_2O_3)	45.89 (Ce_2O_3 + La_2O_3)	47.12 (Ce_2O_3 + La_2O_3)	22.23	25.26	22.22
La_2O_3					23.29	23.77	24.04
Fe_2O_3	1.04	Net	—	—	2.21	0.50	—
FeO	Net	Do	—	—	0.14	—	0.35
CaO	3.34	4.56	1.70	2.08	6.51	3.78	1.52
SrO	17.84	9.94	16.73	17.95	11.86	17.10	21.03
BaO	4.13	14.36	3.56	4.31	3.33	0.65	—
$(Na, K)_2O$	Net	Net	—	—	0.57	—	—
CO_2	17.06	21.00	21.89	—	20.13	22.33	23.28
H_2O	7.55	6.66	6.85	—	6.23	5.77	6.52
P_2O_5	—	—	—	—	2.57	—	—
Others	0.44	—	—	—	0.84	0.08	—
Total	95.77	99.64	96.62	—	99.91	99.24	98.96
Analyst	M.E. Kazakova	A.V. Bykova		M.V. Kukharchik and E.A. Fabrikova		M.E. Kazakova	Mauzelius
Author	Yu.L. Kapustin, 1964				M.P. Orlova et al., 1963	E.I. Semenov and M.E. Kazakova, 1959	O.B. Böggild, 1901
Color	Colorless	Yellow	Violet	Violet	Red		
Sp. gr.	4.10	4.15	4.00	3.97	3.78	3.987	3.95
$-2V^{o}$	—	72	70	—	71	68	—
n_g	1.764	1.760	1.745	1.760	1.754	1.740	1.735
n_m	1.732	—	1.718	—	1.730	1.705	1.700
n_p	1.635	1.630	1.621	1.631	1.625	1.638	1.638

*Formulas of samples analyzed:

1. $(Ca_{0.03}Sr_{0.85}Ba_{0.12})_{1.00}Ce_{1.26}(CO_3)_{2.00}(OH)_{1.40} \cdot 1.20H_2O$;
2. $(Sr_{0.40}Ba_{0.35}Ca_{0.34})_{1.09}Ce_{1.00}(CO_3)_{2.00}(OH)_{1.00} \cdot 1.05H_2O$;
3. $(Sr_{0.73}Ba_{0.12}Ca_{0.12}Ce_{0.03})_{1.00}Ce_{1.06}(CO_3)_{2.00}(OH)_{1.00} \cdot 1.00H_2O$.

straight extinction. The mineral from Bearpaw Mountain is orthorhombic (Fig. 26.9) with the cell dimensions: $a_0 = 9.57$, $b_0 = 12.65$ Å; $z = 4$ (Pecora and Kerr, 1953). This mineral from the USA has the formula $TR_2(CO_3)_3 \cdot 4H_2O$. Bykova found 55.21% TR_2O_3 in this mineral from the Vuoriyarvi massif. Spectral analysis showed the presence of La, Ce, Yb, Y, Ca, Mn, Sr, and Fe. In Vuoriyarvi calkinsite occurs only at a depth of 70 m, where the rocks are affected by weathering. At the surface this mineral is either absent or is replaced by lanthanite.

Lanthanite $TR_2(CO_3)_3 \cdot 8H_2O$. This mineral is relatively rare but occurs in some rare-earth deposits (Bastnaes, Sweden, Bethlehem, USA—Dana et al., 1953) where rare-earth minerals are formed by weathering. We observed lanthanite in Karelia. It develops as thin crystalline and powdery incrustations

Table 30. Interplaner distances of calkinsite and lanthanite

Calkinsite								Lanthanite			
1		2		3		4		5		6	
I	*d*, Å	*I*	*d*, Å	*I*	*d*, Å	*I*	*d*, Å	*I*	*d*, Å	*I*	*d*, Å
10	6.35	10	6.54	2	2.00	3	2.009	10	8.20	10	8.46
3.5	4.81	4	4.78	1	1.98	0.5	1.985	3	4.92	2	4.71
3	4.50	3	4.49	1	1.942	3	1.945	3	4.30	2	4.45
1	4.21	0.5	4.24	1	1.925	1	1.925	2	4.16	2	4.24
2	3.87	2	3.87	1	1.900	2	1.902	2	4.10	2	4.14
1	3.70	2	3.71	1	1.840	1	1.840	1	3.90	2	3.96
2	3.20	5	3.27	1	1.780	1	1.786		—	1	3.84
1	3.15	1	3.17	1	1.630	1	1.634	1	3.20	3	3.24
2	2.93	3	2.931	1	1.590	1	1.591		—	1	3.15
1	2.90	2	2.897		—	0.5	1.570	6	3.00	4	3.02
	—	0.5	2.713		—	0.5	1.548	1	2.94	1	2.945
1	2.65	0.5	2.654	1	1.525	0.5	1.527	1	2.80	1	2.809
1	2.60	1	2.595	1	1.500	1	1.502	1	2.70	1	2.696
1	2.43	0.5	2.433		—	1	1.446	1	2.50	2	2.563
	—	0.5	2.393		—	1	1.421	1	2.421	1	2.425
2	2.34	0.5	2.338	1	1.350	1	1.357		—	1	2.295
1	2.28	0.5	2.281		—	0.5	1.319	1	2.152	1	2.157
1	2.24	1	2.248	1	1.300	1	1.300	2	2.120	1	2.125
1	2.20	0.5	2.207		—	0.5	1.262	1	2.096	1	2.093
	—	0.5	2.179	1	1.220	0.5	1.221	3	2.050	1	2.058
4	2.13	3	2.128		—	0.5	1.176	1	2.018	2	2.016
4	2.11	3	2.115	1	1.155			1	1.969	2	1.968
2	2.070	3	2.074	1	1.087			1	1.873	2	1.873
1	2.020	0.5	2.029	1	0.902			1	1.822	1	1.823

Explanation: 1, 3, 5—after author (Karelia); 2, 4—after Pacora and Kerr, 1953; 6—after ASTM Bulletin, (1943). X-ray was taken (from Karelia) in RKD diffractometer, $2R = 57.3$ mm, $2r = 0.6$ mm with Cu-Ni radiation. Analyst: R.A. Alexandrova.

on the surface of burbankite in associatton with aragonite and celestine. Probably lanthanite is more widespread than is thought today, as white powdery encrustations containing TR are widely found in weathered carbonatites. But the constant presence of impurities and the very thin incrustations (< 0.1 mm) of lanthanite make it difficult to collect pure material. It is white in color and powdery. Under the microscope minute concretions form radiate structure. The properties of this mineral from Karelia massifs are given in Table 31.

Table 31. Chemical composition and physical properties of lanthanite and calkinsite

Components	Calkinsite	Lanthanite			
	Bearpaw Mountain	Kola		Bethlehem	Bastnaes
	Wt. %	Wt. %	Atomic quantity	Wt. %	Wt. %
TR_2O_3	54.42	50.90	0.3328	55.03	54.55
CaO	1.46	—	—	—	—
(Sr, Ba) O	4.77	—	—	—	—
CO_2	22.40	22.44	0.5100	21.95	21.95
H_2O	12.00	23.20	1.2889	24.21	23.40
Others	5.42	—	—	—	0.13
Total	100.47	96.54		101.19	100.03
Analyst		V.N. Arkhangel'skaya			
Author	W.T. Pecora and J.G. Kerr, 1953			D. Dana et al., 1953	
Sp. gr.	3.28			2.84	2.70
n_g	1.686	1.613			1.613
n_m	1.657				1.587
n_p	1.569	1.515			1.520
$-2V^0$	54				63

The sp. gr. of this mineral cannot be determined due to the presence of impurities. X-ray pattern is close to standard (Table 30). X-ray analysis of finely powdered material gives picture not of distinct lanthanite but of La_2O_3 (probably this material is formed during grinding). Biaxial, – ve. Earlier it was thought to be rhombic with cell dimensions: $a_0=9.52$, $b_0=17.1$, $c_0=9.02$ Å; $z=4$. The chemical composition of the mineral from the Karelia massif can be expressed as $TR_2(CO_3)_3 \cdot 8H_2O$. With rising temperature lanthanite loses some of its water content and at 80°C changes into calkinsite. The remaining water vaporizes at 100–200°C (Fig. 22, *13*) with the decomposition of the mineral. The composition of TR in lanthanite varies widely (Table 18).

Lanthanite is formed during the weathering of rare-earth minerals, chiefly burbankite. Sometimes identification is difficult due to the constant presence of powdery monazite in the zone of weathering of hypergene carbonatites.

Manasseite $Mg_6Al_2(CO_3)(OH)_{16} \cdot 4H_2O$. This mineral was first noticed by Rimski-Korsakov in Kovdor and also by us in Vuoriyarvi within the ankeritic veins intersecting the brecciated picrite porphyrites and their relics. It forms individual flattened crystals and xenomorphic monocrystaliine grains occurring around ankerite (Vuoriyarvi) or druses of hexagonal and barrel-shaped crystals within geodes (Kovdor). It is associated with magnesite, podolite, pyrite, and sometimes with collinsite. Manasseite crystals are well developed and show hexagonal bipyramidal forms with truncated basal pinacoids. Individual grains are striated parallel to the basal pinacoid and show tarnishing with no distinct luster. An appreciable part of the crystals show complex twinning. Twinning develops with repetition of one of the pyramids making 30° with z axis. Twinning is occasionally developed parallel to the basal pinacoid. The crystals are rarely segregated.

Manasseite shows various colors from white, sky-blue, yellow, to brown. The mineral often shows color zoning which is parallel to the margin of bipyramidal grains, and is sometimes rhythmically graded or segregated. It shows perfect basal pinacoid cleavage with strong pearly luster on the cleavage plane. X-ray analysis is close to standard (Table 32); properties and composition similar to the typical mineral from Norway (Table 33). Uniaxial, −ve. At a latest age of the process of mineral formation manasseite is replaced by fine-grained aggregates of the podolite or magnesite. Under hypergene condition it becomes dull and is covered with ocher. In Kovdor, manasseite sometimes forms an intimate intergrowth with hydrotalcite, making them difficult to isolate one from the other. Spectral analysis of manasseite indicates the presence of Sr, Ba, Mn, Yb, Zn, and Pb. Thermal curves (Fig. 24, *15*) show two endothermic peaks due to the presence of water (at 180–230°C) and isolation of CO_2 (at 410°C).

Hydrotalcite $Mg_{18}Al_6(OH)_{48}(CO_3)_3 \cdot 12H_2O$. This occurs with manasseite, often forming an intimate intergrowth. It is reported from Kovdor and Vuoriyarvi; in Kovdor it occurs in fair quantities. It is associated with podolite and pyrite in ankeritic veins intersecting the picrites. Physical properties and chemical composition of hydrotalcite are similar to those of manasseite. It differs from manasseite only in cell dimensions (Table 33). Debye grains and thermal curves of both the minerals (Table 32) are also similar to those of manasseite (Figs. 24, *15,16*).

Table 32. Interplaner distances of manasseite and hydrotalcite

Manasseite							Hydrotalcite				
1		2		3			4		5		
I	*d*, Å	*I*	*d*, Å	*I*	*d*, Å	*hkl*	*I*	*d*, Å	*I*	*d*, Å	*hkl*
10	7.71	10	7.69	100	7.67	006	10	7.70	100	7.69	006
9	4.12	9	4.07	80	4.05		8	3.89	70	3.88	$0.0.\underline{12}$; 10
8	3.87	8	3.83	20	3.83	004	3	2.60	20	2.58	024
5	2.72	4	2.67	50	2.60	201; 333	3	2.31	20	2.30	0.2.10
4	2.54	3.5	2.55	30	2.49	202	2	1.96	20	1.96	125; $0.2.\underline{16}$
3	2.37	3	2.39	40	2.34	203	1	1.860	10	1.85	$2.1.\underline{10}$
3	2.20	3	2.20	40	2.17	204; 115		—	10	1.75	2.1.13; 2020
3	2.00	3	2.01	40	2.00	210; 205	1	1.651	10	1.65	$2.1.\underline{16}$
4.5	1.844	4	1.851	60	1.84	206	2	1.525	20	1.53	220; 223
3	1.550	4	1.551	20	1.56	208	1	1.504	20	1.50	226
3	1.520	3	1.515	30	1.52	221	1	1.285	10	1.28	$4.0.\underline{10}$
2	1.440	1	1.432	30	1.49	119	1	1.201			
1	1.309	2	1.328	10	1.33		1	1.105			
1	1.290	1	1.294		—		1	1.089			
1	1.260	1	1.259	10	1.25						
1	1.233	2	1.233	10	1.24						
1	1.180	1	1.182	10	1.17						
1	1.152	1	1.152								
1	1.092	1	1.090	10	1.09						
1	1.004	1	1.004								
1	0.974	1	0.971								
		1	0.956								
		1	0.933								
		1	0.888								
		1	0.878								

Note: 1, 2, 4—after author (Vuoriyarvi and Kovdor); 3, 5—ASTM Bulletin, 1943. X-ray of the samples (Kola) was taken in RKD diffractometer, $2R$=57.3 mm, $2r$=0.6 mm with Cu–Ni radiation. Analyst: R.A. Alexandrova.

Phosphates

Phosphorus is one of the characteristic elements of carbonatites and phosphates are formed in almost all the stages of the formation of carbonatites. But only apatite occurs in appreciable quantities; the other phosphates occur in negligible amounts.

Apatite $Ca_{10}P_6O_{24}$ (F, Cl, CO_3 (OH))$_2$. This is the typomorphic accessory mineral for ultrabasic and alkaline rocks. It also occurs in minor quantities in olivinites and pyroxenites. The quantity sharply increases in alkaline rocks (ijolites, melteigites, and turjaites), in which it is also a metasomatic product. In nephelinitic pyroxenites the apatite content rises to 25% (Vuoriyarvi, Ozernaya Varaka, South Siberian massifs). Apatite occurs in particularly high proportions in carbonatites at the contact zones, where there is intensive apatitization. In apatitized magnetite-forsterite rocks apatite develops large masses in several zones 50–100 m in length (Vuoriyarvi—50 m, Kovdor—100 m). Such apatite has developed somewhat early in the process of carbonatite formation and occurs in a zone surrounded by metasomatites. It is believed to be of the 1st generation.

Table 33. Chemical composition (in wt. %) and physical properties of manasseite and hydrotalcite

Components	Manasseite			Hydrotalcite		
	Kovdor	Vuoriyarvi	Norway	Kovdor	Norway	
Al_2O_3	16.48	21.94	16.59	14.50	15.32	14.42
Fe_2O_3	—	FeO–2.42	0.21	2.00	1.89	2.44
MgO	39.70	33.71	39.38	39.81	39.72	39.52
CaO	0.11	Traces	—	—	—	–
CO_2	7.50	7.32	7.48	7.42	7.60	7.33
H_2O	36.23	34.48	36.34	36.01	35.46	36.28
Others	—	—	—	—	0.72	0.56
Total	100.02	99.87	100.00	99.74	100.71	100.55
Analyst	T.N. Capitonova	A.V. Bykova		T.N. Capitonova		
Author			D. Dana et al., 1951		D. Dana et al., 1951	
Sp. gr.	2.03	2.05	2.05	2.02	2.06±0.03	
n_0	1.526	1.524	1.524	1.517	1.511	
n_e	1.510	1.510	1.510	1.498	1.495	
a_0, Å		6.12	6.13		6.14	
c_0, Å		15.39	15.37		46.24	

In carbonatites of the 1st stage uniform distribution of apatite (2nd generation) is a constant feature, but it is principally present near the periphery and the central parts of carbonatites (see above.) A significant amount of apatite is found to occur in carbonatites of the 2nd stage (3rd generation), in which it is disseminated within the rock mass. Such apatites occur on the margin of carbonatites or are concentrated along the axis of veins; it also occurs as schlieren, pockets, and microveinlets in calcite masses or small veins. This 3rd generation apatite is formed later than calcite.

In early carbonatites apatite is persistently associated with accessory rare-earth minerals, namely, dysanalyte (2nd generation), and rarely with sphene, pyrochlore, and baddeleyite (3rd generation). These minerals show intergrowths with apatite while the other minerals are xenomorphic with respect to apatite. There is a sympathetic relation among all these minerals.

In early carbonatites apatite is present within the rock mass. Apatite crystals are distributed only within the interstices of the calcite grains. Individual crystals of apatite (0.1 to 2 mm, chiefly 0.1 to 0.5 mm) are idiomorphic in relation to all other minerals. Prismatic grains are always equigranular and lath-shaped grains are absent. Larger crystals are more rounded in shape. In the apatite-rich part of the rock individual crystals of apatite develop a mosaic structure. Due to the process of dolomitization-amphibolitization of early carbonatites apatites are redistributed in them. In the first stage they form segregation and independent veins (together with clinohumite, pyrrhotite, and 4th-generation niobozirconolite) and afterward these are crushed and gradually dissolved. Apatite here shows an antipathic relation with dolomite: in dolomitized rocks apatite is completely absent. Accumulation of apatite in the first stage is probably due to intensive migration from deeper zones. Apatite of the 5th generation (podolite) is always found in ankeritic veins. This was not observed earlier. Such apatite occurs in all the massifs of the Kola Peninsula (Kapustin, 1964; Kukharenko et al., 1965) and similarly in the South Siberian massifs (authors). Podolite forms independent veinlets in the gneisses around Namo-Vara; the proportion may be as high as 60–90%. It is associated with monazite, barite, strontianite, anatase, and sulfides, and shows an antipathic relation to fluorite and fluor-carbonates (Siberia). It also develops veinlets within ankerite and dolomite masses.

Staffelite (carbonate apatite) cemented with rock fragments in pipe-shaped zones of breccia (postcarbonatitic) in several massifs (Kovdor, Vuoriyarvi, Eastern Sayan, Gulinkskii, Magnet Cove) represents 6th-generation apatite. In Vuoriyarvi and Kovdor staffelite is associated with vermiculite and zeolite and forms a radiate mass; sometimes it is covered by chabazite, natrolite, and needle-shaped calcite crystals (Kovdor, Vuoriyarvi). Apatites of the first four generations are fluorapatite and contain Sr, Ba, and TR (Table 34). Apatite of the 4th generation shows an increase in H_2O and CO_2. In ankeritic veins of several massifs independent hydrated carbonate-apatites

(usually under the name of podolite) rich in Sr and Ba occur. Staffelite is the typical carbonate-apatite and is almost free of Sr, Ba, and TR but contains Cu.

Under hypogene conditions apatite is markedly stable and accumulates as placers (Brazii—Guimaraes and Ilchenko, 1954).

Isokite $CaMgPO_4F$. Isokite is found in the oxidized dolomite-ankerite carbonatite veins of Isoka (Nkombwa—Deans and McConnel, 1955) in association with pyrite, barite, monazite, and sellaite. Isokite forms spherulites and white or pink-colored radiate masses with pearly or silky luster. Hardness 4–5, sp. gr. 3.32 (theoretically 3.29); cleavage along (010). Biaxial, +ve, n_p= 1.590; n_m=1.595, n_g=1.615; $2V$=51°. It fluoresces blue under ultraviolet light. Chemical composition of the mineral (wt.%) is as follows: CaO 29.57, SrO 1.60, BaO 0.21, TR_2O_3 0.16, MgO 21.18, FeO 0.41, MnO 0.13, P_2O_5 37.36, F 9.52, H_2O 0.46, total 96.59. Isokite is formed under hydrothermal conditions along with sellaite and other low-temperature minerals of late veins.

Monazite ($CePO_4$). This often occurs in late carbonatites as an accessory mineral. In volcanic veins of Kangankude monazite is widely and uniformly distributed (Garson, 1957–1958; McKie, 1962). It is also well known from Nkombwa (Reeve and Deans, 1954), Ravalli County and Fremont County (Heinrich and Levinson, 1961; Heinrich and Dahlem, 1965; Heinrich, 1967), Mountain Pass (Olson et al., 1954; Jaffe, 1955), and as an accessory mineral in the late carbonatite massifs of the Kola Peninsula and Siberia (authors). It is usually associated with quartz, sulfides, barite, chlorite, and strontianite, but shows an antipathic relation to fluor-carbonate and fluorite. It occurs as small (up to 1 mm) flat, granular crystals in geodes with striations on the grains (Fig. 26, *11*) or as granular masses, powdery accumulations, sheaf-like and radiate growths (Kukharenko et al., 1961). The properties and composition of this mineral are normal, but it is often crowded with inclusions and in several veins it shows anomalous composition (Table 35); it becomes very rich in SO_3 and under this condition develops another variety like sulfate-monazite (Kukharenko et al., 1961).

The presence of a significant amount of Ca, H_2O, Fe_2O_3, and SO_3 in sulfate-monazite is probably due to mechanical inclusions of gypsum, limonite, and copiapite, thin encrustations of which were observed on the monazite crystals. R.I. and thermal curves of monazite are like those of rhabdophane.

Rhabdophane ($CePO_4 \cdot H_2O$). This is not a typical mineral for carbonatites but was found to occur as powdery encrustations on weathered cyrtolite crystals (Kovdor) and ancylite (Sallanlatva). Rhabdophane is white in color, uniaxial, +ve; n_e=1.700, n_0=1.667; X-ray data like the standard. Major-element analysis (analyst: M.E. Kazzkov) gives 62.81% TR_2O_3, and spectral

Table 35. Chemical composition and physical properties of monazite from carbonatites

Components	Siberia		Kola Peninsula			
	Wt.%	Atomic quantity	Wt.%	Atomic quantity	Wt.%	Wt.%
SiO_2	0.17		—		0.70	—
ThO_2	0.07		0.02		5.77	0.09
TR_2O_3	68.92	0.4181	68.31	0.4140	50.61	68.21
Fe_2O_3	0.44		—		6.10	—
CaO	0.09	0.0018	0.12	0.0021	4.60	—
H_2O	0.26	0.0278	—		3.50	—
P_2O_5	29.96	0.4220	30.02	0.4228	25.84	29.90
SO_3	—		—		3.12	—
Others	—				0.23	—
Total	99.91		98.47		100.47	98.20
Analyst	G.E. Cherepivskaya				K.A. Baklanova	M.V. Kukharchik
Author					A.A. Kukharenko et al., 1961	
Sp. gr.	5.28		5.31		4.54	5.28
n_g	1.84		1.84		1.776	1.80
n_p	1.80		1.80		1.730	1.77

analysis indicates the presence of P, Th, Zr, Ca, Ba, La, Y, Yb, and Ce. Rhabdophane probably formed under hypogene conditions.

Crandallite $CaAl_3(PO_4)_2(OH)_6$. This mineral occurs in the staffelitic carbonatites of Kovdor (Kukharenko et al., 1965), where it is intimately associated with staffelite, forming conchoidal and reniform aggregates within the geodes. We found crandallite, showing the same association, in Vuoriyarvi and in one of the Siberian massifs. This mineral is either white or yellowish in color. Its crusts develop radiate or thin, flattened structures. Uniaxial, +ve; X-ray data close to standard. Properties and compositions are normal (Table 36). Crandallite is formed in the epithermal stage along with staffelites.

Goyazite $SrAl_3(PO_4)_2(OH)_6$. This mineral occurs in carbonatites of Kangankunde and Vigu (McKie, 1962), but the analysis of this mineral indicates a composition intermediate between goyazite and florencite (Sr-bearing florencite). A mineral similar in composition to goyazite was observed in one of the Sayan massifs, occurring as fine-grained crystalline aggregates and also as powdery coatings and crusts on quartz crystals within the rock cavities.

It is associated with pyrite, barytocalcite, sphalerite, and strontianite. Small crystals of florencite and colorless quartz grow on goyazite. In goyazite crusts individual grains are oriented perpendicular to the surface of the crusts and show a hexagonal parallel structure. It is white in color; X-ray pattern close to standard; uniaxial, +ve. The properties and composition of the mineral are normal (Table 36).

Florencite $CeAl_3(PO_4)_2(OH)_6$. This mineral occurs in alumino-phosphatic alkaline deposits (Dana et al., 1953). It rarely occurs in carbonatites, but is found in one of the Sayan massifs (Somina and Bulakh, 1966) and Kangankunde (McKie, 1962) where it occurs in significant amounts. It is a typical mineral for dolomite-ankerite veins and is associated with sulfides and minerals that contain Sr, Ba, and TR, forming granular aggregates and druses within the geodes. The symmetry is trigonal with rhombohedral and cubic-octahedral forms (Somina and Bulakh, 1966). It is either colorless or pink, uniaxial, +ve; X-ray pattern is close to standard. The properties of this mineral depend on its composition (Table 36). Sp. gr. increases with the increase in Ba and TR; R.I. is directly proportional to TR content. The composition of this mineral from carbonatites of Africa and Siberia is intermediate in nature between florencite, $CeAl_3 (PO_4)_2 (OH)_6$ and goyazite, $SrAl_3(PO_4)_2(OH)$.

Gorceixite $BaAl_3(PO_4)_2(OH)_6$. This mineral occurs in weathered carbonatites of Mrima Hill (Goetzee and Edwards, 1959), where it forms accumulations and concretions together with other products of hypergene weathering. Kukharenko (Kukharenko et al., 1965) observed a mineral similar in composition to gorceixite in oxidized dolomitic carbonatites of Lesnaya Varaka. To date gorceixite has not been recorded from carbonatites. In Mrima Hill it is associated with the products of lateritic weathering, indicating its hypergene origin.

Gorceixite often forms a porcelaneous cryptocrystalline mass. It is white in color but often also gray, yellow or brown. Uniaxial, +ve; X-ray pattern is similar to crandallite. Gorceixite from Mrima Hill differs from the other occurrences in the presence of more Ca and Fe (Table 36).

Svanbergite $SrAl_3(PO_4SO_4)(OH)_6$. This mineral occurs in negligible amounts in the upper part of the carbonatite stocks of Sallanlatva within the weathered ankeritic carbonatites. It is associated with barite, staffelite, and crystalline pyrolusite, and forms flattened porcelaneous crusts 1–3 mm thick and veinlets in oxidized and limonitized siderite-barite rocks. The crusts are fine-grained with radiate structures (rare). Grayish-yellow inclusions of other materials are always found in it. Svanbergite is yellowish in color with sporadic white or gray patches. X-ray pattern is similar to the crandallite

Table 36. Chemical composition (in wt.%) and physical properties of crandallite group of minerals

Components	Crandallite		Goyazite	Goyazite-Florencite			Florencite	Gorceixite		Svanbergite	
	USA	Kovdor	USA	Kangan-kunde	Vigu	Sayan	Brazil	Mrima Hill	South Africa	Ural	Sallan-latva
SiO_2	—	—	0.96	0.3	—	1.95	0.48	1.9	1.25	1.03	—
TR_2O_3	—	—	—	14.1	17.6	19.19	28.00	—	7.00	—	0.54
Al_2O_3	34.15	36.21	32.30	29.8	29.8	34.49	32.38	35.9	37.96	39.84	—
Fe_2O_3	—	0.04	0.90	—	—	1.41	0.76	—	3.76	0.28	—
MgO	2.06	—	—	—	—	0.81	—	—	1.28	—	—
CaO	15.30	11.59	—	0.9	1.6	—	1.31	—	—	4.01	1.38
SrO	—	2.15	18.43	10.9	9.0	7.87	—	—	—	14.16	15.71
BaO	—	0.68	4.00	1.7	0.1	—	—	16.0	11.88	—	0.72
$(Na, K)_2O$	—	0.15	0.74	—	—	—	—	—	—	—	0.02
P_2O_5	32.23	30.35	28.92	24.1	26.0	23.28	25.61	28.1	22.39	19.82	—
SO_3	—	—	—	3.2	1.7	—	—	—	—	5.27	—
H_2O	17.50	18.16	12.00	—	—	11.11	10.87	—	15.05	15.85	—
Ignition loss	—	0.43	—	14.5	12.9	—	—	16.6	—	—	—
F	—	0.50	1.93	1.2	1.6	—	—	—	—	—	—
$-O=F_2$	—	0.21	0.81	0.50	0.7	—	—	—	—	—	—
Total	101.24	100.05	99.37	100.2	99.6	100.11	99.31	98.5	100.57	100.26	—

Analyst		Z.V. Vasileva				T.A. Burova				L.I. Pokrobskaya	L.I. Baum
Author	D. Dana et al., 1954	A.A. Kukharenko et al., 1965	D. Dana et al., 1954	McKie, 1962		M.Ya. Somina and A.G. Bulakh, 1966	D. Dana et al., 1954		D. Dana et al., 1954	L.I. Lukanina, 1959	
Sp. gr.	2.92	2.92	3.16–3.28	3.31			3.586		3.185	3.22	3.21
n_e	1.62	1.631	1.630	1.661		1.664–1.7	1.705		1.625	1.640	1.638
n_0	1.618	1.624	1.620	1.663		1.658–1.691	1.680			1.626	1.627
a_0, Å			6.97	6.971	6.982	6.97–6.99	6.96			6.94	
c_0, Å			16.51	14.42	16.54	16.48–16.49	16.34			16.7	
a_{rh}			6.82							6.87	
α			61°28′				53°13′30″			60°40′	

group of minerals. The properties of svanbergite and other minerals of the crandallite group are shown in Table 36.

The crandallite group of minerals was formed in the last stage of the formation of ankeritic carbonatites but before hematitization. Part of them (chiefly svanbergite and gorceixite) probably were hypergene in nature. But genetically it is more closely related to the formation of staffelitic breccia, which has been very poorly studied. Both hypergenetic and hypogenetic minerals occur around these breccias. In all cases the minerals of this group were formed by cooling of the phosphatic solutions within the carbonatites. The presence of Ca, Sr, Ba, or TR in them probably depends on the association of these elements with the mixed rocks and on temperature. Florencite and goyazite were probably formed with early rare-earth and strontium-rich minerals (fluor-carbonates, burbankite, monazite, and others), while crandallite and svanbergite were deposited from calcitic or strontium-phosphatic low-temperature solutions. These minerals are not typical for carbonatites. They are rare and occur in insignificant quantities.

Vivianite $Fe_3(PO_4)_2 \cdot 8H_2O$. This is a characteristic mineral of the hypergene zone, rare in carbonatites, and is formed in a late stage of development of dolomite-ankerite veins. It occurs in Kovdor (Kukharenko et al., 1965) and Vuoriyarvi at great depths, in the cavities of dolomite veins in association with chlorite, podolite, marcasite, and quartz. It forms hexagonal crystals and radiating incrustations up to 2 cm in size. It is greenish-white or sky-blue in color. Sp. gr. 2.72; X-ray pattern close to standard. Biaxial, +ve; n_p=1.580–1.593, n_m=1.600, n_g=1.63–1.64. Refractive index, strength of pleochroism, and intensity of the color of vivianite increase (dark-blue) with oxidation. Besides the hypogene vivianite, hypergenetic earthy vivianite also occurs.

Bobierrite $Mg_3(PO_4)_2 \cdot 8H_2O$. This mineral was observed in Kovdor (Kukharenko et al., 1965) in the cavities of dolomitic veins together with pyrite, calcite, and hydromicas. It occurs as white-colored fine grains. Biaxial, +ve; n_p=1.512, n_m=1.520, n_g=1.541. It was formed under hydrothermal conditions, probably by the alteration of primary apatite.

Collinsite Ca_2 (Mg, Fe) $(PO_4)_2 \cdot 2H_2O$. This mineral is rare in occurrence. Earlier it was reported from phosphatic deposits of French Lake, Canada (Dana et al., 1954). It also occurs in Kovdor (Kukharenko et al., 1965). It forms reniform radiate structures and sometimes individual hexagonal prismatic crystals (up to 2 mm in length) with the development of ridge-like growths on the paraankerite crystals within the cavities of ankeritic veins. Veins with collinsite are developed in the zone of carbonatization of picrites. Collinsite is associated with magnesite, manasseite, pyrite, and vermiculite.

It is yellowish-white, pink or sky-blue in color with subvitreous luster; two sets of distinct prismatic cleavages at an angle of 80°; biaxial, +ve. Its properties and composition (Table 37) are similar to the mineral from Canada. The mineral from Kovdor (Kukharenko et al., 1965) contains CO_2, Al_2O_3, and BaO in significant amounts. As this sample is not pure it differs in composition from the standard one. The properties of all the samples are practically identical and so also the X-ray data (Table 38). The mineral from Canada is triclinic, with $a_0=5.71$, $b_0=6.73$, $c_0=5.39$ Å; $\alpha=96°48'$; $\beta=107°16.5'$; $\gamma=104°32'$; $z=1$. The formula of the sample analyzed is $Ca_{2.03}(Mg_{0.96}Fe_{0.07})_{1.02}PO_4 \cdot 2.5H_2O$, which is very close to the sample from Canada but differs from the one analyzed by Kukharenko (Kukharenko et al., 1965). Refractive index α was found to increase with an increase in the Fe content of the mineral. The value of n_p increases substantially. Dehydration of collinsite takes place at temperatures above 400°C. It is easily decomposed under hypergene conditions and is covered with ocher.

Table 37. Chemical composition and physical properties of collinsite

Components	Kovdor			Canada
	Wt. %	Atomic quantity	Wt. %	Wt. %
Al_2O_3	Nil		2.51	—
FeO	1.44	0.0180		6.86
MgO	11.14	0.2784	11.33	6.34
CaO	33.37	0.5960	28.81	32.16
MnO	0.66	0.0082	—	—
(Sr, Ba) O	—		4.74	—
$(K, Na)_2O$	—		0.20	—
H_2O	12.65	1.4056	12.11	12.28
P_2O_5	40.00	0.5634	38.51	39.83
Others	0.35		2.15	2.37
Total	99.61		100.36	99.84
Analyst	A.V. Bykova		Z.V. Basileva	
Author			A.A. Kukharenko et al., 1955	D. Dana et al., 1953
Sp. gr.	2.98		2.93	2.95
n_g	1.648		1.651	1.657
n_m	1.633			1.642
n_p	1.606		1.613	1.632
$2V°$	78		80	80

Sulfates

Minerals of this class, except barite, are not so important for carbonatites, although the presence of sulfur is a characteristic feature of carbonatites.

Barite ($BaSO_4$). This occurs in late carbonatites. Large veins and zones of barite-carbonate rocks occur in the massifs of Alnö (Eckermann, 1950), Chilwa (Garson and Smith, 1955), Kangankunde (Garson, 1958), Nkombwa (Deans and McConnel, 1955), Sallanlatva, Vuoriyarvi, Karonge (Thoreau et al., 1958), Ravalli County and Fremont County (Heinrich et al., 1961, 1965, 1966, 1967), and also in Siberian massifs, where barite constitutes 10–30% of the veins. Two generations of barite occur. One is colorless and the other is

Table 38. Interplaner distance of collinsite

1		2			1		2		
I	*d*, Å	*I*	*d*, Å	*hkl*	*I*	*d*, Å	*I*	*d*, Å	*hkl*
2	6.41	30	6.3	010	2	1.839	40	1.831	031
1	5.12	20	5.01	001	1.5	1.803	5	1.797	022; $\bar{3}21$
	—	10	4.51	—	3	1.767	40	1.765	220; $22\bar{2}$
	—	10	3.54	100; $11\bar{1}$	3	1.707	20	1.695	$20\bar{3}$
1	3.30	20	3.26	—	7	1.672	60	1.669	$\bar{1}13$; $\bar{1}40$
3	3.15	50	3.14	101		—	10	1.629	$0\bar{2}3$; $\bar{3}22$
7	3.04	80	3.04	$0\bar{2}1$	2	1.406			
10	2.70	100	2.69	$\bar{1}21$; $1\bar{2}1$	2	1.373			
2	2.56	10	2.54	$0\bar{1}2$	2	1.344			
1.5	2.30	10	2.30	$\bar{2}21$	3	1.316			
2	2.25	30	2.25	—	2	1.230			
1.5	2.21	5	2.13	030; $0\bar{3}\bar{1}$	1.5	1.207			
2	2.13	30	2.10	$1\bar{1}2$; $12\bar{2}$	1.5	1.147			
2	1.977	20	1.982	$\bar{1}31$; $\bar{1}22$	1.5	1.125			
1	1.877	5	1.910	—	1.5	1.083			

Note: 1—author's data (Kovdor massif); 2—according to ASTM Bulletin, 1943. Condition of photography of samples from Kovdor massif: Camera RKD, 2R=57.3 mm, 2r=0.6 mm; radiation Cu–Ni. Analyst R.A. Alexandrova.

yellowish-orange. The colorless type is associated with carbocernaite, anatase, marmatite, and pyrite, forming pinacoidal flattened crystals with the development of rhombic prismatic grains (210), pinacoid (010), and particularly the pinacoid (001) (Fig. 26, *10*). Orange-colored barite is associated with monazite, strontianite, and cleiophane, and occurs as rhombic-prismatic crystals with the development of such forms as (011), (201), (210), (110) and (001). Individual crystals of barite show zoning, the center being colorless and the periphery orange in color. Biaxial, +ve. The properties and composition of colorless and orange barite tally with those of strontiobarite and pure barite respectively (Table 39).

Earlier generation barites (colorless) are rich in Sr, while yellowish barites containing less Sr are intimately associated with strontianite. Barite is fairly stable and does not transform even in the last stage of the transformation process.

Table 39. Properties and composition (in wt. %) of barite
Analyst: M.V. Kukharchikh and L.A. Baum

Properties	Vuoriyarvi		Sallanlatva		Kovdor		Siberia	
	1st generation	2nd generation	1st generation	2nd generation	1st generation	2nd generation	1st generation	2nd generation
Sp. gr.	4.46	4.52	4.44	4.50	4.45	4.54	4.48	4.54
n_g	1.640	1.646	1.638	1.645	1.641	1.647	1.640	1.645
n_p	1.630	1.634	1.630	1.632	1.633	1.635	1.631	1.633
CaO	0.23	0.06	0.30	0.09	0.24	0.08	0.12	0.10
SrO	5.24	0.43	4.30	0.85	3.18	0.51	2.29	0.31
BaO	56.95	65.08	58.50	64.91	60.74	65.86	61.50	66.02
TR_2O_3	0.07	0.02	0.09	0.01	0.04	—	—	0.01

Celestine ($SrSO_4$). This mineral is rare in carbonatites. Carbonatites rich in hematite veins contain a significant amount of celestine, as in Tuva. Rare crystals of celestine occur within the weathered products of burbankite along with barite and aragonite (Vuoriyarvi). Celestine forms druses of small flattened crystals showing pink and colorless patches. Sp. gr. 3.93; X-ray pattern close to standard; biaxial, +ve, $n_p=1.614$, $n_g=1.623$. It is formed under late hydrothermal or hypergene conditions under the influence of a burbankite-rich sulfatic solution.

Anglesite ($PbSO_4$). This mineral is mostly found in dolomitic veins in negligible quantitites. Independent anglesite crystals do not occur, but it is developed in the form of crusts and rims around galena (Namo-Vara, Kovdor, Sallanlatva). The properties of this mineral are normal; X-ray pattern is close to standard. Major-element analysis of this mineral was not possible. Spectral analysis (N.V. Lizunov) indicates the presence of Pb, Ba, Zn, and traces of Sr, Ca, and Cu.

Anglesite occurs in association with other minerals at depths that indicate hypogene origin. Probably it is formed after galena in late stages of the development of ankeritic veins together with chlorite, quartz, and hematite.

Anhydrite ($CaSO_4$). This was observed by Ilinski in hematitized parts of late carbonatite of Vuoriyarvi (Kukharenko et al., 1965) and was identified by its optical properties; $n_g=1.610$–1.612. We did not observe it in any carbonatite.

Silicates

The silicate content of carbonatite is not especially high (up to 20%); rarely the percentage increases in zones of metasomatism, where it is derived from the mixed rocks. In carbonatites the most important among the silicates are mica, pyroxene, forsterite, and richterite. Less important are albite and chlorite; other minerals are found in negligible quantities. The silicate minerals in carbonatites are discussed in the following order: orthosilicate, chain-silicate, ring-silicate, sheet-silicate, layered-silicate, and framework-silicate.

Schorlomite garnet $Ca_3(Al, Fe, Zr, Ti)_2 (Si, Ti)_3O_{12}$. This is the characteristic mineral of ijolites in the zone of nephelinization. It is rare in carbonatites, but occurs in rocks of the 1st stage in Vuoriyarvi, Kovdor, Magnet Cove, Oka, and Siberia, where it is associated with dysanalyte, pyroxene, phlogopite, or monticellite (Oka). Schorlomite forms idiomorphic tetragonal-trioctahedral crystals with rounded apex and shows intergrowths with apatite and calcite in some parts. Properties of this mineral are normal but sometimes it is rich in Zr (Borodin and Bykova, 1961; Milton et al., 1961), which is more conspicuous in schorlomites from alkaline rocks. Zr-rich schorlomite belongs to the andradite group (Table 40), with ZrO_2 content between 5 and 15%. The position of Zr in the schorlomite structure is not clear. Probably it replaces partly Ti and Fe^{3+} and partly Al and Si, but not Ca, which remains constant in quantity (Borodin and Bykova, 1961). This unusual garnet from Magnet Cove belongs to the grossular series, and distinctly differs from the Vuoriyarvi sample in the similar amount of Si and Fe and higher Al content. R.I. increases with an increase in $Fe^{3+}+Ti$, sp. gr. with an increase in the $(Ti+Fe^{3+})/Al$ ratio (Kukharenko and Bagdasarov, 1962; Kukharenko et al., 1965). In carbonatites this garnet is more or less stable, but it is sometimes replaced by sphene and, in late stages, by richterite and ilmenite aggregates.

Forsterite (Mg_2SiO_4). This is the typical rock-forming mineral of hypabyssal olivinites. It is also associated with alkaline ultrabasic effusives and dikes (Butakova and Egorov, 1962; Heinrich, 1967). It is the principal mineral of magnetite-forsterite rocks and occurs persistently in carbonatites (forsteritic facies—Vuoriyarvi, Kovdor, Siberian massifs, Palabora, Alnö, Jacupiranga, Magnet Cove, Sebl-Yavr). In carbonatites around magnetite-forsterite rocks it is often present as relics of the latter, in which forsterite shows replacement by phlogopite. At the contacts of carbonatites with forsterite-bearing rocks forsterite recrystallizes, becomes free of iron (1% FeO), and has a powdery appearance. In early carbonatites of the 2nd stage it is not usually altered, but in rocks of the 1st stage it is sometimes partly replaced by serpentine without, however, showing marked changes in the parent rock (Fig. 13). It develops a rounded inequigranular texture and sometimes forms anhedral

Table 40. Chemical composition (in wt. %) and physical properties of garnets

Components	Melteigites		Ijolites	Turgites		Pyroxenites	Carbonatites		
	Oka	Ozernaya Varaka	Kovdor	Salmagorski	Turi Bay	Gulinskii	Vuoriyarvi	Magnet Cove	Oka
SiO_2	33.86	28.20	28.99	31.15	33.10	23.10	22.56	9.6	32.0
TiO_2	2.07	12.03	12.80	8.02	6.34	14.60	12.36	5.0	5.0
ZrO_2	0.30	0.96	—	0.18	—	10.73	13.11	29.9	3.7
Al_2O_3	—	6.47	4.60	0.85	3.36	—	2.50	11.0	3.8
Fe_2O_3	20.93	18.36	17.46	25.23	21.37	16.84	14.49	13.14	14.0
FeO	1.72	3.72	3.53	1.36	1.10	2.84	1.84	0.8	—
MnO	1.05	0.36	0.18	0.18	0.28	0.17	0.25	—	2.6
MgO	1.08	2.07	1.10	Traces	1.09	1.09	2.00	0.5	1.0
CaO	32.34	27.59	30.06	33.03	32.36	29.72	29.00	29.8	42.0
$(Na, K)_2O$	0.31	0.34	0.45	0.26	0.22	—	0.74	—	—
Others	6.36	0.38	0.39	0.24	0.20	0.69	1.16	1.0	—
Total	100.02	100.48	99.56	100.50	99.42	99.84	100.01	100.74	104.1
Analyst		B.N. Melentev	V.M. Kovyazina			A.V. Bykova			
Author	G. Perrault, 1959	A.A. Kukharenko et al., 1965				L.S. Borodin and A.V. Bykova, 1961		C. Milton et al., 1961	G. Perrault, 1959
Sp. gr.	3.692	3.745	3.769	3.86	3.72	3.79	3.76	4.0	3.70
n	1.85	1.95	1.95	1.965	1.897	—	1.97	—	1.94
a_0, Å		12.10				12.29	12.28	12.46	

Table 41. Chemical composition (in wt. %) and physical properties of orthosilicates of Mg and Ca

Components	Forsterite								Monticellite		Clinohumite	
	Olivinites			Magnetite-forsteritic				Carbonatites				
	Kygda	Lesnaya Varaka	Afrikanda	Kovdor			Vuoriyarvi	Oka	Kovdor		Vuoriyarvi	
	1	2	3	4	5	6	7	8	9	10	11	12
SiO_2	40.59	40.37	37.02	39.80	41.08	41.75	41.70	39.36	33.32	37.72	36.09	36.69
TiO_2	—	0.12	1.31	Traces	Nil	0.01	0.02	0.28	—	0.01	2.86	3.66
Al_2O_3	0.87	0.36	0.39	0.55	Do	—	0.04	—	2.55	—	—	1.15
Fe_2O_3	2.08	2.10	2.32	1.05	0.20	0.14	0.18	0.86	0.92	0.13	—	1.48
FeO	8.91	11.66	10.78	4.70	4.57	2.15	2.80	2.84	6.25	3.26	9.26	2.02
MnO	0.32	0.33	0.30	0.38	0.78	0.80	0.01	4.73	—	—	0.31	0.26
MgO	46.88	43.55	43.63	51.82	53.08	54.66	54.50	49.15	21.50	23.48	49.20	51.30
CaO	0.27	0.61	2.08	0.96	Nil	0.50	0.41	1.49	32.14	34.81	—	2.33
Others	0.56	0.41	2.12	1.60	Traces	—	—	1.45	3.39	0.40	2.85	1.39
Total	100.48	99.51	99.95	100.86	99.71	100.01	99.66	100.16	100.07	99.81	100.57	100.28
Analyst			M.N. Sukoiova		A.D. Demidova	V.A. Klassen			H. Ulk	V.A. Klassen		M.N. Peterson
n_g	1.700	1.695	1.700	1.678–1.685		1.672	1.673	1.685	1.671	1.665	1.705	1.700
n_m	—	—	1.679	1.658–1.662		1.650	1.652	1.668	—	—	1.681	1.676
n_p	1.660	1.660	1.660	1.642–1.648		1.633	1.637	1.659	1.654	1.648	1.672	1.670
$2V^\circ$	−89	+89	−89	+83; +84; −86		+83	+83	—	—	−72	—	—

Note: 1—After E.L. Butakova and L.S. Egorov (1962); 4, 5, 11—After A.A. Kukharenko et al. (1965); 8, 9—After G. Perrault (1959).

Formulas of samples analyzed:

7. $(Mg_{1.96}Fe_{0.05}Ca_{0.01})_{2.02}SiO_{4.02}$; 8. $(Mg_{1.96}Fe_{0.04}Mn_{0.01}Ca_{0.01})_{2.02}SiO_{4.02}$;

11. $(Ca_{0.99}(Mg_{0.90}Fe_{0.08})_{0.98}SiO_{3.94}$;

12. $(Mg_{0.30}Fe^{2}_{0.18}Fe^{3}_{0.14}Mn_{0.02}Al_{0.07}Ti_{0.29})_{9.00}(Si_{0.97}Al_{0.03})_{1.00}O_4(O_{0.51}F_{0.34}(OH)_{0.29})_{1.14}$.

grains within the calcite grains. When recrystallized it is markedly granular in nature (Rimskaya-Korsakova, 1959).

The properties and composition of forsterite from different rocks also differ (Table 41). More ferruginous forsterite (up to 12% FeO) occurs in olivinites, while in magnetite-forsterite rocks the iron content decreases (to 4% FeO); in carbonatite forsterite is almost free of Fe and hence approaches its theoretical formula, Mg_2SiO_4. Part of the iron in forsterite is probably due to the constant presence of powdery magnetite inclusions. In late carbonatites forsterite is replaced by serpentine.

Monticellite ($CaMgSiO_4$). This is the characteristic mineral of alkaline skarns of superficial facies. It also occurs in melilitic rocks, picrite porphyrites, and damkjernites. In carbonatites monticellite is rare, but it occurs as a typomorphic mineral of early carbonatites of the 1st stage with distinct monticellite grade, where it is associated with phlogopite or biotite, melilite, schorlomite, and dysanalyte (Magnet Cove, Oka, Kovdor). Monticellite occurs as rounded crystals in calcite. The properties and composition of monticellite are normal (Table 41).

Clinohumite $Mg_9(SiO_4)_4(F, OH)_2$. This mineral often occurs in picrite, damkjernite, and the picritic zone of magnetite-forsterite rocks. It is also present in early carbonatites of Palabora (Russel et al., 1954), Alnö, Vuoriyarvi, Kovdor, and in forsterite-bearing rocks undergoing cataclasm and amphibolitization in Siberia, where it is accompanied by tetraferriphlogopite, pyrite, and richterite. Clinohumite forms rounded or flattened orange-red crystals, the crystals showing granular habit. Under the microscope clinohumite is strongly pleochroic with a yellowish tinge ($N_g > N_m > N_p$) and shows polysynthetic twinning. Biaxial, +ve; X-ray pattern is close to standard. The properties and composition of this mineral are more or less constant (Table 41). The intensity of pleochroism is directly proportional to the Ti content of the mineral (titanian-clinohumite). The occurrence of clinohumite is related to the contact metasomatism accompanying magnetite-forsterite rocks and carbonatite of the 2nd stage and also to autometasomatic amphibolitization-dolomitization.

Zircon ($ZrSiO_4$). This mineral is seen in the contact zone of nepheline and alkaline syenites with the early carbonatites of the 2nd stage, showing the biotite-aegirine assemblage (the massifs of Siberia, Chilwa, Sukulu, Alnö, Lueshe). Part of the accessory zircon is derived from the mixed rock, and it quickly disappears toward the center of carbonatite body. Zircon is associated with aegirine, biotite, orthoclase-perthite relics (derived from syenites), and pyrochlore. The presence of zircon at the margin of carbonatite is possible principally because of the availability of silica there (Maurice,

1949), but there is no doubt that zircon is derived from mixed rock (Dixey et al., 1955).

Zircon is always found in carbonatites that have been subjected to amphibolitization; it is accompanied by ilmenite, pyrochlore, and richterite. It replaced early minerals of Zr (baddeleyite and niobium-zirconolite) and is surrounded by crystals of the latter minerals. It also occurs in late carbonatites in very minor proportions (Bulakh and Kurbatova, 1959). It forms idiomorphic tetragonal-bipyramidal crystals or xenomorphic grains filling the interstices of dolomite crystals. It is brown, opaque, uniaxial, +ve; X-ray pattern close to standard; composition and properties are normal (Table 42). Spectral analysis indicates the presence of Hf, Y, Pb, Mn, and Ca. The composition of TR is rich in Y with a large amount of Ce and La (Table 18).

The formula of the sample analyzed is close to the theoretical formula: $ZrSrO_4$, with some Hf.

Table 42. Chemical composition (in wt. %) and physical properties of zircon

Components	Vuoriyarvi	Kovdor		Sebl-Yavr	Siberia	Bolshe-tagninskii
SiO_2	34.40	34.53	34.00	31.34	—	—
ZrO_2	63.58	63.74	63.58	66.57	66.70	64.82
HfO_2	1.61	1.59	1.45	1.52	1.3	1.4
TR_2O_3	0.27	0.10	—	0.17	0.33	0.25
Fe_2O_3	0.16	0.30	0.40	0.27	—	—
Others	0.17	0.36	0.44	0.13	—	—
Total	100.19	100.62	99.87	100.00	—	—
Analyst	M.V. Kukharchik	E.A. Isaeva			V.N. Arkhangelskaya	
Author		A.A. Kukharenko et al., 1965				
Sp. gr.	4.60	4.42	4.48	4.67	4.63	4.54
n_e	1.95	1.97–2.00			1.96	1.98
n_o	1.93	1.92–1.95			1.93	1.95

Sphene ($CaTiSiO_5$). This is a typical mineral of alkaline rocks and persistently occurs in ijolites and nephelinized pyroxenites, replacing perovskite. It is also observed in early carbonatites of the 1st stage. Often it is associated with contact metasomatic silicates that are rich in Ti-bearing ultrabasites (Vuoriyarvi, Kovdor) and melanocratic fenites (Kovdor, Ozernaya Varaka). In Kovdor the central part of carbonatite veins (occurring around sphene-rich fenitized amphibolites) is rich in sphene. Sphene is associated with apatite, pyroxene, and biotite, forming well-developed idiomorphic crystals (up to

5 cm) with an adamantine luster. Properties of sphene are normal; X-ray pattern close to standard; sp. gr. 3.54. Chemical analysis gives the following result (wt.%) : Nb_2O_5 1.03–1.98, SrO 0.68–1.17, TR_2O_3 0.35–2.18, ZrO_2 0.73 (Kovdor, Vuoriyarvi, and Ozernaya Varaka). The composition of TR from sphene is as follows: La_{16} Ce_{46} Pr_8 Nd_{22} $Sm_{2.2}$ $Eu_{0.3}$ Gd_2 $Tb_{0.3}$ Dy_1 $HO_{0.1}$ Er_2 $\cdot Yb_{0.1}$ (Kovdor) and $La_{21}Ce_{48}Pr_6Nd_{24}Gd_1$ (Vuoriyarvi).

In the last stage of the process of mineral formation sphene is replaced by ilmenite, calcite, and richterite aggregates (Fig. 27).

Thorite ($ThSiO_4$). This mineral occurs in minute quantities in late ankerite-dolomitic veins (Kola Peninsula, Ravalli County). It develops anhedral grains around carbonates, often giving rise to poorly developed crystals (in Kovdor—pseudohexagonal forms) and is associated with labuntsovite, sulfide, quartz, and fluorite. It is brown in color, shows normal properties, and is always metamict. X-ray pattern is close to standard; sp. gr. 4.89–5.12; isotropic (metamict) or uniaxial, –ve; $n=1.742$–1.782 (metamict variety), $n>1.8$ (crystalline variety). The mineral from the Kola Peninsula (analyst: M.V. Kukharchik) contains 1.57% TR_2O_3. Spectral analysis of thorite indicates the presence of Th, La, Yb, Si (>1%); Y, Mn, Fe, Ti, and Mg (0.01 to 0.001%).

Cerite ($Ce_3Si_2O_8F$). This mineral occurs as inclusions in the individual grains of late calcitic veins of the Kola Peninsula (Kapustin, 1964), Ravalli County (Heinrich and Levinson, 1961), and Mountain Pass (Olson et al., 1954). It develops anhedral or prismatic crystals similar to the forms of zircon (pseudotetragonal), less than 0.1 mm in size. It is brown in color. It is associated with fluorcarbonates of TR, ancylite, thorite, chlorite, sulfide, and quartz. Uniaxial, +ve; $n_e=1.83$, $n_0=1.82$. X-ray pattern is close to standard and shows diffused nature. The interrelation of cerite with other minerals is not clear.

Ramsayite ($Na_2Ti_2Si_2O_9$). This mineral is typical for agpaitic nepheline syenites and thin pegmatites (Hibinski and Lovozersky massifs, Tuva) and was also found, in a single instance, in the carbonatized fenites of Kovdor at the contact with early carbonatites of the 2nd stage (Kapustin, 1964). Ramsayite is associated with zircon, replacing lamprophyllite and sphene. It forms needle-shaped, brown crystals within the rock cavities. Properties of this mineral are normal; sp. gr. 3.46; X-ray pattern similar to the standard; biaxial, –ve; $n>1.9$. Spectral analysis indicates the presence of Ti, Na, Si, Mg, Fe, V, and Zr. The origin of ramsayite is not clear; it is probably formed during the alteration of fenites.

Melilite (Ca, Na) $MgSi_2O_7$. This is a typical mineral for the alkaline ultrabasic complex. It is found in melilitic rocks (turjaites, melilitites) and in superficial volcanoes, in alkaline dikes and effusives (Changit, Turi Bay, Africa). It is rare in carbonatites and occurs only in early 1st stage rocks of the monticellite-melilite facies in Kovdor and Oka (okaites). Melilite is associated with monticellite, dysanalyte, biotite, and pyroxene, forming independent corroded grains (up to 1 cm). The presence of unaltered melilite in carbonatites is rare. Often, at the contact of carbonatites with melilitic rocks, melilite develops in large contact-metasomatic zones (autoreactivated skarn) (Epshtein, 1959) containing calcite and apatite. In Kovdor and Gulinskii, at the contact of carbonatite bodies of both stages, melilitic rocks are intensively altered, and melilite itself undergoes heterogeneous changes with inclusions of fine-grained diopside, phlogopite, wollastonite, and calcite aggregates (Kovdor, Gulinskii, South Siberian massifs).

The properties and composition of melilite are more or less constant in nature (Table 43) and show similarity to akermanites that are rich in Na-bearing melilite (10–35%) and gehlenite (4–10%). In most of the well-known massifs melilitic rocks are usually unstable and undergo intensive and polyphase alterations.

Orthite $CaTRFeAl_2Si_2O_7SiO_4(OH)$. This mineral is rare in carbonatites and is found only in late dolomite-ankeritic veins with barite, chlorite, sulfide, TR minerals, and thorite in Kovdor, Siberia (Zdorik et al., 1966) and the USA (Heinrich, 1967). It is often associated with quartz and hematite, with which it is coordinate in development; it replaces earlier rare-earth carbonates (burbankite, carbocernaite and accessory bastnaesite—Zdorik, 1966), forming pseudomorphs after them. It often develops crystalline accumulations and veins in carbonate masses. In carbonatites it is crystalline and shows normal properties; X-ray pattern close to standard; sp. gr. 4.07 (Siberia) to 4.12 (Kovdor); biaxial, $n_p = 1.784$, $n_m = 1.813$, $n_g = 1.827$; $2V = -85°$ (Siberia) and $n_p = 1.776$, $n_m = 1.802$, $n_g = 1.819$ (Kovdor). Dorofeev has presented the following analysis of orthite (wt.%): SiO_2 30.12, TiO_2 0.22, ThO_2 0.10, UO_3 0.51, Al_2O_3 11.66, Fe_2O_3 5.74, TR_2O_3 28.07, FeO 11.31, MnO 0.15, MgO 0.30, CaO 6.44, SrO 3.72, Na_2O 0.27, K_2O 0.10, H_2O 0.07, F 0.03, Total 98.82. Peterson determined 30.15% of TR_2O_3 in this mineral from the Kola Peninsula. The interrelation of rare-earth elements in orthite from Siberia and Kovdor is as follows: Siberia—$La_{35}Ce_{40}Pr_{7.5}Nd_{16.7}Sm_{1.9}Eu_{0.1}$ (Zdorik, 1966); Kovdor—$La_{20}Ce_{55}Pr_6Nd_{16}Sm_2$.

Niocalite ($Ca_{3.5}Nb_{0.5}Si_2O_7F_{0.5}O_{0.5}$). This is a rare silicate found in early carbonatites (1st stage) of Oka (Nickel, 1956), in association with pyroxene and biotite. It occurs as yellowish prismatic crystals. Cleavage not prominent, fracture conchoidal; hardness 5.5–6; biaxial, –ve. Properties and composition are given in Table 44. X-ray pattern is close to that of the lavenite-wöhlerite group of minerals, to which niocalite belongs with the retention of

Table 43. Chemical composition (in wt. %) and physical properties of melilites

Components	Turgites					Okaites		Carbonatites		
	Kugda	Odikhincha	Tury Bay	Kovdor		Oka				Kovdor
SiO_2	43.38	43.50	42.93	42.97	43.36	39.78	38.68	39.64	39.98	38.95
TiO_2	0.10	Traces	—	Traces	0.39	—	—	—	—	0.07
Al_2O_3	3.05	9.08	8.34	7.20	5.98	10.33	10.60	6.62	4.47	4.80
Fe_2O_3	1.32	1.31	1.54	0.74	1.88	2.02	0.45	1.47	1.89	0.67
FeO	2.22	3.09	3.40	1.96	0.89	1.44	1.81	2.01	2.59	0.91
MnO	0.07	0.12	Traces	0.08	0.06	0.38	0.35	0.91	1.21	0.09
MgO	10.70	6.31	6.26	8.06	9.17	7.06	7.66	7.72	7.29	9.04
CaO	36.80	32.49	31.93	35.00	34.88	33.02	34.28	34.32	34.86	36.43
(Sr, Ba) O	—	—	—	—	—	0.97	0.44	1.44	1.60	2.88
Na_2O	2.24	4.24	4.08	2.97	2.92	3.69	3.92	3.35	3.08	2.36
K_2O	0.13	Traces	0.48	0.31	0.37	0.24	—	0.24	0.12	0.98
H_2O	0.62	0.44	0.08	0.65	0.36	0.44	0.37	1.12	0.86	0.92
Others	0.05	—	—	—	—	0.87	1.25	1.42	2.44	1.35
Total	100.68	100.58	99.04	99.94	100.26	100.24	99.81	100.26	100.39	99.45
Analyst				V.M. Kovyazina		W.H. Herdsman	H. Ulk	W.H. Herdsman		V.A. Klassen
Author	E.L. Butakova and L.S. Egorov, 1962		A.A. Kukharenko et al., 1965			G. Perrault, 1959				
n_0	1.633	1.632	1.633		1.626	1.633	1.633	1.633	1.635	1.633
n_e	1.623	1.627	1.623		1.618	1.627	1.625	1.628	1.629	1.626

its own end members, namely, the calcium-niobium member of this group of minerals. The formula of niocalite is as follows: $Ca_{14}Nb_3(Si_2O_7)_4(O_{8.6}F_{1.8})_{10.4}$ or $Ca_{3.5}Nb_{0.75}(Si_2O_7)(F_{0.45}O_{2.15})_{2.60}$.

Niocalite occurs as an independent stable mineral at the early stage of phosphorus-free carbonatites and ultimately is dissolved or replaced by latrappite (or pyrochlore?). Growth of latrappite on the corroded crystals of niocalite was observed in several samples, but the relation of niocalite to pyrochlore is not clear. Possibly niocalite is replaced by pyrochlore during the formation of carbonatites of the 2nd stage in which apatite starts to appear.

Lavenite $(Na, Ca, Mn)_3(Zr, Ti)Si_2O_7(F, O)$. This is a rare mineral, well known in the alkaline pegmatites of Lovozero massif (Semenov et al., 1958),

Table 44. Chemical composition (in wt. %) and physical properties of niocalite and lavenite

Components	Niocalite		Lavenite		
	Oka		Kovdor	Lovozero	Norway
Nb_2O_5	16.56	18.86	2.66	2.97	5.20
SiO_2	29.70	29.90	28.80	30.94	29.63
TiO_2	0.22	0.26	8.30	5.28	2.35
ZrO_2	—	—	23.00	23.20	28.79
Al_2O_3	1.31	0.16	0.60	FeO—3.73	—
Fe_2O_3	0.54	0.54	4.98	2.29	4.73
MnO	1.28	0.99	5.62	6.00	5.59
CaO	47.50	46.96	11.36	13.61	9.70
Na_2O	0.78	0.55	12.60	9.74	10.77
F	1.70	1.73	4.00	2.41	2.24
$-O=F_2$	0.71	0.73	1.68	1.00	0.94
Others	1.06	0.95	—	0.11	—
Total	99.94	100.08	100.24	99.28	98.06
Analyst			A.V. Bykova	M.E. Kazakova	P. Kleve
Author	E.H. Nickel, 1956		Yu.L. Kapustin, 1964	E.I. Semenov et al., 1958	W.C. Brögger, 1906
Sp. gr.	3.32	3.32	3.43	3.41	3.42
n_g	1.730	1.720	1.755	1.759	1.760
n_m	1.700	1.701	1.720	1.713	1.713
n_p	−56	−56	−78	−78	−80
a_0, Å	10.83	10.42			10.93
b_0, Å	10.42	20.39			9.99
c_0, Å	7.38	7.38			7.18
β	109°40′				110°18′

South Norway (Brögger, 1906), and in carbonatized fenites of Kovdor massif (Kapustin, 1964) where lavenite is associated with calcite, dysanalyte, apatite, and nepheline. Lavenite forms rounded crystals of 0.2–1.0 mm in diameter and is intimately intergrown with calcite and apatite. It is orange in color, biaxial, –ve; pleochroic in shades of yellowish tinge with $N_g > N_p$; X-ray pattern close to that of niocalite and titanium-lavenite from the Lovozero massif.

The chemical composition and properties of lavenite from Kovdor (Table 44) are similar to those of titanium-lavenite from the Lovozero massif (Semenov et al., 1958). The formula of the mineral from Kovdor is as follows: $(Na_{1.70} Ca_{0.85} Mn_{0.33} Fe^{3+}_{0.12})_{3.00} (Fe^{3+}_{0.16} Sr_{0.78} Ti_{0.43})_{1.37} Si_2O_7 (F_{0.88} O_{1.33})_{1.21}$. Spectral analysis indicates the presence of V, Sr, Ba, and La.

The wöhlerite-lavenite group of minerals is developed in rocks rich in calcium (and sodium) but poor in silica (Semenov, 1958; Kapustin, 1964), namely carbonatites. Lavenite is possibly formed in the process of carbonatization of fenites, with materials derived from the latter. Sergeev (1962) optically identified wöhlerite, whose properties fully tally with lavenite. Sergeev classified this mineral under titanium-bearing wöhlerite (to which lavenite also belongs). Independent wöhlerite was not observed in complex massifs.

Lamprophyllite $(Na, Ca, Mn, Sr)_3 Ti_2 (Si_2O_7)_2 (OH, F)$. This is a relatively rare mineral and is reported from only a few places in the world (Kola Peninsula, Aldan, USA, South Africa). It is typical for agpaitic nepheline syenites and their pegmatites, in which it is associated with eudialyte, loparite, and rinkolite. Lamprophyllite is formed at the contact of early carbonatites with the carbonatized fenites of Kovdor massif (Kapustin, 1964). Fenites contain microcline and aegirine-augite and, in places, are albitized and develop vugs. Lamprophyllite occurs intimately associated with hornblende or in the form of individual needle-shaped or flattened crystals in the rock cavities. It is brown in color with perfect cleavage along z axis, sp. gr. 3.51; biaxial, +ve, $n_p = 1.751$, $n_g = 1.782$, $2V = 55°$; $r > v$; z: $N_g = 0–4°$; X-ray pattern close to standard. Sufficient material was not available for major analysis. Spectral analysis indicates the presence of Ti, Na, Ca, Sr, Ba, Si, Al, TR, Nb, and Zr. Partial analysis of lamprophyllite by Fabrikov's photometric method gave the following result: SrO 11.04, BaO 6.71, CaO 1.26, Na_2O 16.14, K_2O 1.12%. Lamprophyllite is probably formed in fenites along with early stages of albitization and carbonatization.

Labuntsovite $(K_2 Ba) (Ti, Nb) Si_2O_7 \cdot 2H_2O$. This is a rare mineral in alkaline pegmatites of the Chibina and Lovozero massifs (Semenov and Burova, 1955), in dikes and fenites of Turi-Mis (Kukharenko et al., 1965), and in dolomite formations of Green River (Milton et al., 1958), probably associated with the eroded regions of ancient carbonatitic volcanoes (Heinrich, 1967). We observed labuntsovite in late calcitic veins of Vuoriyarvi and

Kovdor (Kapustin, 1964), where it forms two varieties: prismatic and tabular. The prismatic variety of labuntsovite is associated with pyrite, ancylite, orthoclase, and quartz (1st generation) and forms well-developed colorless or orange-colored granular crystals showing rhombic prisms with truncated

Table 45. Chemical composition (in wt. %) and physical properties of labuntsovite

Components	Labuntsovite				Nenadkevichite			
	Kovdor		Tury Bay	Green River	Lovozersky			
SiO_2	34.61	37.68	39.40	39.53	39.59	40.42	42.48	37.15
TiO_2	22.26	24.92	26.66	25.56	25.49	19.15	20.92	12.12
Nb_2O_5	14.30	1.12	0.83	0.25	1.45	9.85	13.75	24.61
Al_2O_3	Nil	Nil	0.29	0.42	1.30	0.64	0.40	1.15
Fe_2O_3	1.21	2.52	2.02	0.42	1.56	1.57	0.71	0.80
MgO	Nil	1.70	Nil	1.86	0.42	1.23	0.12	0.52
MnO	—	0.20	0.29	—	2.34	3.56	—	2.90
CaO	1.32	0.11	Nil	0.02	1.19	7.28	5.14	2.75
BaO	5.54	9.56	9.85	9.25	8.61	—	6.02	1.39
Na_2O	2.75	5.41	5.18	5.66	3.18	2.65	1.18	4.16
K_2O	4.48	8.56	7.05	7.16	7.23	—	0.62	2.24
H_2O	13.65	8.06	7.68	9.25	7.91	14.91	9.32	9.84
Others	—	—	1.03	—	—	—	—	0.30
Total	100.12	99.84	100.28	99.38	100.27	101.26	100.66	99.93
Analyst	M.E. Kazakova		V.N. Kovyazina		T.A. Burova		M.E. Kazakova	
Author	Yu.L. Kapustin, 1964		A.A. Kukharenko et al., 1965	C. Milton et al., 1958	Yu.L. Kapustin and E.I. Semenov, 1964			
Color	Pink	Orange			Brown			Pink
Sp. gr.	2.89	2.96	3.02	2.90	2.94	2.87		2.86
n_g	1.790	1.814	1.839	1.795	1.795	1.770		1.785
n_m	1.786	1.693	1.698	1.702	1.702	1.670		1.686
n_p	1.675	1.688	1.684	1.689	1.689	1.660		1.669
$2V_0$	38	33	30	20	41	35		46
a_0, Å	7.7		14.14		7.7			
b_0, Å			13.70		13.7			
c_0, Å			15.41		14.2			
β			117°06′		117°03′			

basal pinacoids. The tabular variety of labuntsovite is associated with zeolite, catapleiite, ancylite, and vinogradovite, forming pink-colored thin layers. The layering is formed by one of the pinacoids under stress. X-ray pattern is close to standard (Kapustin and Semenov, 1964), but the properties and composition of the end-members (Table 45) of the isomorphous series pure labuntsovite (titanium variety) to nenadkevichite (titanium-niobium variety) vary widely. Decrease in Ti in labuntsovite is accompanied by a decrease in Ba and K and increase in Ca and H_2O. Sp. gr. and R.I. of this mineral increase with increasing Ba and Ti, monoclinic (Semenov and Burova, 1955) or triclinic (Kukharenko et al., 1965). Nenadkevichite is either monoclinic (Kuzmenko and Kazakova, 1955) or orthorhombic (Semenov, 1959) in symmetry. Both these minerals are hydrothermal alteration products of early Ti-rich minerals.

Vinogradovite ($Na_3AlTi_3Si_6O_{21} \cdot 3H_2O$). This mineral is found rarely in alkaline pegmatites (Semenov, 1959). In Kovdor (Kapustin, 1964) it occurs in late zeolite-calcitic veins together with catapleiite, niobolabuntsovite, and marcasite. It forms small (up to 4 mm in diameter) spherulites composed of thin needle-shaped crystals or fibrous aggregates. X-ray pattern is close to standard; the properties and composition are normal (Table 46). It is color-

Table 46. Chemical composition (in wt. %) and physical properties of vinogradovite

Components	Kovdor	Chinbina		Lovozero	Inagli
SiO_2	45.48	40.70	41.26	40.83	45.43
TiO_2	28.51	33.60	32.08	35.86	31.57
Al_2O_3	3.70	6.20	7.60	4.88	3.68
Fe_2O_3	2.75	—	—	—	0.68
MgO	—	0.36	—	0.42	—
CaO	Traces	1.00	0.32	0.66	0.27
BaO	1.10	—	—	—	—
Na_2O	10.90	12.00	12.66	10.39	6.08
K_2O	2.00	1.78	2.38	2.10	3.05
H_2O	5.30	4.50	4.16	5.50	7.82
Total	99.74	100.14	100.46	100.64	98.58
Analyst	A.V. Bykova	V.A. Moleva			M.E. Kazakova
Author		E.I. Semenov, 1965			A.F. Efimov et al., 1963
Sp. gr.	2.85	2.878			
n_g	1.773	1.775			
n_m	1.770	1.770			
n_p	1.734	1.745			
$2V^0$	−41	−41			

less, biaxial, – ve; bositive elongation; $a_0 = 24.28$, $b_0 = 8.53$, $c = 5.23$ Å; $\beta = 101°$; $z = 2$; symmetry class *Cc* or C^2/c (Semenov, 1965). Within the fibrous aggregates of vinogradovite relics of sphene, labuntsovite, or biotite containing about 3.67% of TiO_2 are often found. In pegmatites of the Lovozero and Chibina massifs vinogradovite replaces titanium-bearing minerals (ramsayite, sphene, lamprophyllite) in the hydrothermal process and accompanies zeolites (Vlasov et al., 1959).

Eudialyte $(Na, Ca, Mn)_5\,ZrSi_6O_{17}\,(Cl, OH)$. This is a typical accessory mineral of agpaitic nepheline syenites (Fersman et al., 1937), in which it occurs sporadically; it is, however, segregated in late intrusive phases, particularly in pegmatites. Eudialyte often occurs in alkaline ultrabasic rocks. It also occurs in fenites, melilitites, nepheline syenites and pegmatites (Borodin and Nazarenko, 1957b; Kukharenko et al., 1965), but in small quantities. It occurs as an accessory in veins of early carbonatites of the 2nd stage around albitized fenites on the southwestern border of the Kovdor massif (Kapustin, 1964). Eudialytes are of two varieties: pinkish (pure eudialyte) associated with sphene, pyroxene, and biotite at the margin of carbonatites and yellowish (eukolite) associated with apatite, magnetite, and phlogopite at the center of carbonatites. Both these varieties form rounded crystals (up to 1 cm) within the calcite mass. X-ray pattern is close to standard; properties and composition are normal (Table 47). A few samples rich in TR and Mn occur in carbonatites. Formulas of the two samples analyzed are close to that specified for eudialyte (Borodin and Nazarenko, 1957b), $(Na, Ca, Mn, TR)_5\,ZrSi_6O_{17}$ (Cl, O, OH): (1) $(Na_{2.96}Ca_{1.28}Mn_{0.36}Fe^{2+}_{0.32})_{5.10}(Zr_{0.83}Fe^{3+}_{0.20})_{1.03}Si_6O_{17}\,(OH)_{0.70}$ $Cl_{0.10}$; (2) $(Na_{2.28}Ca_{1.67}Mn_{0.82}Fe^{2+}_{0.28})_{5.05}\,(Zr_{0.80}Fe^{3+}_{0.20})_{1.00}Si_6O_{17}\,(OH)_{0.82}O_{40}$.

R.I. of this mineral shows correlation with $(CaO + FeO + MnO)$ contents; sp. gr. is greater when Na_2O is present. In carbonatites it is formed in the early stage of the decomposition of fenites which also contain eudialyte and lavenite. Under hydrothermal condition eudialyte is replaced by catapleiite.

Wadeite $(K_2ZrSi_3O_9)$. This is a rare mineral; it was first reported from alkaine rocks of Australia (Prider, 1939), and later from the Chibina massif (Tikhonenkov et al., 1960). Now it has been reported from late calcitic carbonatites of Kovdor (Kapustin, 1963). It is associated with labuntsovite, thorite, and phlogopite, and develops rounded crystals (up to 5 mm in diameter) showing hexagonal bipyramidal forms with truncated basal pinacoids. It is bright violet in color; X-ray pattern close to standard; uniaxial, + ve; properties and composition more or less constant in nature (Table 48). The violet color is possibly related to Ti^{3+} content. Spectral analysis indicates the presence of Mn, V, Zn, Cu, and Be.

In carbonatites wadeite is very rare and occurs in calcitic veins containing potassic minerals, namely labuntsovite, phlogopite, orthoclase etc.

Table 47. Chemical composition (in wt. %) and physical properties of eudialyte

Components	Carbonatites		Fenites		Malignite	Pegmatite nepheline syenite	
	Kovdor		Tury Bay			Chibina	
$(Nb, Ta)_2O_5$	1.54	—	1.00	0.85	0.61	3.68	—
SiO_2	47.46	47.53	50.50	49.73	50.88	46.02	48.22
TiO_2	0.77	—	0.16	0.50	1.13	1.02	0.27
ZrO_2	12.88	12.19	10.95	12.33	12.23	10.99	12.05
TR_2O_3	2.17	2.06	1.10	0.09	—	0.80	2.85
Al_2O_3	Traces	—	1.45	—	—	1.82	—
Fe_2O_3	2.41	2.61	0.10	0.76	0.96	1.88	—
FeO	3.32	2.85	5.71	4.10	3.70	—	5.83
MnO	3.43	7.81	1.12	0.78	0.82	10.79	3.00
MgO	0.34	—	0.72	—	0.27	Traces	0.34
CaO	8.98	12.32	12.82	15.87	15.04	10.96	10.33
(Sr, Ba) O	1.15	—	0.78	—	—	0.48	—
Na_2O	12.71	8.92	7.27	11.35	11.63	7.47	13.24
K_2O	0.61	0.61	1.26	0.96	1.10	0.46	0.51
H_2O	0.92	1.04	4.50	2.26	1.45	2.70	1.32
(F, Cl)	0.64	—	0.69	0.82	0.62	0.72	1.39
$-O=Cl_2$	0.26	—	0.16	0.20	0.14	0.16	0.30
Total	99.07	97.94	99.97	100.20	100.30	99.63	99.05
Analyst	M.E. Kazakova		K.A. Baklanova	E.A. Isaeva	I.I. Nazarenko	M.E. Kazakova	P.E. Vlodavetz
Author	Yu.L. Kapustin, 1964		A.A. Kukharenko et al., 1965		L.S. Borodin and I.I. Nazarenko, 1957b	V.S. Saltikova, 1959	E.E. Kostileva, 1937
Sp. gr.	3.01	3.12	2.93				2.86
n_0	1.627	1.634	1.610–1.619	1.601–1.603			1.594
n_e	1.625	1.628	1.608–1.616	1.603–1.607			1.599

Catapleiite $(Na, Ca)_2ZrSi_3O_9 \cdot 2H_2O$. This mineral occurs with vinogradovite and niobiumlabuntsovite in natrolite-calcitic veins of the Kovdor massif (Kapustin, 1964), in the form of flattened crystals within the prismatic grains of natrolite. It is often found in the ankerite-chloritic rocks of Sallanlatva, where it forms sporadic small flattened crystals (up to 5 mm) in association with barite, ancylite, and pyrite. It is brown in color with distinct (0001) cleavage; hexagonal in symmetry with glossy luster; uniaxial, +ve; X-ray pattern is close to standard; properties and composition are normal (Table 49).

Table 48. Chemical composition (in wt. %) and physical properties of wadeite

Components	Kovdor	Kimberley	Chibina
SiO_2	46.36	39.43	42.80
TiO_2	1.03	1.63	0.24
ZrO_2	29.62	21.29	26.66
Al_2O_3	Nil	5.98	1.92
CaO	0.47	5.22	3.10
SrO	0.06	0.16	—
BaO	—	1.20	—
Na_2O	1.28	2.82	1.50
K_2O	20.99	18.40	19.21
Others	0.18	4.83	4.63
Total	99.99	100.96	100.06
Analyst	M.E. Kazakova		M.E. Kazakova
Author	Yu.L. Kapustin, 1963		I.P. Tikhonenkov et al., 1960
Sp. gr.	3.10	3.10	3.130
n_e	1.658	1.655	1.653
n_0	1.627	1.625	1.624

Table 49. Chemical composition (in wt. %) and physical properties of catapleiite

Components	Kovdor	Sallanlatva	Chibina	Vishnevogorsky
SiO_2	42.17	42.65	44.77	42.32
TiO_2	0.86	0.14	0.28	0.20
ZrO_2	31.50	30.18	29.85	29.93
Al_2O_3	0.73	—	1.02	0.73
CaO	3.30	4.22	3.72	5.70
Na_2O	10.64	10.47	10.29	9.05
K_2O	Traces	0.56	1.02	0.65
H_2O	10.00	10.03	9.56	10.44
Others	—	—	0.056	0.02
Total	99.20	98.25	100.566	99.04
Analyst	A.V. Bykova		E.E. Kostileva	T.A. Kapitonova
Author	Yu.L. Kapustin, 1964		A.K. Fersman et al., 1937	A.G. Zhabin et al., 1961
Sp. gr.	2.71	2.73	2.73	2.77
n_e	1.625	1.627	1.624	1.627
n_0	1.596	1.597	1.596	1.596

The formula of catapleiite from Kovdor is $(Na_{1.50}Ca_{0.21})_{1.71}$ $Zr_{1.00}$ $Si_3O_{6.86}\cdot 2H_2O$ and from Sallanlatva is $(Na_{1.46}Ca_{0.34})_{1.80}$ $Zr_{1.17}Si_3O_{9.41}\cdot 2.17H_2O$. These are very close to the theoretical formula $(Na, Ca)_2ZrSi_3O_9\cdot 2H_2O$, differing only in the smaller Ca and Na contents, which are characteristic of catapleiite undergoing hypergene alteration. Catapleiite crystals in Kovdor are covered with a thin powdery white incrustation which gives an X-ray pattern similar to that of zircon.

Pyroxene (Na, Ca) (Mg, Fe^{2+}, Fe^{3+}) Si_2O_6. This is one of the principal rock-forming minerals of all the rocks of the formations observed (Sobolev, 1951). In carbonatites pyroxene is more or less constant in nature, and is very similar to micas in distribution. In early carbonatites of the 1st stage pyroxene is distributed in almost all places, but it is typical in massifs of superficial and subvolcanic types where there is an abundance of dark-colored minerals in carbonatites (Kaiserstühl, Kruidfontein, Mrima Hill, Hudini, Chilwa, Napak). It is also well distributed in massifs of hypabyssal nature (Kovdor, Bolshetagneinskii, southern and eastern Siberian massifs, Alnö, Fen, Tapira, Magnet Cove). In the 1st group of massifs pyroxene occurs chiefly at the peripheral and central parts of the carbonatite body. Along the axial part of the carbonatite body it is replaced by mica. The quantity of pyroxene and other silicates sharply increases in carbonatites that occur in the fractured zones and also at the intersection with mixed rocks.

In the early carbonatites of the 2nd stage pyoxrenes are rare and confined to the central and peripheral parts of the body, but in biotite-aegirine carbonatite it is the principal rock-forming silicate, occurring in all the veins along the axial part. Pyroxene also replaces biotite, which is more widespread in the peripheral zones. Carbonatites of this facies occur in Lueshe and in one of the Siberian massifs (Frolov et al., 1969). In other massifs such carbonatites are not found, because their overall composition is similar to carbonatites of the 1st stage. It should, however, be mentioned that the composition of the accessory minerals and of the chief rock-forming minerals of these 2nd stage carbonatites (by which these rocks are differentiated) were not determined.

Pyroxenes are stable in carbonatites of both stages. In the mixed pyroxenic rocks of the zone of carbonatization, pyroxene recrystallizes and acquires the composition that is typical for carbonatites of a particular stage. At the contact of the rocks of both stages with fenites, almost monomineralic zones and druses of pyroxene crystals are found. These disappear in the carbonatites away from the contact (Fig. 15, *a*). Pyroxene is formed at the contact of carbonatites with the pyroxene-free rocks (biotite fenites and nepheline syenites). In carbonatites of the 1st stage it is associated with dysanalyte, biotite phlogopite, schorlomite, and calzirtite. In rocks of the 2nd stage it is associated with phlogopite, biotite, magnetite, and pyrochlore (hatchettolite).

Table 50. Chemical composition (in wt. %) and physical properties of pyroxenes

Components	Pyroxenites		Ijolite-meltigites				Okaites		Basalts	Phonolites
	Salmagorsky	Kovdor	Afrikanda		Kovdor		Oka		Kaiserstühl	
SiO_2	50.00	49.87	49.05	50.30	49.86	50.44	39.89	47.16	45.83	49.75
TiO_2	1.47	0.48	1.32	0.63	0.81	2.92	2.30	0.24	3.57	1.45
Al_2O_3	1.86	4.52	3.66	0.50	2.77	1.41	14.94	1.49	7.47	0.53
Fe_2O_3	3.93	3.00	5.07	6.22	4.50	9.09	5.62	5.33	4.90	12.23
FeO	1.96	2.01	5.30	5.60	6.30	6.98	2.01	6.61	4.11	9.66
MnO	0.08	0.06	0.20	0.23	0.17	0.25	0.21	1.36	—	1.09
MgO	15.36	14.56	11.47	12.16	11.59	7.48	10.14	10.92	10.92	4.55
CaO	24.10	24.50	22.57	22.46	21.94	18.49	24.33	23.70	22.83	16.72
Na_2O	0.53	0.33	0.74	0.73	1.45	2.20	0.13	1.11	—	2.26
K_2O	0.10	0.61	0.26	0.20	0.42	0.40	0.20	1.14	—	—
Others	0.80	0.24	0.77	1.02	0.64	0.63	0.16	0.59	—	—
Total	100.19	100.18	100.41	100.05	100.45	100.29	99.93	99.65	99.63	98.24
Analyst			O.P. Boyarshirova				H. Ulk	W.H. Herdsman	Katerin	
Author	A.A. Kukharenko et al., 1965				N.D. Sobolev, 1951		G. Perrault, 1959		A. Knop, 1892	
Sp. gr.	3.31	3.21	3.335	3.283	3.331		3.399	3.518		
n_g	1.712	1.703	1.728	1.726	1.711	1.737	1.745	1.725		
n_p	1.686	1.680	1.701	1.697	1.691	1.712	1.725	1.703		
$2V^0$	51	57	59	65	66	75	61	66		
$z : N_g^0$	41	44	52	53	50	63	35	22		

Components	Fenites		Carbonatites									
	Alnö		Ozernaya Varaka	Kovdor	Siberia		Oka		Kaiserstühl	Alnö		
SiO_2	49.61	48.35	52.14	53.48	53.84	51.22	48.75	53.60	52.09	43.34	45.60	50.65
TiO_2	0.50	1.55	0.29	0.18	0.53	1.76	0.66	0.07	0.95	1.23	0.94	0.61
Al_2O_3	2.75	3.27	2.20	0.45	0.19	0.90	2.04	Nil	1.18	9.36	8.01	2.18
Fe_2O_3	15.49	6.26	11.86	2.76	1.71	16.27	5.32	1.12	1.59	6.74	4.70	8.15
FeO	4.90	9.39	6.24	2.05	2.08	2.58	5.30	1.33	1.57	2.48	4.31	6.51
MnO	1.62	0.80	0.32	—	—	0.44	1.83	1.33	Traces	0.18	0.13	0.55
MgO	4.64	7.53	7.00	15.23	15.72	6.05	11.73	16.38	18.10	11.25	11.08	8.85
CaO	15.80	20.16	14.82	24.96	24.48	12.87	22.12	25.33	23.56	21.91	23.59	19.56
Na_2O	4.67	2.27	4.29	0.22	0.71	6.36	1.62	0.05	0.96	1.18	1.19	2.11
K_2O	0.36	0.05	—	—	—	0.22	0.09	0.07	—	0.37	0.28	0.42
Others	0.03	0.12	0.84	—	—	—	0.05	0.42	—	0.08	0.09	0.03
Total	100.37	99.75	100.00	99.33	99.26	98.67	99.51	99.70	100.00	98.12	99.92	99.62
Analyst	R. Blix	T. Berggren	T.A. Capitonova		B.A. Klassen		H. Ulk	O. Jngumels		T. Berggren	H. von Eckermann	T. Berggren
Author	H. von Eckermann, 1966						G. Perrault, 1959		A. Knop, 1892	H. von Eckermann, 1966		
Sp. gr.	3.513	3.460	3.25	3.32	3.30	3.28	3.570	3.29		3.325	3.328	3.476
n_g	1.768	1.740	1.737	1.711	1.700	1.80	1.722	1.710		1.728	1.738	1.733
n_p	1.731	1.706	1.703	1.682	1.680	1.751	1.700	1.685		1.700	1.706	1.708
$2V^0$	±90	73	86	61	—	64	64	56		61	68	75
$z : N_g^0$	20	29	70	43	43	0	44	40		37	29	30

The composition of pyroxenes from different rock types shows marked variations. The presence of augite-diopside with more than 70% diopsidic molecules and the large quantity of Al_2O_3, Fe_2O_3, and FeO (Table 50) is characteristic of pyroxenes of alkaline rocks (ijolites, turjaites) and pyroxenites. In carbonatites two types of pyroxenes are found. In rocks of the 1st stage and in rocks of diopsidic facies of the 2nd stage, diopside occurs with an appreciable proportion of molecules of the other type ($>20\%$). It may be mentioned that augite (Pozharitzkaya and Epshtein, 1963, 1964; Pozharitzkaya, 1966; Gaidukova et al., 1962) occurs in these rocks as a relic in the zone of carbonatization (composition was not studied). In carbonatites of the 2nd stage of aegirinitic facies (Lueshe, one of the Siberian massifs—Frolov et al., 1969) pyroxene has constant composition (aegirine-diopside with diopside molecules 40-60%; see Table 49). The optical properties of pyroxene change with the variation in composition. With increasing alkalinity the R.I., bire-fringence, and extinction angle of pyroxene also increase, while z: N_g decreases. With an increase in Fe^{3+} and Ti the intensity of color and pleochroism also increases. The Siberian pyroxene without Ti is bright greenish in color and its pleochroism is weaker than that of Ti-rich aegirine from Chibina.

Wollastonite ($CaSiO_3$). This mineral occurs in ijolites, fenites, and apomelilitic rocks with no spatial relation with carbonatites (Kovdor, Vuoriyarvi, Alnö, Fen, Magnet Cove, Gulinskii, Oka). In carbonatites wollastonite is rare. It occurs at the margin of the veins of the 1st stage surrounding the zone of carbonatization. It also occurs in the melilitic rocks, which are replaced by fine-grained aggregates of diopside, phlogopite, and wollastonite (Gulinskii, Oka). In Kovdor wollastonite occurs in the marginal parts of the carbonatites of the 1st stage that contain fragments of fenites with wollastonite. With the melting of the fenites segregation of pyroxene and wollastonite takes place. Toward the center wollastonite gradually disappears. It forms hexagonal aggregates and individual flattened crystals (up to 5 cm), containing calcite and apatite inclusions. The properties and composition of wollastonite are normal (Table 51). The question of the primary or relict origin of wollastonite is still unanswered (Eckermann; 1967). Decomposition of wollastonite and its replacement by calcite indicate the increase of CO_2.

Pectolite $NaCa_2Si_3O_8(OH)$. This mineral is formed along with zeolites under hydrothermal conditions in alkaline pegmatites, and is widely distributed in fenites (Kovdor, Afrikanda, Vuoriyarvi, Ozernaya Varaka, Siberian massifs, near the contact of the massifs and sometimes within the massif at the contact zone with pyroxenites) (Afrikanda). In carbonatites pectolite is rare but it occurs in the zones of carbonatized fenites of Kovdor and Vuoriyarvi. The properties and composition of pectolite are normal (Table 51). It is sometimes replaced by wollastonite along the periphery.

Table 51. Chemical composition (in wt. %) and physical properties of wollastonite and pectolite

Components	Wollastonite				Pectolite	
	Vuoriyarvi	Siberia	Oka	Kovdor	Afrikanda	Tury Bay
SiO_2	50.48	—	50.15	49.41	52.25	51.16
Al_2O_3	0.09	—	0.14	0.62	0.24	0.92
Fe_2O_3	0.21	—	0.04	0.46	0.11	0.93
CaO	47.69	47.29	46.97	46.32	34.07	32.30
Na_2O	0.08	0.71	0.35	0.17	9.17	8.00
K_2O	0.06	0.16	0.05	0.06	Nil	0.84
H_2O	—	—	0.38	0.04	1.78	4.90
Others	1.28	—	2.01	2.28	1.80	1.09
Total	99.89	—	100.09	99.36	99.42	100.14
Analyst	V.A. Klassen	L.I. Baum		T.P. Kiseleva		V.I. Vlodavetz
Author				A.A. Kukharenko et al., 1965		N.D. Belyankin et al., 1924
Sp. gr.	2.93	2.90	2.859	2.92	—	—
n_g	1.634	1.633	1.633	1.634	1.635	1.633
n_p	1.619	1.618	1.618	1.619	1.596	1.599
$z : N_g^0$	13	14	13	13		

Schizolite [Na (Mn, Ca)$_2$Si$_3$O$_8$ (OH)]. This mineral occurs in carbonatized and albitized fenites of Kovdor, forming fan-shaped aggregates on the surface of individual rocks. It is yellowish in color, biaxial, +ve; $n_p = 1.612$; $n_g = 1.657$; X-ray pattern is close to standard.

Amphiboles. These minerals occur in almost all the massifs, and each species can be distinguished by its own characteristic composition. In pyroxenites black amphiboles are associated with segregations of titaniferous magnetite or perovskite or micaceous veins, but most amphiboles are developed in nephelinized and apatitized zones (Vuoriyarvi, Afrikanda, Kovdor, Siberian massifs, Magnet Cove). This type of amphibole constitutes up to 30% of the altered pyroxenites of Afrikanda and Pesochni, and is always found as impregnations in ijolites, nephelinite dikes, phonolites, alnöites and damkjernites (Vuoriyarvi, Kovdor, Siberian massifs, Alnö, Fen, Iron Hill, Nagualla).

Colored amphibole, i.e. richterite, is associated with carbonatites. The properties and composition of this mineral are more or less uniform in all the massifs. It is developed around fragments of pyroxenite and ijolite, in magnetite-forsterite rocks, and in picrites or at the contact of early carbonatites of

Table 52. Chemical composition (in wt. %) and physical properties of amphiboles

Components	Ijolites			Pyroxenites			Alnöites		
	Sebl-Yavr	Ozernaya Varaka			Vuoriyarvi	Afrikanda	Oka	Siberia	Lesnaya
	1	2	3	4	5	6	7	8	9
Nb_2O_5	—	0.12	0.06	0.08	0.06	0.04	—	0.06	0.04
SiO_2	39.50	39.20	38.37	37.10	38.50	40.86	38.70	39.10	56.18
TiO_2	1.56	2.71	2.52	2.65	1.80	1.36	1.33	1.16	0.22
Al_2O_3	12.27	14.51	13.89	15.44	13.93	12.33	14.52	14.27	0.30
Fe_2O_3	7.23	4.93	5.54	6.73	5.61	7.34	5.99	4.87	5.44
FeO	7.71	7.32	6.55	5.60	6.25	5.63	5.46	5.92	0.90
MnO	0.36	0.13	0.17	0.12	0.15	0.28	0.10	0.18	0.12
MgO	12.85	14.48	13.80	13.69	14.03	14.83	15.51	15.45	22.52
CaO	12.90	12.35	12.91	12.39	12.17	12.74	13.08	12.88	3.76
Na_2O	2.39	1.94	2.78	2.55	2.72	2.54	1.14	2.61	7.29
K_2O	1.47	1.16	1.67	1.91	1.85	1.57	2.42	2.39	1.51
H_2O	1.77	0.80	Nil	—	2.70	0.56	1.24	0.81	2.05
F	0.15	0.35	—	—	—	0.28	—	—	0.28
Others	0.03	—	1.98	1.44	—	0.06	0.33	—	0.34
$-O=F_2$	0.06	0.15	—	—	—	0.11	—	—	0.11
Total	100.13	99.85	100.24	99.70	99.77	100.31	99.82	99.70	100.84
Analyst	V.M. Kovyazina		T.A. Kapitonova			Z.T. Kataeva	W.H. Herdsman	Z.T. Kataeva	
Author	A.A. Kukharenko et al., 1965						G. Perrault, 1959		
Sp. gr.	3.22	3.19	3.21	3.22	3.23	3.12	3.135	3.12	
n_g	1.699	1.691	1.692	1.690	1.693	1.672	1.650	1.661	1.627
n_p	1.672	1.663	1.664	1.662	1.662	1.652	1.670	1.674	1.618
$-2V^0$	68	84	83		85	80	77	73	
$z:N_g^0$		19	23	19	21	10	10	11	26

Components	Carbonatites									
	Varaka	Iron Hill		Libby	Vuoriyarvi	Sebl-Yavr	Siberia			
	10	11	12	13	14	15	16	17	18	19
Nb_2O_5	—	—	—	—	0.01	0.01	0.03	0.03	—	0.01
SiO_2	56.21	54.30	52.94	56.74	55.75	56.03	55.22	52.83	50.84	50.78
TiO_2	0.23	0.04	1.32	0.28	Traces	—	0.28	0.54	0.31	0.52
Al_2O_3	1.42	2.02	3.30	0.71	0.60	0.18	1.60	2.69	1.00	1.39
Fe_2O_3	5.48	7.37	9.87	4.71	4.42	4.52	5.79	9.82	13.88	20.37
FeO	0.16	2.98	4.24	0.87	0.80	0.24	2.33	4.67	8.55	12.52
MnO	—	0.52	0.15	0.07	0.10	0.08	0.19	0.18	0.39	0.12
MgO	23.26	17.71	15.02	21.95	22.29	22.94	18.00	14.93	9.00	5.43
CaO	3.81	3.30	3.98	6.15	6.30	5.56	3.70	2.30	4.40	0.33
Na_2O	8.24	7.80	7.01	5.15	6.52	6.30	8.10	7.72	7.00	5.21
K_2O	0.37	2.10	0.48	1.80	1.83	1.67	1.60	1.92	0.56	1.12
H_2O	1.40	0.61	1.24	0.87	0.91	0.80	2.78	2.60	3.56	2.61
F	—	2.14	0.78	1.30	1.63	1.59	—	—	—	0.31
Others	—	—	—	—	—	—	—	—	0.10	—
$-O=F_2$	—	0.90	0.33	0.54	0.69	0.68	—	—	—	0.13
Total	100.58	99.99	100.00	100.06	100.47	99.24	99.62	100.23	99.59	100.59
Analyst	Z.T. Kataeva	F.A. Gonier			Z.T. Kataeva				P.I. Fershtatter	Z.T. Kataeva
Author		E.S. Larsen, 1942					V.S. Gaidukova et al., 1962			
Sp. gr.	3.10	3.13	3.132	3.051	3.10	3.11	3.25	3.29		3.13
n_g	1.647	1.641	1.670	1.627	1.636	1.635		1.666	1.674	1.680
n_p	1.632	1.623	1.651	1.612	1.616	1.615		1.650	1.650	1.634
$-2V^0$		87	72		66				68	70
$z : N_g^0$	21				17	14		5	11	16

the 2nd stage (Vuoriyarvi, Sebl-Yavr). Large-scale formation of richterite starts at the beginning of the process of dolomitization and amphibolitization, replacing all early silicates and a part of the magnetite. In some places carbonatites are altered to richterite-carbonate schists (Vuoriyarvi, Sebl-Yavr). Richterite occurs in small quantities in almost all the carbonatite massifs (Iron Hill, Magnet Cove, Oka, Mrima Hill, Chilwa, Palabora), except in effusive carbonatites. The quantity of richterite depends on the composition of the carbonatites and the mixed rocks, and increases when the latter show cataclasis and dolomitization. The quantity of richterite increases significantly in melanocratic carbonatites and in ultrabasites (Lesnaya Varaka, Kovdor, Vuoriyarvi), but only slightly in leucocratic carbonatites and nepheline syenites (Siberian massifs) or fenites (Kovdor). The iron content of richterite is higher in Fe-rich rocks (ultrabasites) and lower in leucocratic fenites and syenites.

A minor quantity of amphibole forms at the beginning of the formation of late veins. These amphiboles replace the primary silicates but they are higher in iron content and very similar to magnesium-arfvedsonite.

The amphiboles may be grouped into two types: black (barkevikite-cataphorite) and bright (richterite). Compositions of both types have been well studied in all the massifs. Black amphibole is similar to hastingsite-barkevikite-cataphorite but shows lower bire-fringence, strong pleochroism (N_g= brown, N_p=dark-blue) and higher content of Al and Fe^{2+} (Table 52). Bright amphiboles from the amphibolitized zone are characterized by weak pleochroism in shades of sky blue (sometimes with a violet tinge) and higher content of Mg, Na, and Fe^{3+}, and form discontinuous series from less ferruginous richterite to more ferruginous magnesium-arfvedsonite; pleochroism, R.I., and sp. gr. increase along with the iron content in these amphiboles. Richterite in iron-rich rocks, particularly in late carbonatites, contains a higher amount of iron (Table 52).

Micas: phlogopite and biotite $K(Mg, Fe)_3 AlSi_3O_{10} (OH, F)_2$. These are widely distributed in ultrabasic alkaline rocks and carbonatites (Palabora, Spitzkop, Magnet Cove, Gulinskii, Kovdor, Vuoriyarvi, Sebl-Yavr). Micas are formed in all stages of the formation of massifs, but are more prevalent in ultrabasites and melilitic rocks (Ternovoi, 1960; Tokmakov, 1961; Rimskaya-Korsakova and Sokolova, 1964; Kukharenko et al., 1965; Chernisheva and Gormasheva, 1966; Krasnovsky, 1948). Phlogopite constitutes 90% of the micas. Muscovite is absent and biotite occurs in the early carbonatites of the 1st stage and in aegirine-biotite facies of the 2nd stage.

Early micatization is associated with olivinites. Uniform, extensive micatization is also found in pyroxenites (Afrikanda, Vuoriyarvi, Sebl-Yavr, Fen, Jacupiranga, Palabora) but it is not so prominent in alkaline rocks and nephelinized zones. Large deposits of phlogopite are formed by metasomatic changes of the melilitic rocks. Magnesium-iron-rich micas are typical for early carbonatites, and the micatization process accompanies the formation of carbonatite bodies in all the argillaceous rocks, nepheline syenites (Siberia), fenites, schists (Siberia, Vuoriyarvi), and ijolites (Sallanlatva). Micas are present in all the carbonatite facies, but each facies is characterized by a particular type of mica. Four generations of micas are found in these rocks. In the first generation biotite is found in rocks of the 1st stage that are surrounded by zones of silica matasomatism developed along with the alkaline rocks. Biotite is associated with dysanalyte, pyroxene, and schorlomite. Biotite in rocks of the 1st stage often gives rise to greenish phlogopites typical for large intrusive bodies occurring in any kind of rock (Kovdor, Vuoriyarvi, Siberia, Magnet Cove). Along the contact of the injected alkaline veins strips of black biotite are formed. At the center of the veins it is replaced by phologopite. Micas in the rocks of the 1st stage form poikilitic crystals which enclose calcite.

In early carbonatites of the 2nd stage biotite and phlogopite (2nd generation) are found, that is, biotite in the rocks of aegirine facies, and phlogopite in rocks of the forsterite facies (Kovdor, Siberian massifs, Mrima Hill, Lueshe). The iron content of micas depends markedly on the composition of the carbonatites and of the mixed rocks, increasing sharply due to intermingling with alkaline rock materials. In the zones of brecciation and intensive metasomatism Fe-rich micas are developed, while magnesium-rich micas are formed in large intrusive bodies. Micas in the rocks of the 2nd stage form independent layers uniformly distributed in calcite; such micas contain inclusions of segregated idiomorphic prisms of apatite and octahedral pyrochlore.

Reddish-brown micas showing a reverse pleochroic scheme occur in all the massifs. These were considered earlier as manganophyllite (Larsen, 1942; Heinrich, 1967), but Mn is not present in appreciable amounts (Krasnovsky, 1948). Rimskaya-Korsakova and Sokolova (1964) regarded these micas as an independent variety, namely, tetraferriphlogopite, in which Al is replaced by Fe^{3+}. This type is formed at the contact of magnetite-forsterite rocks and sometimes at the contact of early carbonatites. This type is also persistent in the zones of amphibolitization and dolomitization, where it is the typical mineral and is associated with richterite and pyrrhotite, which are earlier. The composition of reddish-brown micas depends on the composition of the rocks in which it is formed. The iron content of these micas is directly proportional to the iron content of the mixed rocks (these micas are colorless and poor in iron in leucocratic carbonatites and rich in iron and dark-colored in pyroxenites).

Phlogopite of the 4th generation is formed at the beginning of the formation of late carbonatites (calcitic) together with burbankite and rarely with anatase and brookite.

The composition of the micas also varies in different rocks (Table 53). They are magnesium-rich in olivinites and turjaites, iron-rich biotites or iron-rich phlogopites in pyroxenites, and mostly biotites in nephelinites. In carbonatites the composition of micas changes depending on the type of facies. Rare-earth minerals (pyrochlore, dysanalyte, niobozirconolite) always occur in micas but are very difficult to isolate. Nb, Ta, and Zr are mostly present as inclusions in micas. Li, Rb, and Cs contents of micas from carbonatites are negligible ($<0.1\%$). Under hypergene conditions micas undergo hydration. Many micas with definite compositions in association with other characteristic minerals act as index minerals for carbonatites.

Chlorite group $(Fe, Mg)_5 (Fe, Al) (Si_3AlO_{10}) (OH)_8 \cdot nH_2O$. These minerals are found in fair amounts in late ankeritic carbonatites, replacing different ferruginous and argillaceous rocks. They are associated with barite, anatase, pyrite, and strontianite. Chlorite often replaces ankerite or, particularly, siderite. Microveinlets of chlorite always intersect the late carbonatites. These veinlets show a radial arrangement and resemble colloform-like banding but are formed by metasomatism. Chlorites are weakly pleochroic in different shades of green; $n_p = 1.570$–1.600, $n_g = 1.579$–1.612. Usually different varieties of chlorites are formed together, but isolation of these varieties is not possible. The more widespread among the minerals of this group are clinochlore, jenkinsite, and ripidolite. Less prominent are delessite, penninite, and amesite.

Serpentine $Mg_5Si_4O_{10} (OH)_8$. This mineral occurs occasionally in early carbonatites of the 1st stage along with forsterite, but it is more characteristic of the late carbonatites occurring in olivinites. Serpentinization is always associated with dolomite-ankerite veins in olivinites, while the serpentine mass replacing forsterite forms large aureoles around these veins. Serpentine is white or greenish in color. The properties are normal.

Talc $Mg_3Si_4O_{10} (OH)_2$. This occurs in negligible quantities in the carbonatites of Siberia (Pozharitzkaya, 1966) and the Kola Peninsula (Kovdor, Vuoriyarvi), particularly in dolomitized forsterite-bearing carbonatites. It is developed after forsterite and rarely after clinohumite, forming scaly pseudomorphs. The properties of talc are normal; biaxial, $-$ve; $n_p = 1.540$, $n_g = 1.590$.

Nepheline $(NaAlSiO_4)$. This is a typical mineral of alkaline rocks. In carbonatites it occurs rarely and is replaced by biotite or cancrinite; it is associated with calcite in ijolites (Kovdor, Siberian massifs, Vuoriyarvi, Alnö), nepheline syenites (Vuoriyarvi Lake, Laacher Sea—Brauns, 1919, 1926), or calcitic dikes (Zhabin, 1967). In Kovdor and in one of the Siberian massifs it

occurs in carbonatites of the 1st stage, where it forms pure transparent hexagonal-prismatic crystals with rounded grains. It is uniformly distributed in the calcitic mass and is associated with pyroxene and apatite. Its properties and composition are normal (Table 54); uniaxial, –ve.

Table 54. Chemical composition (in wt. %) and physical properties of nepheline and cancrinite

Components	Nepheline						Cancrinite	
	Ijolites-melteigites					Okaites	Carbonatites	Turgites
	Bikhit	Pechosni	Kovdor	Oka		Kovdor		Tury Bay
SiO_2	42.97	41.10	39.71	40.86	37.88	42.94	36.43	36.02
Al_2O_3	33.08	35.51	33.84	33.64	31.57	33.05	30.27	29.54
Fe_2O_3	0.94	0.83	0.81	1.21	0.13	0.07	—	—
FeO	0.17	0.37	Nil	0.16	0.30	0.23	—	—
MgO	Traces	0.58	0.06	0.07	0.39	—	—	0.30
(Ca, Sr) O	0.25	1.30	2.80	0.89	5.81	0.18	6.69	7.12
Na_2O	17.40	16.10	14.94	14.74	15.85	16.77	18.14	16.02
K_2O	5.30	3.57	5.54	6.78	7.47	6.15	2.74	1.77
Others	0.45	0.89	0.92	1.48	0.33	0.84	5.71	8.76
Total	100.56	100.25	99.62	99.83	99.73	100.23	99.98	99.53
Analyst		A.S. Akeleva	M.M. Stukolova	H. Ulk		V.A. Classen		
Author	E.L. Butakova and L.S. Egorov, 1962	A.A. Kukharenko et al., 1965		G. Perrault, 1959				E.H. Kranck, 1928
n_0		1.538	1.542	1.545	1.543	1.543	1.524	1.522
n_e		1.534	1.534	1.540	1.538	1.539	1.503	1.501

Cancrinite ($3NaAlSiO_4 \cdot CaCO_3 \cdot H_2O$). This is widely distributed in intrusive syenites (principally in post-carbonatitic syenites—Kovdor) and fenites, where two generations of cancrinite, namely, primary and secondary, are observed. Primary cancrinite occurs as small individual crystals in dikes of alkaline rocks, sometimes showing a preferred orientation (Vuoriyarvi, Kovdor), and often occurring in considerable proportions in massive nepheline and cancrinite syenites (Lueshe—Meyer and Bethune, 1958, 1960). Secondary cancrinite is formed after nepheline at the contact of late calcitic carbonatites or in the dolomitized-amphibolitized zones. Cancrinite is pink or yellowish in color; its properties and composition are normal (Table 54); uniaxial, –ve.

Orthoclase and microcline. Potash feldspars are not so characteristic of carbonatites, but early carbonatites of both stages often retain relics of corroded and albitized microcline (Siberia). It is only found along the peripheral parts of the carbonatite body; at the center it disappears.

Orthoclase of later generation forms small independent crystals or aggregates in late ankeritic veins around ultrabasites and ijolites (Vuoriyarvi, Kovdor). It is associated with quartz, pyrite, and anatase, forming rounded and tabular grains in the carbonatite mass. The properties of these minerals are normal. Orthoclase from ankeritic veins of Vuoriyarvi contains 2.89% Ba (analyst: L.I. Baum) and has $n_p = 1.540$, $n_g = 1.546$.

Albite ($NaAlSi_3O_8$). This mineral is rare in carbonatites. It is replaced by orthoclase at the contact zones of the carbonatite veins. However, sometimes thick zones of albitization (alkaline and nepheline syenite and fenites) are associated with bodies of early carbonatites of the 2nd stage (Vuoriyarvi, Siberian massif). In Africa albitization usually took place around volcanic carbonatite veins (Chilwa, Toror, Mrima Hill) (Heinrich, 1967). In late ankeritic veins albite is more prominent but rarely in crystalline form. Zones of albitization are well developed along with these ankeritic rocks, forming aureoles in the schists in contact (Siberia). The properties of albite (No. 5–10) are normal.

Natrolite ($Na_2Al_2Si_3O_{10} \cdot 2H_2O$). This mineral occurs only in late carbonatites and in zeolitized parts of the early carbonatites. Natrolite constitutes up to 40% (Kovdor, Vuoriyarvi) and is the principal constituent of rocks in which idiomorphic (rhombohedral) crystals of calcite occur. Within the rock cavities natrolite forms druses of hexagonal crystals. Its properties are normal; biaxial, +ve; $2V = 80°$, $n_p = 1.481$, $n_g = 1.495$. Spectral analysis indicates the presence of Sr, Mn, Ca, Fe, and Ba.

Chabazite $(Ca, Na)_2Al_2Si_4O_{12} \cdot 6H_2O$. The mineral occurs within the cavities of ankeritic veins in the Vuoriyarvi and Kovdor massifs, and is widely distributed in the staffelite-bearing fenites of Kovdor undergoing intensive decomposition and pelite formation. It is associated with natrolite, staffelite, and needle-shaped calcite, and forms granular pseudocubic crystals (up to 2 mm) within the rock cavities. Chabazite crystals are formed on the surface of staffelite. It is colorless; its properties are normal; X-ray pattern similar to the standard; biaxial, +ve; $n_p = 1.478$, $n_g = 1.480$. Spectral analysis indicates the presence of Ca, Na, Al, Si (>1%) and traces of Ba, Sr, Mg, Nb, and Zn.

Chapter VI

LAWS GOVERNING THE FORMATION OF COMPLEX MASSIFS OF ALKALINE ULTRABASIC ROCKS AND CARBONATITES

1. Alkaline ultrabasic massifs and carbonatites showing their own characteristic volcano-plutonic origin are widely prevalent in different regions. They show the following features: (a) Inclination toward the platforms. (b) Association with regional dislocation of moderate depths. (c) Stock-like forms of moderate size. (d) Formation of diapiric dome-shaped structures around the massifs. (e) Several phases with successive formation of rocks, namely ultrabasites-alkaline rocks—carbonatites. (f) Vertical zoning with the prevalence of ultrabasites at the bottom and carbonatites at the top levels. (g) Development of volcanoes with characteristic effusives. (h) Intensive fenitization of the mixed rock. (i) Richness in Ti, Nb, Ta, Zr, Sr, Ba, and TR.

2. There is no doubt as to the exclusive inclination of the carbonatite massifs toward the rigid, consolidated platforms and shields. These massifs occur within the regional dislocations and are developed either on platforms in association with the formation of nearby geosynclines (Siberia, Baltic Shield, Canada) or in lineaments (Africa).

Massifs of hypabyssal facies retain their own typical intrusive characters and are rich in crystalline rocks intersecting the mixed structures. At depth distinct domes are formed by expansion of the layers around the massifs of hypabyssal facies. This indicates the great magmatic pressure from the depths. This pressure develops chiefly due to the extensive intrusion of nepheline-pyroxene dikes following the rounded, radial, and oblique systems of fractures in the domes surrounding the massifs; the fractures are supposed to have formed along with the domes. The expansion effect is found in plicated, relatively layered carbonate rocks (Maimecha-Kotui Province), but in large bodies of gneisses (Kola Peninsula) the major effect is the development of small fractured blocks in the domes.

Forms and structures of different massifs of hypabyssal facies that are either horizontal or gently dipping monocline (Maimecha-Kotui Province) belong to a particular type. They are similar to vertical stocks and often occur below massive contacts (conical stocks). Forms and structures of massifs sharply intersecting anisotropic layered structures depend on the configuration of the latter, that is the massifs run in the direction of the strike and show nonuniform distribution. A few hypabyssal massifs intersecting layered structures are known (Magnet Cove). Independent massifs (moderate sizes) intersecting linear, steeply dipping layered rocks and extending toward wide tectonic zones form distinct elongated fissure-type bodies (Eastern Sayan, Kazakhstan).

Alkaline ultrabasic volcanic rocks are rarer than the intrusives and differ in size. Two morphological types can be differentiated, namely, volcanic cones with sheet lava (and submarine necks) and diatremes. Volcanic cones rich in effusive materials are relatively rare. They occur in recent volcanoes like Lengan, Kerimasi, and Kalyango. The remnants of eroded cones occur in Gulinskii, Mbeya, Napak, Kaiserstühl, and elsewhere. Diatremes are typical for this type of magmatism. Classical examples of this structure are the diatremes of Laacher Sea in the Rhine region (and southeast France?). The large trough at Vorotilov of the Moscow syncline (diameter up to 30 km) shows its own diatreme buried under Upper Paleozoic and Mesozoic sediments. In all these cases the diatremes are filled with fragments of different rocks with marginal development of fragments of mixed sediments (Moscow syncline), namely, tuffs, volcanic bombs, and alkaline ultrabasic lavas (Rhine region, Mt. Alban).

Development of diatremes and breccias indicates large-scale eruptions associated with the intruding alkaline ultrabasic magma. Due to this not only are eruptive breccias and cemented intrusive rocks formed but the cones are filled with fragments of mixed rocks and pyroclastic materials. All these indicate the existence of distinct gaseous phases. The eruption took place possibly along with abundant effusion of CO_2 from the magmas, with the attainment of magmatic equilibrium in which dynamic pressure of CO_2 became higher than the hydrostatic pressure of the rocks at the upper level. This explains the existence of eruptive cones in the Russian platform, particularly toward the elevated basement (presence of CO_2 indicates constant development of carbonatization and also explains the discharge of independent CO_2 in the massifs of Mbeya, Napak, and Laacher Sea diatremes in recent times).

3. The structure of multiphase complex massifs is characterized by uniform distribution of rocks of different types in their vertical and horizontal sections (vertical and horizontal zoning). The following constant sequence of rock formation is typical for such massifs: olivinites-pyroxenites-turjaites-ijolites and melteigites-nepheline and alkaline syenites-magnetite-forsterite rocks-picritic porphyrites-carbonatites.

The internal structure of the massifs changes with the change in depth of the erosional surface. The deeper massifs are chiefly composed of ultrabasites, the superficial ones are composed of alkaline rocks and carbonatites. Possibly this is a general feature of the massifs, but this is not true in all cases and there are many exceptions (the upper level of the Gulinskii massif is rich in dunites (80%); carbonatites are totally absent from the Laacher Sea diatremes and the Kontozersky massif; the massifs of the Chilwa group are also very poor in carbonatites). In the intrusive stocks these or other types of rocks are found, but in the upper parts of these stocks there are volcanic cones or diatremes rich in silicate rocks; carbonate materials constitute up to 10–20% and only in independent recent volcanoes (Oldoino-Lengai, Kerimasi, Kalyango) are carbonatite lava flows and carbonatized pyroclastic materials found. The absence of carbonatite from the effusive series of ancient volcanoes (Gulinskii, Laacher Sea, and others) does not necessarily indicate their absence at the primary stage. The sodium carbonate lavas of the Lengai type disappear within a few months of discharge by weathering (these lavas decompose in a humid atmosphere within a few days).

Horizontal zoning has been well studied in several massifs of different regions. Massifs that are mostly rounded in plan show concentric zoning, and the different types of rocks are uniformly concentrated around a single or several centers. Two types of zoning are met with: the central type and peripheral type. The central type of zoning is formed along with the development of the massifs from the periphery toward the center. It is characterized by replacement of older rocks by younger ones from the periphery to the center. This type of zoning is typical for superficial massifs (subvolcanoes). In most cases it comprises alkaline stocks whose nucleus is composed of carbonatites (Sallanlatva, Mbeya, Lulekop, the Siberian and East African massifs). It is developed along with the formation of the massifs from the center toward the periphery, while the individual body and rounded (arch-like) zones are arranged with younger rocks around the older ones. This zoning cannot be grouped with the typical rounded ones: its development does not indicate the formation of a rounded fracture system. The formation of this zone is obscure near the rigid centers (olivinites and pyroxenites), which are affected by younger magmatic and metasomatic processes. Depending on the forms of the massifs and the structures of the mixed tectonic zones, complete circular structures, e.g. the Kovdor massif, or asymmetric structures, e.g. Vuoriyarvi and Gulinskii massifs, are formed. More detailed discussion (see below) indicates that the carbonatites were formed under conditions different from that of the silicate rocks. The carbonatites differ in their depth of formation and also in structure. Development of carbonatite at the center of the massifs and its rarity at the contacts indicate a definite relation with the forms of the massifs and the mixed structures. Thus the complex massifs are not only characterized by the central type of zoning but are also dominated by both peripheral (hypabyssal facies) and central types (subvolcanic) of zoning.

4. With the development of characteristic structures of the massifs three

phases emerge, each of which is associated with a typical independent system of tectonic deformation differing from the others in plan, depth of occurrence, and spatial distribution. Each phase is characterized by a definite set of minerals.

In the first phase, subfluvial canals are formed and ultrabasic magma starts rising through these canals. In hypabyssal massifs the first phase is divided into two subphases in which the formation of olivinites (first subphase) is followed by pyroxenites (second subphase). Intrusive olivinites are often steeply dipping, show elongated forms (in plan) similar to dikes, and are of smaller dimensions. In most massifs these constitute up to 20% of the area but in some massifs more than 50% (Lesnaya Varaka, Bor-Uryak, Gulinskii). Pyroxenites of the second subphase intersect the olivinites, retaining the xenoliths of the latter. Pyroxenites form larger bodies, occupying about 40 to 80% of the total area of the massifs and in some massifs even greater areas (Kovdor), replacing olivinites. Ultrabasites of the first phase are composed of asymmetric stocks which are sometimes similar to interstratal bodies (laccoliths and others—Gulinskii massifs).

Alkaline rocks (postcarbonatite) are placed in the second phase, which forms four successive subphases: (i) turjaites; (ii) ijolites-melteigites; (iii) nepheline and alkaline syenites; (iv) dike series.

Nepheline syenites within the surrounding structural setup differ from nepheline syenites of the first two subphases of rocks. But, as shown earlier, melilitic and nepheline-pyroxenitic rocks are always accompanied by ultrabasites, while the syenite group shows an antipathetic relation to ultrabasites. In most massifs syenites occur in the dike series of the second phase. Development of rocks of the first two subphases is controlled by the zone of tectonic deformation and takes place at the contacts of ultrabasite nuclei. Sometimes, when the ultrabasites of the first phase are absent, these rocks develop independent stocks (Sallanlatva, Siberian massifs, Lueshe, Rangwa, Tapira), but in such cases it is possible that ultrabasites occur at depths (the ijolites of Sallanlatva contain xenoliths of pegmatoid pyroxenites). Rarely, alkaline rocks form stocks that penetrate the ultrabasite at the center (Pesochni, Magnet Cove). The area occupied by alkaline rocks in complex massifs varies from 0–10 to 80–90%, but on an average it is between 30 and 50%, increasing at the upper levels. Alkaline rocks in complex massifs form diapiric structures, and are brecciated and banded with conformable contacts. These rocks are always found at the nuclei of ultrabasites in different regions. These facts indicate the development of tectonic movements near the contact of ultrabasite nuclei at the second phase. Complex massifs are formed on platforms (without syngenetic folding) and are characterized by intersecting stocks and development of diapiric and tectonic zones near the contacts of ultrabasite nuclei. All this can be interpreted in terms of the magmatic pressure from the depths. With the formation of alkaline rocks the volume of the massifs increases significantly. This indicates the breaking or expansion of mixed piles around the massifs, principally at this stage.

Nephelinitic and alkaline syenites at the upper level of the massifs constitute the stocks. In hypabyssal massifs these rocks are well represented, chiefly by dikes of small isolated massifs (Kovdor). Rarely, in some massifs, syenites intersect the ultrabasite stocks at the center (Spitzkop). Dikes of the alkaline rocks are characterized by typical fractured bodies extended probably toward a hollow belt. Occurrence of such a hollow belt indicates a change in geological conditions (development of concealed fractures together with intensive crushing along the contacts and compaction with the increase in volume of the massif).

The rocks of the carbonatite series belong to the second phase, which has been divided by the authors into five subphases: (i) magnetite-forsterite rocks; (ii) picrite porphyrites; (iii) early carbonatites of the 1st and 2nd stages; (iv) damkjernites; (v) late carbonatites. All these rocks are intimately associated and are developed within the nearby structures. These rocks contain one or more minerals and also carbonatites that are persistent in nature in variable quantities.

The formation of carbonatite rock series in hypabyssal massifs primarily suggests basic changes in the nature of intrusive and metasomatic activities. If the above alkaline rocks are developed in rounded zones of fragments around the ultrabasite nucleus or within it (dikes), the rocks of the carbonatite series form independent stocks, conical and veinlike bodies that are intruded around a single center. Such centers are observed in almost all the massifs or are spontaneously extended to the zone of contacts (principally in zones where asymmetric stocks of silicate rocks diminish, e.g. in Vuoriyarvi—southeastern contact, Kovdor—southwestern contact, Gulinskii—southern contact, Iron Hill—western contact, Spitzkop—southwestern contact, etc.). In shallower massifs (subvolcanic type), carbonatites and the associated rocks occur at the center (Lueshe, Rangwa, Toror, Sallanlatva) and often form independent conical stocks or a system of ring dikes developed around a single center and accompanied by rare dikes of alkaline rocks.

Magnetite-forsterite rocks form independent veins only in Vuoriyarvi and Kovdor, but the layered stocklike bodies of these rocks in the same massifs are intimately associated both with the early carbonatites and with the carbonatized and apatitized parts of the massifs. In Lolekek phlogopite-apatite-magnetite-forsterite rocks surround the circular zones of the early carbonatite stock. Picrite porphyrites form cross-cutting stocks or veinlike bodies in parts rich in carbonatites and magnetite-forsterite rocks. These picrite porphyrites are rich in rounded xenoliths of the mixed rocks carried up with them from a considerable depth. Picrite porphyrite bodies intersect the magnetite-forsterite rocks and, in turn, are intersected by early carbonatite veins.

The structure of early carbonatites shows a distinct character of its own, identical in 90% of the massifs. These rocks (early carbonatites) form large conical stocks and cone-sheets around them. In contrast with the pseudo-circular ijolitic bodies the structural pattern of carbonatites depends very little on the form of the massif. The vein-systems intersect the rocks of the massifs and the mixed rocks without changing their trends. The size of the carbonatites apparently increases (Kovdor) due to the parallel orientation of carbonatite veins with the mixed layered rocks. Conical stocks and veins are formed from a single focus (sometimes two, e.g. Oka, Gulinskii), and the succeeding generations of these stocks and veins are associated with deeper foci (Eckermann, 1948a). Carbonatites of the 1st stage often form stocks and that of the 2nd stage, conical veins. In massifs developed over a large linear belt, carbonatites similarly form a linear system of veins parallel to the general trend of the massifs. Damkjernite forms small dikes and pipes around which rocks of the carbonatite series are developed and also intrude into the stocks of carbonatites, but these are mainly confined to the boundaries of massifs.

Late carbonatites are concentrated in the zones of linear tectonic deformations. They cut across all the earlier rocks and develop metasomatically from the early carbonatite stocks. In the last case, late carbonatites develop pseudo-stocks and pseudoconical structures, often forming at the center of the body of the early carbonatite (Chilwa, Kangankunde, Mbeya, Siberian massifs). In such cases the structure of the late carbonatites completely depends on the structures of the conical stocks of early carbonatites.

5. The formation of multi-phase massifs, with their magmatic processes frequently changing to metasomatic and the wider development of the latter, indicates complex and contiguous processes. In spite of the accumulation of various facts and information, comparative study of these massifs was started only recently and the main genetic aspects are still debatable. The intrusive origin of the ultrabasites is doubtful, and Borodin (1963a) showed the possibility of the formation of metasomatic olivinite rocks, but in massifs such as those of Kovdor, Lesnaya Varaka, Bor-Uryak, Gulinskii, and Dorova olivinites are of primary intrusive nature. Pyroxenites vary in grain size with intensive development of mica and nepheline and rarely retain their primary structures and compositions, but there are differences of opinion regarding their origin in massifs like Vuoriyarvi, Afrikanda, Odikhincha, Jacupiranga, Lolekek and Eastern Sayan, and most researchers class them with primary magmatic rocks. The wide development of secondary processes is probably due in part to autometasomatism, but the major part is genetically related to alkaline rocks and the process of nephelinization.

The first intrusive phase in complex massifs (ultrabasitic) gives rise to the formation of relatively common stock-like bodies or laccoliths which do not differ in form from normal hyperbasitic massifs of gabbro-peridotite composition. The characteristic features of the massifs indicate the formation of these bodies in the second phase, when alkaline (melilitic and nepheline-pyroxenitic) rocks are developed. In hypabyssal massifs the phases characteristically associated with tectonic deformations around ultrabasite nuclei containing alkaline rocks give rise to dome-shaped structures in the mixed rocks. Tectonic movements, probably due to the development of magmatic pressure from below, give rise to zones of crushing and deformation in the peripheral parts of ultrabasites and in the mixed rocks. Shrinkage develops at this stage before the open fractures and layering occur. The alkaline rocks that crystallize under lateral pressure from all sides in the zones of crushing around the ultrabasites do not form veins, but enclose the fragments of ultrabasites and fenites, form unstable structures (usually tectonic) and compositions with the materials of these rocks, and contain relics of minerals. When the alkaline rocks are concentrated in the tectonic zones they are layered along the contact of ultrabasite nuclei.

Alkaline rocks in complex massifs are divided into two successive groups: melilitic and nepheline-pyroxenitic (closely associated genetically and in space but formed in succession). Melilitic rocks have been regarded by most workers (Orlova, 1959, 1963; Kukharenko, 1958, 1967; Kukharenko et al., 1965; Lapin, 1960, 1962) as metasomatic in origin and developed from olivinites under the influence of alkaline solutions in the latter. Orlova regarded melilitic rocks as postijolitic, while Lapin (1962) and Egorov (1963) regarded them as preijolitic. The presence of xenoliths of apomelilitic rocks and persistent intrusions of turjaite dikes in the ijolites of Kovdor indicate the later origin of ijolites, although in Turi Mis and Iron Hill the interrelations between turjaites, pyroxenites, and melteigites are not clear. Probably turjaites are formed metasomatically from olivinites under the influence of alkaline solutions, but the formation of turjaites is preceded by the formation of ijolites, as bimetasomatic exchanges between the components of olivinites and ijolites are not possible in such cases. From the study of Maimecha-Kotui Province, Egorov (1966) showed the wider development of melilitic dikes, indicating their magmatic origin. They were formed by differentiation of alkaline ultrabasic magma, and part of them is formed at the beginning of the pneumato-hydrothermal process associated with this magma. Linear dikes of fine-grained melilitic rocks that intersect the ultrabasites occur along with turjaite bodies containing fragments and relics of ultrabasites and their minerals.

The possibility of the occurrence of magmatic melilitic rocks is best illustrated by the occurrence of melilitic basalts in the different massifs. The Gulinskii intrusives accompany thick alkaline basalts (Aridzangsky and Delkansy suite) containing nepheline, olivine, melilite, and pyroxene. Most workers have pointed out the genetic relation of these effusives with the complex Gulinskii massifs. Similar effusive formations (tuffs, lavas, and agglomerates) are known in several volcanoes of East Africa. Effusives containing nepheline, melilite, olivine (sometimes leucite or calcite) are found in the volcanic craters of Nyiragongo, Baruta, Skhageru, Homa-richuru, Cameroon, Enclave (Denaeyer-Schellink, 1965). A few occur in dikes of melilitic rocks. There is no doubt as to the magmatic origin of melilitic rocks in volcanoes.

In hypabyssal massifs the melilitic rocks around the ultrabasite nuclei vary in composition. They are crushed along the contacts and also contain relics of ultrabasite; there is a transitional zone between them. The metasomatic transformation of olivinites into turjaites under the influence of an alkaline solution is possible but, if so, the role of the magmatic material that occurs in the zones of crushing of olivinites giving rise to hybrid rock loses its importance. Probably the metasomatic process gives rise to the formation of turjaites from olivinites at the eutectic point. With the attainment of eutectic composition local melting of turjaites starts, giving rise to intrusive dikes. It is unfortunate that the melilite system has not been studied in the field. The eutectic composition (if it occurs) must contain about 55–65% melilite (a similar composition is found in kugdite and turjaite dikes—Egorov, 1966).

Nepheline-pyroxenitic rocks are formed by different processes. Earlier workers, such as, Brögger (1921), Högbom (1895), Shand (1947), and also most later workers (Butakova, 1956; Volotovskaya, 1958; Kukharenko, 1958, 1967; Kukharenko et al., 1965; Vorobeva, 1960; Sheinmann et al., 1961; Ginzburg et al., 1958; Pozharitskaya et al., 1963; King and Sutherland, 1960), regarded nepheline-pyroxenitic rocks as magmatic in origin. Borodin (1958a, b, 1959, 1962, 1965a), however, on the basis of his detailed study of these rocks from the Kola region, showed that they are metasomatic in origin. Eckermann (1948a, b, 1958), Gittins (1961), Kononov (1957), and Portnov (1967) similarly showed that nephelinization is associated with the formation of alkaline rocks which engulf the mixed metasediments. A similar process takes place in the pyroxenites and fenitized schists of Eastern Sayan. Development of veinlets and nepheline crystalloblasts in pyroxenes and schists, retention of primary textures and structures, and the wide development of aegirinization of pyroxene (formation of zoned crystals) in pyroxenites simply indicate the metasomatic origin of nepheline-pyroxenic rocks. However, these facts do not refute the magmatic origin of ijolites. Borodin showed that independent massifs composed of equigranular ijolites (Sallanlatva) or numerous dikes of these rocks differing in composition and configuration occur in every hypabyssal massif and may be intrusive in nature. Probably the ijolitic bodies that occur around olivinite nucleus without showing nephelinization (Kovdor) may also be of magmatic origin, wholly or in part. In all cases the development of directive (layering) and taxitic textures is restricted to rocks occurring in the zones of crushing with numerous fragments of ultrabasites (and also melilitic rocks).

The magmatic origin of part of the nephelinitic rock is confirmed by remnants of hepheline-bearing effusive in Gulinskii massifs and also by the remnants of nephelinite flows in the African volcanoes. Probably nephelinization of pyroxenites and melanocratic fenites converts them into an ijolitic composition having a nepheline-pyroxene ratio of 1 : 2. After the formation of rounded zones of ijolites partial melting took place locally, giving rise to intrusive bodies and dikes.

Alkali metasomatism has a great role in the formation of massifs. This process has given rise to the formation of abundant mixed rock with pyroxenites because the latter occupy large areas. Fenitization is always developed around the massifs (even without ijolites). Fenitized parts form aureoles around massifs, ranging in width from 50 m (near steep contacts) to 2–3 km. Away from the massifs magmatic schists, gneisses, and other rocks are subjected to weak albitization and recrystallization, retaining the relic structures in all places, but near the massifs gneissosity and schistosity disappear. All the dark-colored minerals and quartz are replaced by aegirine-augite-diopside, while plagioclase is replaced by potash feldspar. This process, as studied by Brögger (1921), Eckermann (1948a, 1950, 1961), King and Sutherland (1960a, b), Sergeev (1959, 1962, 1967), Tikhonov (1962), Ronenson (1966), and other researchers, indicates that near the alkaline massifs the mixed rocks are changed into fenites of a composition similar to alkaline syenites, and often show deformation of the primary structures. In places nepheline and cancrinite are also found. The fenites become more alkaline, cancrinitic, or nepheline-syenitic in composition and structure, so that distinction of the fenites from intrusive rocks becomes difficult. Probably in such cases metasomatic reworking of the mixed rocks gives rise to eutectic compositions, forming local centers of melting and occurrence of intrusive bodies of nephelinitic and alkaline syenites (principally small dikes widely developed around the fenites). These bodies, as mentioned above, intersect the mixed rocks regardless of various associations with the process of fenitization (Lueshe, Kalkfeld, and the massifs of Eastern Siberia). Occurrences of small veins of nephelinitic, cancrinitic, and alkaline syenites intersecting the early carbonatites indicate the continuation of the process of local melting and development right from the outset of late hydrothermal veins (fenitization accompanies the formation of early carbonatites).

In the light of the development of the processes of alkali metasomatism over large areas and along the great vertical lengths near the stock-like ultrabasite bodies, melting of large masses of alkaline rocks may be indicated, but this does not exclude the contribution of an independent magmatic process to their formation. Several large nephelinitic and alkaline syenite intrusives occur, regardless of their varied relations with complex massifs. There is now no confusion as to the existence of independent centers of alkaline magma (whose formation we have been able to determinc).

6. As mentioned earlier, the complex massifs of alkaline ultrabasic rocks, according to most workers, form series of comagmatic rocks with their root in the hypothetical depths of magmatic centers. The composition of these rocks

changes uniformly with time, reflecting the beginning of magmatic evolution. Recently Borodin (1963b), considering the possibility of temporary ruptures between ultrabasites and alkaline rocks, showed the participation of two different magmas, e.g. normal ultrabasic and carbonate-nepheline syenitic, in the formation of massifs in the hypabyssal alkaline massifs of the Aldan Shield. The occurrence of such ruptures is illustrated in the hypabyssal alkaline massifs of the Aldan Shield (Kravchenko and Vlasova, 1962), but in other regions it is not so prominent.

Distinct comagmatic conformity between ultrabasic and alkaline rocks in complex massifs is also a characteristic feature of the effusive series of the Gulinskii massifs, and of numerous volcanoes of East Africa erupting intermittent lavas and tuffs of ultrabasic and alkaline rocks. Effusives containing nepheline, olivine, and melilite also occur in the volcanoes of Nyiragongo, Sakhageru, Baruta, Homa-Richuru, Shein di Rutario, Cameroon, Mbuga. In the volcano of Toro-Ankole (Bunyaruguru) flows of pyroxenite, peridotite, and leucitic rocks are found. The alkaline lavas of Bufumbira contain blocks of massive peridotite and pyroxenites. Tuffs and agglomerates containing nepheline, aegirine, olivine, diopside and up to 15–38% carbonate occur in 30 craters running east from Hauang volcano to Buzutu (Heinrich, 1967). Several typical picrite-alnöite dikes in hypabyssal massifs are genetically related to ultrabasic alkaline magmas and are rich in olivine, pyroxene, melilite, biotite, and nepheline, with persistent admixture of calcite and magnetite. Although extrusive bodies containing olivine, nepheline, and pyroxene are very rarely formed (olivinitic melteigite-porphyrites of Changit and Turi Mis massifs), this also indicates the genetic relation between the ultrabasites and alkaline rocks. This confirms the similarity in age of these rocks in the Maimecha-Kotui Province (Landa, 1967). The structure and the sequence of formation of complex massifs are primarily explained by the usual process of differentiation of a single magma. This is described in the classic works of Bowen and Daly (1936), showing primary early crystallization and segregation of high-temperature dense silicates in the lower part of the magmatic basin, while the easily fusible and lighter materials concentrate near the top of the basin and crystallize later. Such zoning (ultrabasite at the bottom, alkaline rocks and carbonatites at the top) is typical for the massifs studied, but this interpretation is not valid where persistent crushing and intermingling of ultrabasites and alkaline rocks have taken place. The melts from which these formed were supplied from the bottom. If a single magmatic column undergoing differentiation is considered, the alkaline rocks should be disposed more by ultrabasites than crushing. This was postulated by Landa (1967), when considering the essential features and effusive activities associated with ultrabasic alkaline magmatism. Actually the earlier stages of the development of massifs are rich in remnants of effusive materials of alkaine and alkaline ultrabasic composition (alkaline basaltoids, ultrabasites, leucitic rocks, nepheline-pyroxene-melilitic rocks with olivines, micatized rocks and others); the intrusive ultrabasites are formed later. But Landa (and others) recognized intermittent intrusive activity after the formation of ultrabasite intrusives and metasomatic alkaline rocks. Occurrence of earlier (than ijolites and carbonatites) normal ultrabasites, as suggested by Landa, is associated with alnöites, as displayed by dikes of picrite-porphyrites in several massifs, but these rocks are not compositionally similar to typical ultrabasites, nor are they genetically related to carbonatites. From the point of view of areal extent, too, these rocks can in no way be compared to alkaline rocks.

Thus the silicate rocks in complex massifs are formed in different phases. During the first phase, ultrabasic alkaline magma rises from the depths into the weak zones. These magmas then undergo differentiation, giving rise to two series of rocks: alkaline ultrabasic effusives at the top and intrusive ultrabasic bodies at the bottom. At the beginning of the second phase (in the first subphase) magmatic pressure develops from the bottom and new magmas or solutions are derived from the system of tectonic zones along the contacts (rarely at the center) of the ultrabasite bodies. Ultrabasites first undergo melilitization and then nephelinization; and where local partial melting (a melt of eutectic turjaitic and ijolitic composition) takes place, a series of intrusive bodies is formed. After the formation of ijolites, nepheline and alkaline syenites start crystallizing, while part of the melt gives rise to a fenitic solution attaining eutectic composition, but the constant availability of new magma (or melts) is required at each stage of the formation of alkaline rocks.

7. Rocks of the carbonatite series are characterized by particular structures not inherited from the foregoing magmatic phase. The carbonatitic magnetite-forsterite rocks and picrite porphyrites commonly form stocks, although linear bodies are also present. Rocks of both types persistently contain fragments in the wide zone of brecciation. Their formation is related to eruptions (for picritic porphyrites there are undisputed indications that the xenoliths are derived from great depths). Stocks of magnetite-forsterite rocks show evidence of intensive metasomatism, while the linear veins resemble dikes. Development of intensive apatitization and carbonatization in stocks can be taken to indicate the association of these rocks with carbonatites. This is illustrated in Lolekek, where apatite-magnetite-forsterite rocks (forscorites) contain superficial zones of carbonatite nuclei which change toward the periphery to pyroxene-olivine-vermiculite (pegmatoid) rocks metasomatically forming after the surrounding pyroxenites. Probably magnetite-forsterite rocks are formed metasomatically after pyroxenites (Lolekek, Vuoriyarvi) or ijolites (Kovdor), around the centers where early carbonatites are also developed. Small (1–2 cm) margins of forsterite are sometimes found at the contacts of carbonatites of the 2nd stage with pyroxenites, but in size they are negligible compared with the magnetite-forsterite rocks. The general presence of zoned bodies of these rocks and nonuniform structures

suggest their metasomatic origin.

Picritic porphyrites developing along with their analogous alkaline peridotites can easily be placed with the magnetite-forsterite rocks (Kovdor), but they derive xenoliths from greater depths and also from typical intrusive bodies. The composition of this group of rocks is variable. They always contain apatite, titano-magnetite, melilite, and calcite; the variability in composition consists in the occasional presence of forsterite (Vuoriyarvi, Petyaian-Vara, Kovdor), pyroxene (Eastern Sayan), or biotite (Vuoriyarvi, Tuxta-Vara). This composition is intermediate in nature, displaying association with all types of rocks of the complex massifs and characteristics of the magmas. At depths, this composition would be found in small centers until the formation of carbonatites. This magma is not considered similar to ultrabasites. Its alkalinity and reaction activity can explain the transformation of xenoliths of pyroxenite, ijolite, and melilitic rocks into aggregates of calcite, tetraferriphlogopite, and richterite. This change is characteristic of the late (autometasomatic) stages of the development of carbonatites. The last fact indicates the genetic relation of picritic porphyrites with carbonatites.

8. Pure carbonatites in complex massifs, along with their own distinct group of rocks, always occur with the general series of rocks. Despite much discussion in many papers regarding the genetic history of formation of carbonatite, no generalization has been finalized. Since the first report on carbonatite there have been many discussions, and many hypotheses regarding its origin have been formulated, but none of them is unanimously accepted. These hypotheses may be divided into three groups:

a) Metamorphic-rheomorphic;

b) Hydrothermal-metasomatic;

c) Magmatic.

The hypothesis of metamorphic-rheomorphic origin was postulated by earlier workers. According to this hypothesis the origin of carbonatites is the reaction of alkaline magma with carbonate metasediments. Blocks of these were believed to be derived from depths (Daly, 1918; Shand, 1921, 1947) or, conversely, dropped from the roofs. Shand believed the sources of alkaline magmas to be the assimilation by normal granitoid magma of carbonate rocks. The association of these rocks with alkaline intrusives is therefore logical, while the occurrence of silicates and other minerals in carbonatites is explained as skarn formation (Hackman, 1925; Daly, 1936). Earlier workers (Högbom, 1895; Brögger, 1921) showed the constant association of carbonatites with ultrabasic and alkaline rocks, but further investigations, principally in East Africa, did not support the hypothesis of simple engulfing of limestones by alkaline magma. Some modifications of this hypothesis were suggested by Strauss and Truter (1951a). According to them carbonatites were originally sedimentary rocks that were rheomorphosed under deep-seated metamorphic condition, acquiring high mobility, as a result of which they were intruded into overlying rocks (the process is similar to the diapiric intrusion of a salt dome). However, later isotopic research on C, Ca, Mg, and Sr in carbonatites showed that carbonatites differ in composition from carbonate sediments (Kirilov and Rilov, 1963; Baertsohi, 1957; Eckermann et al., 1952; Hayatsu et al., 1965; Hamilton and Deans, 1963; Gittins et al., 1965; Faure and Hurley, 1963; Hurley, 1963; Deans and Powell, 1968). This hypothesis has now been discarded, although it explained the source of carbonate quite well.

The hydrothermal-metasomatic hypothesis for the origin of carbonatites was advanced long ago. It has also been advocated in recent times by workers like Bulakh (1961), Volotovskaya (1958), Ginzburg et al. (1958), Kukharenko (1958, 1966), Kukharenko et al. (1955), Lavrenev et al. (1958), Pozharitzkaya et al. (1963, 1964), Epshtein et al. (1968), Davies (1952), Heinrich et al. (1961), King (1949), Kranck (1928), and Saether (1958). This hypothesis ascribes the origin of carbonatites to the infiltration of a solution that is genetically related to alkaline rocks and carbonate materials. The principal feature of this hypothesis is the constant, widespread, intensive replacement of any type of rocks by carbonatites. Metasomatism accompanying carbonatites has an important role, principally during the advanced stage of tectonic activity. It is most active in the zones of brecciation and least active in steeply segmented open fractures and beddings. The intensity and rate of change of mixed rocks in carbonatites are very high and marked by the solution of fragments of rocks of different compositions. In several carbonatite bodies of the Kola Peninsula and Sayan, fragments of mixed rocks are localized in the zones of brecciation; the fragments are of different sizes and compositions. They are calcitized and surrounded by reaction rims, while the fragments of melanocratic (ultrabasic and alkaline) rocks are often totally phlogopitized. Individual fragments, as evidenced early, dissolve and active minerals accumulate from this solution. This process is illustrated in Kovdor, Vuoriyarvi, East Siberian and several other massifs. However, the hypothesis of metasomatic replacement does not explain some peculiarities of carbonatites.

It is difficult for the metasomatic replacement hypothesis to explain the presence of large veins and stocks of leucocratic carbonatites (up to 4–8 km^2—in Gulinskii, African, and Siberian massifs) where the thickness of the reaction zones is insignificant (this is very important, not exceeding 10 m, and in Siberia a few centimeters).

The presence of fragments and erratic relics of mixed rocks indicates their preliminary brecciation and not their replacement (which is marked by brecciation).

The occurrence of large bodies of leucocratic carbonatites containing negligible amounts (<10 to 5%) of silicates and magnetite derived from the mixed rocks, suggests (in a metasomatic tract) acquisition of all the materials (except oxygen), but it cannot be proved that all the materials have been derived from other sources.

If carbonatites are formed from hydrothermal solutions, zones of hydrothermal replacement should develop around them with typomorphic hydrothermal minerals (chlorite, zeolite, quartz, serpentine, sericite, etc.). These minerals, however, are typical only for late carbonatite veins of hydrothermal origin. The high-temperature minerals—diopside, forsterite, magnetite, phlogopite, and apatite—occur along with early carbonatites, and are not typical for hydrothermal origin.

The presence of forsterite and absence of serpentine (primary) along the contact of early carbonatites with olivinites (see above) can be taken to represent a direct relation of early carbonatites with the temperature of formation. The serpentine phase is stable at $T < 500°C$ (and with forsterite at $500 < T < 400°C$), while forsterite is stable at $T > 400°C$ (Bowen and Tuttle, 1950). Temperatures near 500°C indicate the presence of MgO in calcite (Goldsmith et al., 1955), the magnesia being homogeneously distributed in the minerals of carbonatites (Kukharenko and Dontzova, 1962; Evzikova and Moskalyuk, 1964). Orthoclase in these rocks (Baily, 1960; Pecora, 1962), as well as the K_2O content of nepheline (Eckermann, 1948c) and other minerals, is stable at this temperature. This temperature probably exceeds the critical point of water (475°C) and due to this hydrothermal processes rarely become active. The pneumatolitic process does not stand scrutiny, since the transportation of a huge quantity of $CaCO_3$ along with the gaseous phase is difficult to explain.

Most scientists working on carbonatites do not divide them into different types or show any interrelation between different carbonatites. The list of minerals of carbonatites shows consistent groupings like forsterite and serpentine, magnetite and sulfides, pyroxene and chlorite, etc. Even in the recent works of Heinrich (1967) and Tuttle et al. (1967) no such division of carbonatites has been discussed, although Brögger (1921) and Eckermann (1948a, 1958) pointed out the need for it. In the works of Pozharitzkaya and Epshtein (1960, 1963), Gaidukova et al., (1962) and Kapustin (1964), the mineral associations in carbonatites were grouped. From their standpoint the hydrothermal hypothesis, the only possibility for the origin of late carbonatites, can also be adduced in some cases to explain the origin of high-temperature early carbonatites.

In his classic works Brögger (1921) argued for the magmatic origin of carbonatites. Later this suggestion was strengthened in detailed works by Eckermann (1948a, b, c, 1952, 1958), and was supported by other researchers on carbonatites from different volcanoes and subvolcanoes of East Africa. The magmatic hypothesis is supported by the following evidence:

a) Formation of conical stocks and veins in carbonatites;
b) Small size of the zone near the replacement of the large intersecting veins and their stocks;

c) Retention of the composition and configuration of the rocks of different compositions intersected by veins;
d) Transportation of xenoliths along with carbonatites;
e) Presence of carbonatites in volcanic veins (necks, stocks, nucleus);
f) Presence of primary calcite in lavas, tuffs and volcanic agglomerates;
g) Spontaneous eruption of carbonatitic lavas.

The formation of carbonatite bodies of relatively small sizes (10 to 100 m), concentrated in the zones of brecciation and accompanied by intensive metasomatism, is easily explained by the metasomatic hypothesis. Veins of carbonatites in Ozernaya Varaka containing up to 30 to 40% (by volume) relics of gneisses (retaining their primary orientations), which are crowded with quartz and microcline and surrounded by druses of pyroxene crystals, can be placed along with carbonatites. These veins, either crowded with or devoid of different types of materials, indicate the prevalence of metasomatism. Carbonatite bodies of indefinite forms in Mogo-Vidi Mountain (Kovdor) are surrounded by gigantic blocks of phlogopite and thick zones of carbonatization and recrystallization of magnetite-forsterite rocks, with no trace of the reorientation of individual blocks, indicating no intermingling of carbonatite masses and intensive metasomatism. However, in several zones of brecciation: Kovdor and Ozernaya Varaka massifs—the blocks of mixed rocks are reoriented, shattered, and stretched along the dip. They often form lenslike or chainlike bodies, indicating the intermingling of their parallel layered zones from bottom to top. In these zones carbonatites are crowded with partly replaced fragments and relic minerals, indicating intensive metasomatism.

Around the large carbonatite stocks of the Gulinskii massif there is less metasomatic replacement of the mixed rocks. Metasomatic replacement is wholly absent around the large bodies of Kovdor (Pilkoma Selga and Botzu-Vara), because here it pinches out from below. Similar occurrences are observed in several subvolcanoes of East Africa, where the carbonatite nuclei occur in crater pipes around fenitized gneisses and schists (Maumbe, Chilwa, Mwambuto-Hasveta), and also in the layered carbonatite bodies of Keluve (Northern Rhodesia). In these cases it may be suggested that the carbonatites form infilling bodies, but infilling bodies (not intrusive) of such dimensions (up to 5–7 km in length), rich in equigranular aggregates with uniform distribution of minerals, are not found in other types of rocks. If their formation is to be related to alkaline ultrabasic massifs, then it should be remembered that their volume will be proportional to the volume of the massifs (Sallanlatva, Tundulu, Toror), and sometimes will exceed it (East Sayan—two massifs, East Siberia). Analogous hydrothermal bodies of carbonatites have not been met with in recent times; in all cases the volume of material deposited from the hydrothermal solution is commensurate with the volume of intrusion with which the solutions are related. If it is remembered that Ca in carbonatitic solution has the strength $n \cdot 10^{-4}$ (according to Pozharitzkaya, 1966), then for the accumulation of a volume of 5 km^3 of carbonatite $n \cdot 10^3$ km^3 water (!) is required. Moreover, there are no traces of large-scale solfataric activity around young carbonatite veins and stocks (except at Elgon volcano, where deposition of travertine is reported—Heinrich, 1967).

Eruption of carbonatic lavas indicates the possibility of magmatic origin of carbonatites, although the well-studied volcano of Oldoino Lengai erupts calcitic and Na- and Ca-carbonate lavas. Not far from Oldoino Lengai the other volcano, Oldoino Dili, contains intrusive calcitic carbonatites. Vesicular lavas of calcitic composition containing considerable proportions of nephelinites and tuffs occur in several volcanoes of Kizingiri. Individual flows rich in calcitic lavas are found in the volcanic cones of Kerimasi and Kalyango. Primary magmatic calcite occurs in silicate lavas and tuffs of these volcanoes, and in bombs of Laacher Sea diatremes. All these facts directly indicate the possibility of a magmatic origin for carbonatites. However, the possibility of metasomatic replacement cannot be ruled out. It is difficult to postulate the appearance of calcitic lava (non-alkaline), since calcite decomposes at 860–920°C in the atmosphere without melting. At the same time it is difficult to indicate the formation of metasomatic micatization, aegirinization, and albitization accompanying carbonatites if these are subscribed from a single calcitic lava (with inclusions of apatite).

The development of fenitization and occurrence of alkaline minerals at the contacts of carbonatites directly suggest the presence of primary alkaline melts, thereby confirming the metasomatic hypothesis from all sides. If alkalies are thought to be present in primary melts they are equally developed in magmatic solutions. The lavas of Oldoino Lengai rich in alkalies appear along with their analogs (effusives) of the usual early calcitic carbonatites of hypabyssal facies. Enumeration of these facts confirms Eckermann's hypothesis as to the origin of carbonatites in magmatic solutions rich in alkalies. Development of metasomatic activities associated with carbonatites would then be quite normal. A mobile alkaline magma of lower viscosity should possess greater chemical activity (Ginzburg and Epshtein, 1968). This melt is ultra-agpaitic in nature and sometimes it shows $Al/(Na+K) < 1$. Probably the chemical activity of this melt increases with depth, together with the increase of pressure and fugacity of CO_2. Near the surface the chemical activities of such melts should decrease. The richness of the melts in alkalies gives rise to the formation of stable complex carbonates of Ca and Na. This explains the intensive development of metasomatism in the deeper massifs and weak metasomatism in subvolcanoes. The possible occurrence of an alkaline carbonate-silicate melt is confirmed by experimental research (Wyllie and Tuttle, 1960; Wyllie and Hass, 1966; Gittins and Tuttle, 1964).

9. Early carbonatite bodies develop in zones of tectonic activity (catacla-

sis, schistosity), and the fractures formed therein are often parallel to the contact of the bodies. This process is intensively developed in all the hypabyssal massifs, but less developed in superficial subvolcanic stocks. Cataclasis engulfs large bodies of carbonatites, but it is often prominent as a separate entity, chiefly in the contact zones of the bodies. Metasomatism is associated with cataclasis, but the intensity of metasomatism is not always proportional to the intensity of the tectonic activities. The fractured and schistose carbonatites always contain typical minerals like tetraferriphlogopite, pyrrhotite, richterite, and calcite replaced by dolomite. The quantity of these minerals varies widely, with richterite constantly present. Moderately intensive metasomatism is developed in carbonatites that occur around ultrabasites. In carbonatites intersected by leucocratic fenites, ijolites, and nepheline syenites, dolomite is found in small quantities. Development of fibrous richterites take place in zones of intense fracturing.

In the zones of fracturing and cataclasis richterite and dolomite are developed in carbonatite bodies and remnants of mixed rocks. The ultrabasites are intensively phlogopitized. At the beginning of this process an independent carbonatite body is not developed: it is wholly confined to redistributed materials or between carbonatites and mixed rocks. It is therefore irrational to subdivide the independent type (calcite-dolomite, or dolomitized) of carbonatites, as they give rise to their own products of metasomatic changes in rocks formed early. It is believed that dolomitization-amphibolitization precedes the formation of the later group of carbonatites, and the intervening phase is marked by the introduction of damkjernite dikes. Geological structures formed in zones of dolomitization-amphibolitization differ from those present in late carbonatites, and often this formation is separated in space. This phenomenon is autometasomatic in character and infiltrates the zones of fracture of the residual solution, giving rise to bimetasomatic changes between carbonatites and the surrounding rocks. In volcanoes the major part of the vapors and gases escape into the air, but this process is either very weak or does not take place at all.

10. Late carbonatites are concentrated in linear fragmented zones, often cutting across the early rock body and the zones of dolomitization-amphibolitization and moving away from the early carbonatite body for a distance of up to 5 km to form independent zones of veins around the mixed metasedimentary rocks. Late carbonatites are always accompanied by intensive metasomatic changes. The composition and configuration of the veins suggest their formation from a normal hydrothermal solution rich in CO_2, P_2O_5, and sometimes F, but the intensive albitization and occurrence of alkali amphiboles and aegirine with the late carbonatites indicate the presence of alkali in the solution. This is illustrated by the constant recrystallization of quartz at the contacts. Late carbonatites form large bodies only after the metasomatic transformation of the early ones, but in silicate rocks the volume of late veins

sharply diminishes and the quantity of carbonatite is smaller. Sometimes minerals like chlorite (Sallanlatva), barite (Alnö, Sallanlatva), and quartz (Namo-Vara, Vuoriyarvi, Ravalli County) are present. The dependence of the composition of late carbonatites on the composition of the mixed rocks was mentioned earlier. This indicates significant introduction of materials during formation. There is no doubt as to the metasomatic origin of late carbonatites. These are formed by the infiltration of hydrothermal solutions into the zones of tectonic fractures. Often the presence of late carbonatites at the center of stocks and volcanic craters (Nkombwa, Kangankunde, Chilwa) indicates their formation by hydrothermal processes, but in such cases the late rocks often retain the textures of the early ones, confirming their metasomatic origin. The early phase of formation of late carbonatites is marked by the calcitic stage, but dolomite and ankerite are mostly developed in them. With the replacement of early rocks by the latter ones H_2O, Mg, Fe, and S are introduced, while the stable elements are displaced. Due to the development of Mg- Fe-carbonates with lower isomorphic capacity in relation to Sr, Ba, and TR these elements (separating from calcitic solution) form independent minerals. These are also, in part, induced.

11. The successive phases of the formation of carbonatites may be explained as follows: after the crystallization of alkaline silicate rocks in metasomatic centers, alkali-carbonate magma accumulates, penetrating to the upper levels from below. With the attainment of equilibrium of the magma in which the pressure of CO_2 exceeds the hydrostatic pressure of the overlying rocks, massive eruption with the separation of CO_2 begins, forming conical depressions. Part of these is filled up with fragments of mixed rock and the rest by carbonate melts. If the dimensions are large at the surface, volcanoes are developed (Fig. 29) with the eruption of carbonatitic and alkaline lavas. With smaller melts diatremes are formed (Laacher Sea or Vorotilovsky upheaval type), full of fragments of mixed rock and effusive materials. With further diffusion of CO_2 effusives are subjected to carbonatization. Carbonates probably do not always come to the surface, and with smaller melts they form bodies at depths (calcitic) while the alkaline solution in them causes intensive replacement of the surrounding rocks.

The eruptive phenomenon may well be repeated, and after the first eruption and ejection of material around the central carbonatite (1st stage) stock, conical-ring-like fractures are developed in which rocks of carbonatites of the 2nd stage occur, while the solutions associated with them replace the rocks of the 1st stage. After complete cooling of the early carbonatite bodies, fracturing develops with circulation of the solution in this fracture-system, causing autometasomatic dolomitization-amphibolitization. Moreover, from the deeper centers retaining the local concentration of melts, damkjernites intrude, with eruption of carbonatites with distinct melanocratic dike facies. After this, infiltrations of the solution resume in the zone of linear fractures or at the centers of volcanic stocks, and metasomatic late carbonatites are formed. This sequence is similar to the development of normal intrusives of any composition with characteristic sequences: (i) intrusive, (ii) autometasomatic, (iii) dike facies, and (iv) hydrothermal veins.

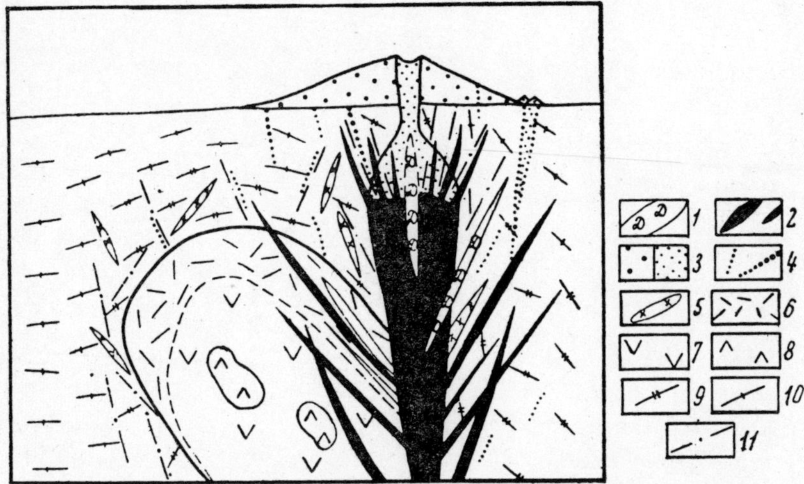

Fig. 29. Structure of complex alkaline ultrabasic rocks and carbonatites.

1—Late carbonatites; 2—Early carbonatites; 3—Effusives and agglomerates; 4—Dikes of alkaline rocks; 5—Nepheline syenites; 6—Ijolites, melteigites, and nephelinitized pyroxenites; 7—Pyroxenites; 8—Olivinites; 9—Fenites; 10—Mixed rocks; 11—Faults.

12. The history of the formation of massifs shows the peculiar formation of specific rocks, depending on their structural positions and age in relation to the carbonatites. The general question of the distinct magmas giving rise to these massifs, their development and origin have not been discussed. The origin of (primary) magma of distinct composition is yet to be clearly explained. Most scientists relate its formation to mantle or deep alkaline basaltoids. In both cases the multi-phase sequence of formation of massifs is associated with magmatic differentiation (Yoder and Tilley, 1965).

From any indefinite erosional section of any massif it is possible to establish neither the phenomenon of differentiation nor the interrelations between the principal members of the series (between ultrabasites, alkaline rocks, and carbonatites). At the same time carbonatites are confined to the top of the massifs. They either decrease in size or are wholly absent at the bottom of massifs, where ultrabasites are prevalent. It is therefore suggested that differentiation starts in a deeper magmatic chamber. The carbonate melt, the last fraction of the differentiation series, rises to the upper level, while the zones of brecciation, carbonatization and alkali metasomatism are retained at depths. Late carbonatites are formed by metasomatic process associated with the filling of fractures of early carbonatites and mixed rocks by a gas-water solution.

BIBLIOGRAPHY

Afanasev, V.A. 1939a. Shchelochnye porody Ozernoi varaki Khabozerskogo raiona (Alkaline rocks of Ozernaya Varaka of Khabozerskii region). *Dokl. AN SSSR*, 25, No. 6.

Afanasev, V.A. 1939b. Olivinity Khabozerskogo raiona (yugo-zapadnaya chast' Kol'skogo polnostrova) [Olivinites of the Khabozerskii region (southwestern part of Kola Peninsula)]. *Dokl. AN SSSR*, 25, No. 6.

Afanasev, V.A. 1940. Shchelochnye porody Khabozerskogo raiona (Alkaline rocks of the Khabozerskii region). In the book: "*Proizvodit. Sily Kol'skogo P-ova*", Kirovsk.

Alves, B.P. 1960. Distrito niobio-titanifero de Tapira. Brasil. Dept. Nac. Fomento Prod. Mineral Bol., 103.

Anderson, E.M. 1936. The dynamics of the formation of conesheets, ring-dykes and cauldron-subsidences. *Proc. Roy. Soc. Edinb.*, LVI, II.

Anderson, A.L. 1960. Genetic aspects of the monazite and columbium-bearing rutile deposits in northern Lemhi County, Idaho. *Econ. Geol.*, 55.

Anderson, A.L. 1961. Thorium mineralization in Lemhi Pass area, Lemhi County, Idaho. *Econ. Geol.*, 56.

Andreev, G.V. 1958. Konderskaya intruziya tsentral'nogo tipa v predelakh Aldanskoi plity (Central-type Konderky intrusive within the Aldan platform). In the book: *Materialy 2-go Vses. Petrograf. Soveshchaniya*. Izd-vo AN SSSR.

ASTM Bulletin (X-ray Diffraction Data Cards. Amer. Soc. Testing Mater.). 1943. Philadelphia.

Atlasov, I.P. 1958. Skhema razvitiya struktury severnoi chasti Sibirskoi platformy (Sketch of the development of structure of northern part of the Siberian platform). *Inform. Byull. NIIGA*, No. 7.

Atlasov, I.P. 1960. Tektonika severo-vostochnoi chasti Sibirskoi platformy (Tectonics of the northeastern part of the Siberian platform). *Trudy NIIGA*, 106.

Baertschi, P. 1957. Messung und Deutung relativer Haufigkeitsvariationen von O^{18} und C^{13} in Karbonatgesteinen und Mineralien. *Schweiz. mineral.*

petrogr. Mitt., 37.

Bagdasarov, E.A. 1959. Shchelochnye pegmatity massiva Afrikanda (Alkaline pegmatite massifs of Afrikanda). *Zap. Vses. Miner. Ob-va*, part 88, No. 3.

Bagdasarov, Yu.A., V.S. Gaidukova, N.N. Kuznetsova and G.A. Sidorenko. 1962. Nakhodka lueshita v karbonatitakh Sibiri (Occurrence of lueshite in the carbonatites of Siberia). *Dokl. AN SSSR*, 147, No. 5.

Bailey, D.K. 1956, 1958. Carbonatites in the Rufunsa Valley. *North. Rhodesia Geol. Surv. Rec.*

Bailey, D.K. 1960. Carbonatites of the Rufunsa Valley, Feira District. *North. Rhodesia Geol. Surv. Bull.*, 5.

Bailey, D.K. 1961. The Mid-Zambezi-Luangwa rift and related carbonatite activity. *Geol. Mag.*, 98.

Balashov, Yu.A. and L.K. Pozharitskaya, 1968. Faktory reguliruyushchie povedenie redkozemel'nykh elementov v karbonatitovom protsesse (Factors regulating the presence of rare-earth elements in the carbonatite process). *Geokhimiya*, No. 3.

Baldock, J.W. 1968. Calzirtite and the mineralogy of residual soils from the Bukusu carbonatite complex, Southeastern Uganda. *Mineral mag.*, 36, No. 282.

Belyaevskii, N.A. 1963. Tektonika i magmatizm grabena Oslo (Tectonics and magmatism of the Oslo grabens). In the book: *Problemy Geologii na XXI Sessii Mezhdunarodnogo Geologicheskogo Kongressa*. Izd-vo AN SSSR.

Belyankin, D.S., V.I. Vlodavets and A. Shimpf. 1924. Gornye porody i poleznye iskopaemye okrestonostei sela Umby i Por'ei guby (Rocks and useful mineral deposits of the outskirts of the village Umba and Porei Bay). *Trudy Severnoi Naurno-promyslovoi Ekspeditsii*, No. 20.

Belyankin, D.S. and V.I. Vlodavets. 1932. Shchelochnoi kompleks Tur'egomysa (Alkaline complex of the Turii Cape). *Trudy Petrogr. In-ta AN SSSR*, No. 2.

Bergstöl, S. and S. Svinndal. 1960. The carbonatite and peralkaline rocks of the Fen area. Petrology. *Norg. geol. undersokn.*, 208.

Betekhtin, A.G. 1953. Gidrotermal'nye rastvory, ikh priroda i protsessy rudoobrazovaniya (Hydrothermal solutions, their nature and processes of ore formation). In the book: *Osnovnye Problemy v Uchenii o Magmatogennykh Rudnykh Mestorozhdeniyakh* . Izd-vo AN SSSR.

Béthune, de. P. 1956. Caractères pétrographiques des carbonatites de la Lueshe (Kivu, Congo Belge). *Soc. Géol. Belgique*, 80.

Bilibin, Yu.A. 1940a. Mineral'nye assotsiatsii magmaticheskikh gornykh porod (Mineral associations in magmatic rocks). *Izv. AN SSSR, ser. geol.*, No. 2.

Bilibin, Yu.A. 1940b. O genezuse shchelochnykh magm (On the origin of alkaline magma). *Zap. Vses. Miner. Ob-va*, part 69, No. 2–3.

Bischoff, G. 1956. Stratigraphie, Tektonik und Magmatismus des Paraná—Beckens (Brasilien). *Z. Dtsch. geol. Ges.*, 106, T. 2.

Björlykke, H. 1934. Norwegische Mikrolithmiineralien. *Norg. geol. tidsskr.*, 14.

Björlykke, H. 1955. The niobium deposits at Söve, Southern Norway. *Mining J.*, 44.

Björlykke, H. and S. Svinndal. 1960. The carbonatite and peralkaline rocks of the Fen area. Mining and exploration work. *Norg. geol. undersokn.*, 208.

Blake, G.S. and H. Smith. 1913. On varieties of zirkelite from Ceylon. *Mineral. Mag.*, 11. No. 77.

Bobrievich, A.P., M.N. Bondarenko, M.A. Gnevushev and others. 1959. Almaznye Mestorozhdeniya Yakutii (Diamond deposits of Yakutia). Gosgeoltekhizdat publishers.

Bogachev, A.I. 1958. O karbonatitakh massiva Vuoriyarvi (On the carbonatite massifs of Vuoriyarvi). *Izv. Karel. i Kol'sk. Fil. AN SSSR*, No. 2.

Boggild, O.B. 1901. Mineralogia groenlandica. *Medd. Gronland*, 26.

Bogomolov, M.A. 1964. O prirode kristallicheskikh shantsev i karbonatnykh porod vblizi Kanderskogo massiva (On the nature of crystalline schists and carbonate rocks near the Kanderskii massif). In the book: *Petrografiya Metamorficheskikh i Izverzhennykh Porod Aldanskogo shchita.* "Nauka" publishers.

Boida, Sh. A. and B.I. Serba. 1958. Novyi massiv shchelochnykh porod i karbonatitov na Kol'skou poluostrove (New massif of alkaline rocks and carbonatites in the Kola Peninsula). *Byull. Nauchn. tekhn. Inform. MGiON SSSR*, No. 3.

Bonshtedt-Kupletskaya, E.M. 1946. Nekotorye dannye o mineralakh gruppy perovskita (Some data regarding the perovskite groups of minerals). In the book: *Voprosy Mineralogii, Geokhimii i Petrografii.* Izd-vo, AN SSSR.

Bonshtedt-Kupletskaya, E.M. 1951. Mineralogiya Shchelochnykh Pegmatitov Vishnevykh Gor (Mineralogy of alkaline pegmatites of Vishnevye mountains). Izd-vo AN SSSR.

Bonshtedt-Kupletskaya, E.M. and T.A. Burova. 1946. Fersmit—novyi Kal'tsievyi niobat iz pegmatitov Vishnevykh gor (Srednii Ural) [Fersmite—the new calcium niobate from pegmatites of Vishnevye mountains (Central Ural)]. *Dokl. AN SSSR*, 34, No. 1.

Borneman-Starynkevich, I.D. and N.V. Belov. 1941, Ob izomorfnykh zameshcheniyakh v karbonat-apatite (On isomorphous replacement in carbonate-apatite). *Dokl. AN SSSR*, 31, No. 3.

Borodin, L.S. 1957. O tipakh karbonatitovykh mestorozhdenii i ikh svyazi s massivami ul'traosnovykh shchelochnykh porod (On the type of carbonatic deposits and their relation with alkaline ultrabasic rocks). *Izv. AN SSSR, ser. geol.*, No. 5.

Borodin, L.S. 1958a. K khimizmu protsessov egirinizatsii i nefelinizatsii piroksena pri obrazovanii metasomaticheskikh nefelinopiroksenovykh porod (On the chemical process of aegirinitization and nephelinitization of pyroxene during the formation of metasomatic nepheline-pyroxene rocks). *Geokhimiya*, No. 4.

Borodin, L.S. 1958b. O protsessakh nefelinizatsii i egirinizatsii piroksenitov v svyazi s problemoi genezisa shchelochnykh porod tipa iiolitov-mel'teigitov (On the process of nephelinitization and aegirinitization of pyroxenites in relation to the origin of alkaline ijolite-melteigite-type rocks). *Izv. AN SSSR, ser. geol.*, No. 6.

Borodin, L.S. 1959. O perovskitivom orudenenii massiva Vuoriyarvi (On the perovskitic mineralization in Vuoriyarvi massif). *Geol. Rudn. M-nii*, No.5.

Borodin, L.S. 1960. Genezis karbonatitovykh mestorozhdenii i ikh geologicheskaya svyaz' s massivami ul'traosnovnykh shchelochnykh porod (Origin of carbonatite deposits and their geological relation with alkaline ultrabasic massifs). In the book: *Doklady na XXI sessii Mezhdunarodnogo Geologicheskogo Kongress*. USSR Academy of Sciences publication.

Borodin, L.S. 1962. K petrografii i genezisu massiva Vuoriyarvi (On the petrography and origin of the Vuoriyarvi massif). *Trudy IMGRE*, No. 9.

Borodin, L.S. 1963a. Perovskit v ultraosnovnykh porodakh Afrikandy i nekotorye voprosy genezisa etogo massiva (Perovskite in ultrabasic rocks of the Afrikanda massif and some problems as to the origin of this massif). *Trudy IMGRE*, No. 15.

Borodin, L.S. 1963b. Karbonatity i nefelinovye sienity (K obshchei petrologii massivov ultrabazikov shchelochnykh porod i karbonatitov) [Carbonatites and nepheline syenites (the general petrology of the alkaline ultrabasic rocks and the carbonatites)]. *Izv. AN SSSR, ser. geol.*, No. 8.

Borodin, L.S. 1965a. Redkie elementy v ultrabazitakh iz kompleksnykh massivov ultraosnovnykh shchelochnykh porod (K probleme genezisa karbonatitov i ikh svyazi s shchelochnym magmatismom) [Rare elements in ultrabasites from complex alkaline ultrabasic massifs (on the problem of the origin of carbonatites and their relation with alkaline magmatism)]. In the book: *Problemy Geokhimii*. "Nauka" publishers.

Borodin, L.S. 1965b. Paragene zisy mineralov Zr, Nb i Ti i fatsii glubinnosti karbonatitov (Paragenesis of Zr, Nb and Ti and the deeper carbonatite facies). In the book: "*Petrologiya i Geokhimicheskie Osobennosti Kompleksa Ultrabazitov, Shchelochnykh Porod i Karbonatitov*. "Nauka" publishers.

Borodin, L.S. 1966a. Perovskitovye i dizanalitovye mestorozhdemiya niobiya i tantala (Perovskitic and dysanalytic deposits of niobium and tantalum). In the book: *Geokhimiya, Mineralogiya i Geneticheskie Tipy Mestorozhdenii Pedkikh Elementov. Vol. 3. Geneticheskie Tipy Mestorozhdenii Pedkikh Elementov*. "Nauka" publishers.

Borodin, L.S. 1966b. Karbonatitovye mestorozhdeniya redkikh elementov

(Carbonatitic deposits of rare elements). In the book: *Geokhimiya, Mineralogiya i Geneticheskie Tipy Mestorozhdenii Redkikh Elementov. Vol. 3. Geneticheskie Tipy Mestorozhdenii Redkikh Elementov.* "Nauka" publishers.

Borodin, L.S. and R.L. Barinskii. 1962. Redkie zemli v perovskitakh (knopitakh) iz massivov ultraosnovnykh shchelochnykh porod [Rare-earth elements in perovskite (knopite) from alkaline ultrabasic massifs]. *Trudy IMGRE*, No. 9.

Borodin, L.S. and A.V. Bykova. 1961. O tsirkonievom shorlomite (On zircon-rich schorlomites). *Dokl. AN SSSR*, 141, No. 6.

Borodin, L.S. and Yu.L. Kapustin. 1962. Berbankit-pervaya nakhodka v SSSR (Burbankite reported for the first time in the USSR). *Dokl. AN SSSR*, 147, No. 2.

Borodin, L.S. and I.I. Nazarenko. 1957a. Khimicheskie sostav pirokhlora i izomorfnye zameshcheniya v molekule $A_2B_2X_7$ (Chemical composition of pyrochlore and isomorphous replacement in the $A_2B_2X_7$ molecule). *Geokhimiya*, No. 4.

Borodin, L.S. and I.I. Nazarenko. 1957b. Evdialit iz shchelochnykh porod Tur'ego mysa i khimicheskaya formula evdialita (Eudialite from alkaline rocks of Turi Mis and its chemical formula). *Dokl. AN SSSR*, 112, No. 2.

Borodin, L.S., I.I. Nazarenko and T.L. Rikhter. 1956. O novom minerale tsirkonalite—cronihou oksle tipa AB_3O_7 (On the new zirconolite mineral—particularly the oxide of AB_3O_7 type). *Dokl. AN SSSR*, 110, No. 5.

Borodin, L.S., A.V. Bykova, T.A. Kapitanova and Yu.A. Pyatenko. 1960. Novye dannye o tsirkonolite i ego niobievoi paznosti (New information on zirconolite and its niobium variant). *Dokl. AN SSSR*, 134, No. 5.

Borodin, L.S., A.G. Zhabin, Yu.L. Kapustin and A.V. Lapin. 1963. Rol' protsessov metasomaticheskogo izmeniya giperbazitov v formirovanii ultraosnovnykh shchelochnykh porod i karbonatitov (Role of the process of metasomatic replacement of hyperbasites in the formation of alkaline ultrabasic rocks and carbonatites). *Tezisy Dokl. na Konf. "Metasomaticheskie Izmeneniya Bokovykh Porod i Ikh Rol' v Rudoobrazovanii".* VSEGEI publishers, Leningrad.

Bowen, N.L. and O.F. Tuttle. 1950. Sistema $MgO\text{-}SiO_2\text{-}H_2O$. Voprosy fiziko-khimii v mineral. i petrogr. (System $MgO\text{-}SiO_2\text{-}H_2O$. Physico-chemical problems in mineralogy and petrology). IL.

Bowen, N.L. 1924. The carbonate rocks of the Fen area in Norway. *Amer. J. Sci.*, 12.

Bowen, N.L. 1938. Lavas of the African rift valleys and their tectonic setting. *Amer. J. Sci.*, 35A.

Branco, W. 1894. Schwabens 125 Vulkan-Embryonen. E. Schweizerbart. Verlagshandl.

Brauns, R. 1919. Einige bemerkenswerte Auswurflinge und Einschlusse aus dem niederrheinischen Vulkangebiet. *Cbl. Mineral.* 1919.

Brauns, R. 1926. Die Bedeutung des Laacher Sees in Mineralogischer und geologischer Hinsicht. *Naturwiss. Heimat*, 1.

Brauns, A. and R. Brauns. 1925. Ein Carbonatit aus dem Laacher Seegebiet. *Cbl. Mineral.*, A(4).

Brock, B.B. 1959. On orogenic evolution, with special reference to southern Africa. *Trans. and Proc. Geol. Soc. South Africa*, 62.

Brögger, W.C. 1906. Die Mineralien des sudnorwegischen Granitpegmatitgange. *Kgl. norske vid. selskab. skr. Mat-naturwis.*, No. 6.

Brögger, W.C. 1921. Die Eruptivgesteinen des Kristianiagebietes. IV. Das Fengebiet in Telemarken, Norwegen. *Kgl. norske vid. Selskab. skr. Mat.-naturwis.*, No. 9.

Broughton, H.J., L.C. Chadwick and T. Deans. 1950. Iron and titanium ores from the Bukusu Hill alkaline complex, Uganda. *Colon. Geol. and Mineral. Resources*, 1.

Bulakh, A.G. 1959. Valunnye daiki Tur'ego mysa (Kol'skii p-ov) [Rubbly dikes of Turi Mis (Kola Peninsula)]. *Inform. sb. VSEGEI*, No. 7.

Bulakh, A.G. 1961. Redkometal'nye ankeritovye karbonatity Sebl'-yavrskogo massiva (Kol'skii p-ov) [Rare metallic ankeritic carbonatites of Sebl-Yavr (Kola Peninsula)]. *Mat-by VSEGEI, nov. ser.*, No. 45.

Bulakh, A.G. 1962. Eksplozivnye brekchii Tur'ego poluostrova i vozrast terskoi svity peschannikov (Kol'skii p-ov) [Breccias of Turi Mis and the age of the Tersky series of sandstones (Kola Peninsula)]. *Geologiya i Razvedka*, No. 3.

Bulakh, A.G. 1963. O tsirkelite i tsirkonolite iz karbonatitov Kol'skogo poluostrova (On the occurrence of zirkelite and zirconolite in carbonatites of the Kola Peninsula). *Zap. Vses. Miner. Ob-va*, part 92, No. 3.

Bulakh, A.G. and N.B. Abakumova. 1960. Sebl'-yavrskii massiv ul'traosnovnykh i shchelochnykh porod i karbonatitov (Kol'skii p-ov) [Alkaline ultrabasic rocks and carbonatites of Sebl-Yavr (Kola Peninsula)]. *Sov. Geologiya*, No. 5.

Bulakh, A.G. and E.P. Izokh. 1967. Novye dannye o karbotsernaite (New information on carbonatites). *Dokl. AN SSSR*, 175, No. 1.

Bulakh, A.G. and G.S. Kurbatova. 1959. Tsirkon iz karbonatitov Sebl'-yavrskogo massiva (Zircon from carbonatites of the Sebl'-Yavr massif). *Mat-by VSEGEI, Nov. ser.*, No. 26.

Bulakh, A.G. and I.D. Shevaleevskii. 1962. K mineralogii i kristallografii kal'tsirtita iz shchelochnykh porod i karbonatitov (On the mineralogy and crystallography of calzirtite from alkaline rocks and carbonatites). *Zap. Vses. Miner. Ob-va*, part 91, No. 1.

Bulakh, A.G., G.A. Il'inskii and A.A. Kukharenko. 1960. Tserkelitiz mestorozhdenii Kol'skogo poluostrova (Zirkelite from Kola Peninsula deposits). *Zap. Vses. Miner. Ob-va*, part 89, No. 3.

Bulakh, A.G., V.V. Kondrateva and E.N. Baranova. 1961. Karbotsernaitnovyi redkozemel'nyi karbonat (Carbocernaite—a rare-earth carbonate). *Zap. Vses. Miner. Ob-va*, part 90, No. 1.

Butakova, E.L. 1956. K petrologii Maimecha-Kotuiskogo kompleksa ul'traosnovnykh i shchelochnykh porod (On the petrology of ultrabasic and alkaline rocks of the Maimecha-Kotui complex). *Trudy NIIGA*, 89.

Butakova, E.L. 1958. Kompleks ul'traosnovnykh i shchelochnykh porod severnoi okrainy Sibirskoi platformy (Complex of ultrabasic and alkaline rocks of the northern part of the Siberian platform). In the book: *Geol. Stroenie SSR*, vol. 2, Gosgeoltekhizdat publishers.

Butakova, E.L. 1959. O roli metasomatoza v obrazovanii shchelochnykh porod (Role of metasomatism in the formation of alkaline rocks). *Miner. Sb. Lvovsk. Ob-va*, No. 13.

Butakova, E.L. 1965. Tektonicheskie usloviya obrazovaniya shchelochnykh porod Vostochnoi Tuvy (Tectonic conditions for the formation of alkaline rocks of the Eastern Tuva). *Geologiya i Geofizika*, No. 5.

Butakova, E.L. and L.S. Egorov. 1962. Maimecha-Kotuiskii kompleks formatsii shchelochnykh i ultraosnovnykh porod (Formation of alkaline and ultrabasic rocks in the Maimecha-Kotui complex). In the book: *Petrografiya Vostochnoi Sibiri*, vol. 1, Izd-vo AN SSSR.

Butakova, E.L. and E.G. Moor. 1958. Ultraosnovnye i shchelochnye porody severnoi okrainy Sibirskoi platformy i ikh genticheskie vzaimootnosheniya (Ultrabasic and alkaline rocks of the northern part of the Siberian platform and their genetic interrelation). In the book: *Mat-by 2-go Vses. Petrograf. Soveshcheniya*. Izd-vo An SSSR.

Butakova, E.L., G.G. Moor and E.M. Epshtein. 1957. Oblast' razvitiya ultraosnovnykh i shchelochnykh porod severa Sibirskoi platformy i svyazannye s neyu endogennye mestorozhdeniya (Region of development of ultrabasic and alkaline rocks in the north Siberian platform and its relation to endogene deposits). *Dokl. Yubil. Sessii Uchenogo Soveta NIIGA*, Leningrad.

Chernysheva, E.A. and G.S. Gormasheva. 1966. O sostave i svoistvakh slyud iz karbonatitov (On the composition and properties of mica from carbonatites). In the book: *Osobennoski Petrologii, Mineralogii i Geokhimii Karbonatitov Vostochnoi Sibiri*. "Nauka" publishers.

Chesnokov, B.V. 1959. Krivye spektral'nogo poglashcheniya nekotorykh mineralov, okrashennykh titanom (Spectra absorption curves of some minerals rich in titanium). *Dokl. AN SSSR*, 129, No. 3.

Christman, R.A., M.R. Brock, R.C. Pearson and Q.D. Singewald. 1959. Geology and thorium deposits of the Wet Mountains, Colorado. *U.S. Geol. Surv. Bull.*, 1072, H.

Coetzee, G.L. and C.B. Edwards. 1959. The Mrima Hill carbonatite, Coast

Province, Kenya. *Trans. and Proc. Geol. Soc. South Africa*, 62.

Daly, R.A. 1918. Genesis of the alkaline rocks. *J. Geol.*, 26.

Daly, R.A. 1925. Carbonate dikes of the Premier diamond mine, Transvaal. *J. Geol.*, 33.

Dana, E.S. 1886. On the brookite from Magnet Cove, Arkansas. *Amer. J. Sci., ser.*, 2, 32.

Davidson, C.F. 1964. On diamantiferous diatremes. *Econ. Geol.*, 59.

Davies, K.A. 1947. The phosphate deposits of the Eastern Province, Uganda. *Econ. Geol.*, 42.

Davies, K.A. 1952. The building of Mount Elgon (East Africa). *Geol. Surv. Uganda Mem.*, 7.

Davies, K.A. 1956. The geology of part of Southeast Uganda with special reference to the alkaline complexes. *Geol. Surv. Uganda. Mem.*, 8.

Dawson, J.B. 1962a. Sodium carbonate lavas from Oldoinyo Lengai, Tanganyika. *Nature*, 195.

Dawson, J.B. 1962b. The geology of Oldoinyo Lengai. *Bull. Volcanol.*, 24.

Deans, T. 1955. Carbonatite investigations in America. *Colon. Geol. and Mineral. Resources*, 5.

Deans, T. 1968. World distribution of carbonatites in relation to volcanism. *Proc. Geol. Soc. London*, 1647.

Deans, T. and J.D.C. McConnel. 1955. Isokite, $CaMgPO_4F$, a new mineral from Northern Rhodesia. *Mineral. Mag.*, 30.

Deans, T. and J.L. Powell. 1968. Trace elements and strontium isotopes in carbonatites, fluorites and limestones from India and Pakistan. *Nature*, 218, No. 5143.

Deli, R.A. 1936. Izverzhennye Porody i Glubiny Zemli (Igneous rocks and the depths of the Earth). ONTI-NKTP publishers, Moscow-Leningrad.

Dena, J.D., E.S. Dena, Ch. Palache, H. Berman and C. Frondel. 1951–1954. *Sistema Mineralogii* (The System of Mineralogy). Vol. I–IV, IL.

Denayer, M.E. and F. Schellink. 1965. Recueil d'analyses des laves du fosse tectonique de l'Afrique Centrale. Bruxelles.

Derby, O.A. 1891. Magnetite ore districts of Jacupiranga and Ipanema, São Paulo, Brazil. *Amer. J. Sci.*, 41.

Dixey, F. 1959. Belikie Afrikanskie Razlomy (The great African dislocations). IL.

Dixey, F. 1946. Carbonatite pipes and ring structures. *Geol. Mag.*, 83.

Dixey, F., W.C. Smith and C.B. Bisset. 1955. The Chilwa series of Southern Nyasaland. *Nyasaland. Geol. Surv. Bull.* 5.

Donnay, G. and J.D.H. Donnay. 1953. The crystallography of bastnaesite, parisite, roentgenite and synchisite. *Amer. Mineralogist*, 38, No. 11–12.

Downie, C. and P. Wilkinson. 1962. The explosion craters of Basotu, Tanganyika Territory. *Bull. Volcanol.*, 24.

Du Bois, C.G.B. 1959. The geology of the Teror Hills alkaline complex,

Central Karamoja, Uganda. Internat. Geol. Congr. 12th Sess. Asoc. Serv. Geol. Africanos.

Du Bois, C.G.B., J. Furst, N.J. Guest and D.J. Jennings. 1963. Fresh natrocarbonatite lava from Oldoinyo Lengai. *Nature*, 197.

Du-Toit, A.L. 1957. Geologiya Yuzhnoi Afriki (Geology of South Africa). IL.

Eckermann, H. von. 1948a. The alkaline district of Alnö Island. *Sevr. geol. undersokn*, Ser. Ca, 36.

Eckermann, H. von. 1948b. The process of nephelinization. Internat. Geol. Congr. 18th Sess. Great Britain, III.

Eckermann, H. von. 1948c. The genesis of the Alnö alkaline rocks. Internat. Geol. Congr. 18th Sess. Great Britain, III.

Eckermann, H. von. 1950. A comparison of Fennoscandian limestone contact minerals and those of the Alnö alkaline rocks, associated with carbonates. *Mineral. Mag.*, 29.

Eckermann, H. von. 1952. The distribution of barium and strontium in the rocks and minerals of the syenitic and alkaline rocks of Alnö Island. *Arkiv mineral och geol.*, 1 (13).

Eckermann, H. von. 1958. The alkaline and carbonatitic dikes of the Alnö formation on the mainland northwest of Alnö Island. *Kgl. svenska vetenskapsakad Handl.*, 7 (2).

Eckermann, H. von. 1960. Contributions to the knowledge of the alkaline dikes of the Alnö region. I–III. *Arkiv mineral och geol.*, 2 (41).

Eckermann, H. von. 1961. The petrogenesis of the Alnö alkaline rocks. *Bull. Geol. Inst. Univ. Uppsala*, 40.

Eckermann, H. von. 1963. Contributions to the knowledge of the alkaline dikes of the Alnö region. X. Carbonatite rich in apatite and quartz from Vintjärns Varv at Sundsvall. *Arkiv mineral. och geol.*, 3 (20).

Eckermann, H. von. 1964. The Swedish kimberlites and a comparison with South African and Russian rocks. *Geol. and geophys.*, 6.

Eckermann, H. von. 1966. The pyroxenes of the Alnö carbonatite (sövite) and of the surrounding fenites. Mineral. Soc. India, IMA Vol.

Eckermann, H. von. 1967. Wollastonite in carbonatite rocks. *Geochim. et cosmochim. Acta*, 31.

Eckermann, H. von., H. von. Ubisch and F.E. Wickman. 1952. A preliminary investigation into the isotopic composition of carbon from some alkaline intrusions. *Geochim. et cosmochim. Acta*, 2.

Efimov, A.F., E.M. Eskova and S.T. Kataeva. 1969. O nakhodke berbankita v shchelochnykh metasomatakh urala (Occurrence of burbankite in alkaline metasomatites of Ural). *Trudy Miner. Muzeya AN SSSR*, No. 19.

Efimov, A.F., S.M. Kravchenko and E.V. Vlasov. 1963. K mineralogii shchelochnykh pegmatitov Inaglinskogo massiva (Mineralogy of alkaline pegmatites of the Inaglinskii massif). *Trudy IMGRE*, No. 16.

Egorov, L.S. 1960a. O tipakh karbonatitovykh mestorozhdenii i ikh svyazi s massivami ultraosnovnykh shchelochnykh porod (On the different types of carbonatite deposits and their relation with alkaline ultrabasic massifs). *Izv. AN SSSR, ser. geol.*, No. 1.

Egorov, L.S. 1960b. K probleme nefelinizatsii i zhelezo-magnezialnokaltsievogo metasomatoza v intruziyakh shchelochnykh i ultraosnovnykh porod (On the problem of nephelinitization and iron-magnesium-calcitic metasomatism in intrusive alkaline and ultrabasic rocks). *Trudy NIIGA*, 114.

Egorov, L.S. 1963. Zernistye melilitovye porody Severa Sibirskoi platformy (Granular melilitic rocks of the north Siberian platform). *Trudy NIIGA*, 136.

Egorov, L.S. 1964. K probleme proiskhozhdeniya karbonatitov (On the problem of origin of carbonatite). *Izv. AN SSSR, ser. geol.*, No. 1.

Egorov, L.S. 1966. O roli intruzivno-magmaticheskogo i metasomaticheskogo protsessov v formirovanii karbonatitov (Role of the intrusive-magnetic and metasomatic processes in carbonatite formation). In the book: *Mat-ly 2-i Konferentsii po Okolorudnomu Metasomatizmu*. VSEGEI publication, Leningrad.

Egorov, L.S. and N.P. Surina. 1961. Karbonatity raiona intruzii Changit na severe Sibirskoi platformy (Carbonatites of the intrusive region of Changit in the north of the Siberian platform). *Trudy NIIGA*, 125, No. 17.

Egorov, L.S., T.L. Goldburt and K.M. Shikhorina. 1959. O forme i mekhanizme obrazovaniya Gulinskoi intruzii (Structure and mechanism of formation of Gulinskii intrusives). *Trudy NIIGA*, 107.

Egorov, L.S., V.M. Rudyachenok and N.P. Surina. 1968. O strukturno-geologicheskom polozhenii ultraosnovnykh shchelochnykh porod v Maimecha-Kotuiskoi provintsii (Structural-geological position of alkaline ultrabasic rocks in Maimecha-Kotui Province). *Dokl. AN SSSR*, 182, No. 1.

Eliseev, N.A. and E.E. Fedorov. 1953. Lovozerskii Pluton i Ego Mestorozhdeniya (Lovozero pluton and its deposits). Izd-vo AN SSSR.

Elyanov, A.A. and V.M. Moralev. 1961. Novye dannye o vozraste ultraosnovnykh i shchelochnykh porod Aldanskogo shchita (New data on the age of alkaline and ultrabasic rocks of the Aldan Shield). *Dokl. AN SSSR*, 141, No. 3.

Emeleus, C.H. 1964. The Grönnedal-Ika complex, South Greenland. The structure and geological history of the complex. *Medd. Grønland*, 172, No. 3.

Epshtein, E.M. 1958. Redkometal'nye karbonatity severa Sibirskoi platformy (Rare-metal carbonatites of the north Siberian platform). *Tezisy Dokl. Na Krasnoyarskom Region. Soveshch.* Gosgeoltekhizdat pub.

Epshtein, E.M. 1959. O karbonatitakh i ikh strukturnom polozhenii v Gulinskom plutone (Carbonatites and their structural significance in the Gulinskii Pluton). *Trudy NIIGA*, No. 2.

Evzikova, N.Z. 1960. Ob orientirovannom narastanii baddeleita na pirokhlore i izmenenii oblika kristallov pirokhlora (On the oriented baddeleyite in pyrochlore and the replacement of crystalline form of pyrochlore). *Zap. Vses. Miner. Ob-va*, part 89, No. 5.

Evzikova, N.Z. and A.A. Moskalyuk. 1964. Gazovo-zhidkie vklyucheniya v karbonatakh karbonatitov (Gaseous-liquid inclusions in carbonate carbonatites). *Dokl. AN SSSR, geol.*, 159, No. 1.

Erickson, R.L. and L.V. Blade. 1963. Geochemistry and petrology of the alkalic igneous complex at Magnet Cove. Arkansas. U.S. Geol. Surv., Profess. Paper. 425.

Faure, G. and P.M. Hurley. 1963. The isotopic composition of strontium in oceanic and continental basalts. Application to the origin of igneous rocks. *J. Petrol.*, 4.

Fawley, A.P. and T.C. James. 1955. A pyrochlore (columbium) carbonatite, Southern Tanganyika. *Econom. Geol.*, 50.

Fersman, A.E. and others. 1937. Mineraly Khibinskikh i Lovozerskikh Tundr (Minerals of Khibinskii and Lovozerskii tundra). Izd-vo AN SSSR, Moscow-Leningrad.

Fick, L.J. and Van der Heyde. 1959. Additional data on the geology of the Mbeya carbonatite. *Econom. Geol.*, 54.

Fockema, R.A. 1949. An occurrence of alkaline and acid lavas and volcanic breccias on the farm Kruidfontein 147, Rustenberg District. *Trans. and Proc. Geol. Soc. South Africa*, 52.

Forster, I.F. 1958. Paragenetical ore mineralogy of the Loolekop—Palabora carbonatite complex, Eastern Transvaal. *Trans. and Proc. Geol. Soc. South Africa*, 61.

Fozzard, P.M.H. 1956. Further notes on the volcanic rocks from Igwisi. *Tang. Geol. Surv. Res.*, VI.

Freitas, de A.J. 1959. A geologia de Mozambique. Lourenzo Marques.

Frolov, A.A. 1960. Nekotorye voprosy detal'nogo geologistrukturnogo izucheniya karbonatitov (Some problems in the geological and structural study of carbonatites). *Geol. Rudnykh M-nii*, No. 5.

Frolov, A.A. 1962. Treshchinnaya tektonika v porodakh shchelochnoultraosnovnogo kompleksa i karbonatitakh (Fracturing tectonics in the rocks of alkaline ultrabasic complex and carbonatites). *Geol. Rudn. M-nii*, No. 2.

Frolov, A.A. 1966a. Poloschatost' v karbonatitakh (Layering in carbonatites). *Izv. AN SSSR, ser. geol.*, No. 4.

Frolov, A.A. 1966b. Orientirovka mineralov v karbonatitakh odnogo iz raionov Sibiri (Orientation of the minerals in carbonatites from one of the regions of Siberia). *Izv. Vysh. Uchebn. Zaved., ser. Geologiya i Razvedka*", No. 7.

Frolov, A.A. and Yu.A. Bagdasarov. 1967. Bolshetanginskii massiv ultraosnovnykh shchelochnykh porod i karbonatitov (Bolshetanginskii massif of alkaline ultrabasic rocks and carbonatites). *Sov. Geologiya*, No. 12.

Frolov, A.A., A.Ya. Volzhenkova and E.A. Nechaeva. 1969. Maloerodirovannyi massiv ultraosnovnykh shchelochnykh porod i karbonatitov v Sibiri (Little eroded alkaline ultrabasic and carbonatite massifs of Siberia). *Geol. Rudn. M-nii*, No. 1.

Fryklund, V.C. Jr., R.S. Harner and E.P. Kaiser. 1954. Niobium (columbium) and titanium at Magnet Cove and Potash Sulphur Springs, Arkansas. *U.S. Geol. Surv. Bull.*, 1015-B.

Gaidukova, V.S. 1960a. Protsessy izmeneniya pirokhlora v karbonatitovykh mestorozhdeniyakh (Replacement process of pyrochlore in carbonatite deposits). *Miner. Syre*, No. 1.

Gaidukova, V.S. 1960b. Razvitie kolumbita i fersmita po pirokhloru (Formation of columbite and fersmite after pyrochlore). *Zap. Vses. Miner. Ob-va*, part 89, No. 4.

Gaidukova, V.S. 1966a. O strontsievom pirokhlore i kaltsievom eshinite iz karbonatitov (On the occurrence of strontianitic pyrochlore and calcitic aechynite from carbonatites). *Geol. M-nii Redkikh Elementov*, No. 30.

Gaidukova, V.S. 1966b. Vanadievyi ilmenorutil i nekotorye voprosy geokhimii vanadiya v karbonatitovom protsesse (Vanadiferous ilmeno-rutile and some problems in the geochemistry of vanadium in the carbonatite process). *Geol. M-nii Redkikh Elementov*, No. 30.

Gaidukova, V.S., L.I. Polupanova and T.I. Stolyarova. 1963. Gatchettolity iz karbonatitov Sibiri (Hatchettolite from carbonatites of Siberia). *Min. Syre*, No. 7.

Gaidukova, V.S., A.I. Ginzburg, L.K. Pozharitskaya and others. 1962. Geologicheskoe stroenie i mineralogo-geokhimicheskie osobennosti redkometal'nykh karbonatitov (Geological structure and mineralogical-geochemical characteristics of rare-metal carbonatites). *Geol. M-nii Redkikh Elementov*, No. 17.

Garson, M.S. 1952–1953. The geology of Chilwa Island. Nyasaland Geol. Surv., Annual Rept.

Garson, M.S. 1955. Flow phenomena in carbonatites in Southern Nyasaland. *Colon. Geol. and Mineral. Resources*, 5.

Garson, M.S. 1957, 1958. Investigation of carbonatites and ring structures. Nyasaland Geol. Surv. Annual Rept.

Garson, M.S. 1959. Stress pattern of carbonatitic and alkaline dyces at Tundulu ring structure, Southern Nyasaland. Internat. Geol. Congr. 20 Sess. Assoc. Serv. Geol. Africanos.

Garson, M.S. 1961, 1962. Research on carbonatites and related structures. Nyasaland Geol. Surv. Annual Rept.

Garson, M.S. 1963. The Tundulu carbonatite ring complex of Southern

Nyasaland. Malawi Geol. Surv. Mem., No. 2.

Garson, M.S. and W.C. Smith. 1958. Chilwa Island. Nyasaland Geol. Surv. Mem., No. 1.

Ginzburg, A.I. and E.M. Epshtein. 1968. Karbonatitovye mestorozhdeniya (Carbonatite deposits). In the book: *Genezis Endogennykh Rudnykh Mestorozhedenii*. "Nedra" publishers.

Ginzburg, A.I., S.A. Gorzhevskaya and G.A. Sidorenko. 1958. O khimicheskom sostave kubicheskikh titano-tantaloniobatov (Chemical composition of cubic titanium-tantaloniobites). *Geokhimiya*, No. 5.

Ginzburg, A.I., Yu.B. Lavrenev, E.A. Nechaeva and L.K. Pozharitskaya. 1958. Redkometalnye karbonatity (Rare-metallic carbonatites). *Geol. M-nii Redkikh Elementov*, No. 1.

Gittins, J. 1961. Nephelinisation in the Haliburton—Bancroft District, Ontario. *J. Geol.*, 69.

Gittins, J. and O.F. Tuttle. 1964. The system CaF_2-Ca $(OH)_2$-$CaCO_3$. *Amer. J. Sci.*, 262.

Gittins, J., D. York and A. Hayatsu. 1965. A reconsideration of the strontium isotope method of distinguishing carbonatites from melted limestones (abstr.). *Canad. Mineralogist*, 8.

Glagolev, A.A. 1962. Rol apatitizatsii v formirovanii zhelezorudnogo i flogopitovogo mestorozhdenii massiva Kovdor (Kolskii p-ov) [Role of apatitization in the formation of ferruginous and phlogopitic deposits of the Kovdor massif (Kola Peninsula)]. *Geol. Rudn. M-nii*, 7, No. 3.

Glushkina, S.E., G.V. Itsikson and B.I. Lovi. 1963. Muaassanite v mestorozhedenii karbonatitov (Moissanite in carbonatite deposits). *Zap. Vses. Miner. Ob-va*, part 92, No. 6.

Gold, D.P. 1964. Minerals from the Oka alkaline complex, near Montreal, Quebec, Canada. Internat. Mineral. Assoc., India.

Goldburt, G.L., L.S. Egorov and others. 1961. Gulinskaya intruziya ultraosnovnykh shchelochnykh porod (Alkaline ultrabasic intrusives of Gulinskii). *Trudy NIIGA*, 122.

Goldsmith, J.R., D.L. Graf, J. Witters and D.A. Northrop. 1962. Studies in the system $CaCO_3$-$MgCO_3$-$FeCO_3$. *J. Geol.*, 70.

Grabert, H. 1960. Zur Tectogenese Nordost-Brasiliens. *Z. Dtsch. geol. Ges.*, 111, Vol. 3.

Grabovskii, M.A. and O.N. Zherdenko. 1965. Damennaya struktura pirrotina iz karbonatitov (Domain structure of pyrrhotite from carbonatites). In the book: *Zhizni Zemli*. MGU pub.

Graham, A.R. 1955. Cerianite. CeO_2 a new rare-earth oxide mineral. *Amer. Mineralogist*. 40.

Grogan, R.M. 1960. Columbium at Powderhorn, Colorado. Colorado School of Mines. *Mines Mag.*, 50.

Guimaraes, D. 1957. Relatorio sôbre a jazida de pirocloro de Barreiro,

Araxá, Minas Gerais. *Brasil. Div. Fomento Prod. Mineral., Bol.*, 103.

Guimaraes, D. 1958. Columbio em Barreiro, Araxá, M.G. *Engenhazia miner., metalurgia*, 28 (168).

Guimaraes, D. 1960. Fundamentos da petrologie e as rochas igneas do Brasil. *Brasil Div. Fomento Prod. Mineral. Bol.*, 107.

Guimaraes, D. and V. Ilchenko. 1954. Apatita de Barreiro, Araxa, *Minas Gerais. Sec. Agric. Bol.*, 7/8, 9/10, 11/12.

Hackmann, V.W. 1925. Das Gebiet der Alkaligesteine von Kuolajarvi in Nordfinland. *Bull. Commiss. geol. Finlande*, No. 72.

Hamilton, E.I. and T. Deans. 1963. Isotopic composition of strontium in some African carbonatites and limestone and in strontium minerals. *Nature*, 198.

Harris, P.M. 1965. Pandaite from the Mrima Hill niobium deposit (Kenya). *Mineral. Mag.*, 35.

Hayatsu, A.D., D. York, R.M. Farquhar and J. Gittins. 1965. Significance of strontium isotope ratios in theories of carbonatite genesis. *Nature*, 207.

Heinrich, E.Wm. 1967. The geology of carbonatites. Chicago.

Heinrich, E.Wm. and R.J. Anderson. 1965. Carbonatites and alkalic rocks of the Arkansas River area, Fremont County, Colorado. 2. Fetid gas from carbonatite and related rocks. *Amer. Mineralogist*, 47.

Heinrich, E.Wm. and D.H. Dahlem. 1965. Unusual characteristics of carbonatites in the Arkansas River Canyon area, Colorado (abstr.). Geol. Soc. America Program 1965 Annual Meeting.

Heinrich, E.Wm. and A.A. Levinson. 1961. Carbonatitic niobium-rare earth deposits Ravalli County, Montana. *Amer. Mineralogist*, 46.

Heinrich, E.Wm. and S.H. Quon. 1963. New type of deposit of aluminofluoride minerals, Fremont County, Colorado (abstr.). *Geol. Soc. Amer. Spec. Paper*, 73.

Heinrich, E.Wm. and J.R. Shapirio. 1966. Alkalic rocks and carbonatites of the Arkansas river Canyon, Fremont County, Colorado. 3. The Amethist carbonatites. *Amer. Mineralogist*, 51.

Heier, K.S. 1964. Layered gabbro, hornblendite, carbonatite and nepheline syenite and carbonatite on Stjernöy, North Norway. *Norsk geol. tidsskr.*, 44.

Hess, H.D. and H.J. Trumpour. 1959. Second occurrence of fermite. *Amer. Mineralogist*, 44.

Hiemstra, S.A. 1955. Baddeleyite from Palabora, Eastern Transvaal. *Amer. Mineralogist*, 40.

Higasy, R.A. 1954. Trace elements of volcanic ultrabasic potassic rocks of Southwestern Uganda and adjoining part of the Belgian Congo. *Bull. Geol. Soc. America*, 65.

Hogarth, D.D. 1961. A study of pyrochlore and betafite. *Canad. Mineralogist*, 6.

Hogarth, D.D. 1957. The apatite-bearing veins of Nisikkatch Lake, Saskatchewan. *Canad. Mineralogist*, 6.

Högbom, A.G. 1892. Syenit omradet på Alnön. *Geol. foren Stockholm forhandl.*, 14.

Högbom, A.G. 1895. Uber des Nephelinsyenitgebiet auf der Insel Alnö. *Geol. foren. Stockholm forhandl.*, 17.

Holbrook, D.F. 1947. A brookite deposit in Hot Spring County, Arkansas. *Arkansas Div. Geol. Bull.*, 11.

Holmes, A. 1950. Petrogenesis of katungite and its associates. *Amer. Mineralogist*, 1959, 35.

Holmes, A. 1952. The potash ankaratrite-melaleucite lavas of Nabugando and Mbuga craters, Southwest Uganda. *Trans. Geol. Soc. Edinburgh*, 15.

Holmes, A. 1958. Spitzkop carbonatite, Eastern Transvaal. *Bull. Geol. Soc. America*, 69.

Holmes, A. and H.F. Harwood. 1932. Petrology of the volcanic fields east and southeast of Ruwenzori, Uganda. *Quart. J. Geol. Soc.*, 88.

Holmes, A. and H.F. Harwood. 1937. The petrology of the volcanic area of Bufumbira. *Geol. Surv. Uganda Mem.*, No. 3, Pt. 2.

Holmquist, P.J. 1893. Pyrochlor från Alnön. *Geol. fören. i Stockholm forhandl.*, 15.

Holmquist, P.J. 1894. Knopit, ett perowskit narstaende, nytt mineral från Alnön. *Geol. foren i Stockholm forhandl.*, 16.

Hussak, E. 1894a. Ueber Brazilit ein neues Tantal- (Niob) Mineral von der Eisenmine Jacupiranga, Sud São Paulo. *Neues Jahrb. Mineral.*, 1894, (II).

Hussak, E. 1894b. Ueber ein neues Perowskitvorkommen un Verbindung mit Magneteisenstein von Catalao, Staat Goyaz, Brasilien (II Teil). *Neues Jahrb. Mineral.*, 1894 (II).

Hussak, E. 1895a. Mineralogische Notizen aus Brasilien (II Teil)—*Tschermak's mineral. und petrogr. Mitt.*, 14.

Hussak, E. 1895b. Ueber den baddeleyit (sin. brasilit) von der Eisenmine in Jacupiranga in São Paulo. *Tschermak's mineral. und petrogr. Mitt.*

Hussak, E. and G.T. Prior. 1895. Lewesite and zirkelite, two new Brazilian minerals. *Mineral. Mag.*, 11.

Hytönen, K. 1959. On the petrology and mineralogy of some alkaline volcanic rocks of Toror Hill, Mt. Moroto, Morulinga in Karamoya, Northeastern Uganda. *Bull. Commiss. geol. Finlande*, 184.

Jaffe, H.W. 1955. Precambrian monazite and zircon from the Mountain Pass rare-earth district, San Bernardino County, California. *Bull. Geol. Soc. America*, 66.

Jaffe, H.W., R. Meyrowitz and H.T. Evans. 1953. Sahamalite, a new rare earth carbonate mineral. *Amer. Mineralogist*, 38.

Jäger, E., E. Niggli and A.H. van der Veen. 1959. A hydrated barium-strontium pyrochlore in a biotite rock from Panda Hill, Tanganyika. *Mineral. Mag.*, 32.

James, T.C. 1956. Carbonatite investigations. *Tanganyika Geol. Surv. Rec.*, IV (1954), 20.

James, T.C. 1959. Carbon dioxide-bearing hot springs in the Songwe River valley, Mbeya district. *Tanganyika Geol. Surv. Rec.*, VII (1957).

James, T.C. and D. McKie. 1958. The alteration of pyrochlore to columbite in carbonatites in Tanganyika. *Mineral. Mag.*, 31.

Johnson, R.L. 1961. The geology of the Dorowa and Shawa carbonatite complexes, Southern Rhodesia. *Trans. Geol. Soc. South Africa*, 64.

Kaiser, E.R. 1956. Preliminary report on the geology and deposits of monazite, thorite, and niobium-bearing rutile of the Mineral Hill district, Lehmi County, Idaho. U.S. Geol. Surv. Open File Rept.

Kapustin, Yu.L. 1960. Geologo-petrograficheskie osobennosti i mineralogicheskii sostav karbonatitov massiv Vuoriyarvi (Geology and petrographical characteristics and mineralogical composition of carbonatites of Vuoriyarvi). *Kratk. Soobshch. po Nauchn-issled. Rabotam IMGRE*, No. 1.

Kapustin, Yu.L. 1963. O novoi nakhodke vadeita v Soyuze (On the new occurrence of wadeite in the USSR). *Dokl. AN SSSR*, 151, No. 6.

Kapustin, Yu.L. 1961. Geologicheskoe polozheniei mineralogicheskii sostav karbonatitov kovdorskogo massiva (Geological position and mineralogical composition of carbonatites of the Kovdor massif). *Tezisy Dokladov 3-i Konf. Molodykh Nauchn. Sotr. IMGRE*. Moscow.

Kapustin, Yu.L. 1964. Aktsessornaya redkometalnaya mineralogiya karbonatitov Kolskogo poluostrova (Accessory rare-metallic mineralogy of carbonatites of the Kola Peninsula). In the book: *Mineralogiya i Geneticheskie Osobennosti Shchelochnykh Massivov*. "Nauka" publishers.

Kapustin, Yu.L. 1965a. O sulfidnoi mineralizatsii v karbonatitakh Kolskogo poluostrova (Sulfide mineralization in carbonatites of the Kola Peninsula). In the book: *Petrologiya i Geokhimicheskie Osobennosti Kompleksa Ultrabazitov, Shchelochnykh Porod i Karbonatitov*. "Nauka" publishers.

Kapustin, Yu.L. 1965b. Norzetit-pervaya nakhodka v SSR (Norsethite-first occurrence in the USSR). *Dokl. AN SSSR*, 161, No. 4.

Kapustin, Yu.L. 1965c. Pozdnie karbonatity s TR, Sr i Ba (Late carbonatites with TR, Sr and Ba). In the book: *Geokhimiya, Mineralogiya i Geneticheskie Tipy Mestorozhdenii Redkikh Elementov. Vol. 3. Geneticheskie Tipy Mestorozhdenii Redkikh Elementov*. "Nauka" publishers.

Kapustin, Yu.L. 1966a. Geneticheskie tipy karbonatitov i osobennosti ikh formirovaniya (Genetical types of carbonatites and peculiarities of their formation). In the book: *Mat-ly 2-i Konferentsii po Okolorudnomu Metasomatizu*: VSEGEI publication Leningrad.

Kapustin, Yu.L. 1966b. Geokhimiya redkozemelnykh elementov v karbonatitakh (Geochemistry of rare-earth elements in carbonatites). *Geokhimiya*, No. 11.

Kapustin, Yu.L. and E.I. Seminov. 1964. Pervaya nakhodka labuntsovita v karbonatitakh i novye dannye o ego svoistvakh (Report on the first occurrence of labuntsovite in carbonatite and its properties). In the book: *Mineralogiya i Geneticheskie Osobennosti Shchelochnykh Massivov.* "Nauka" publishers.

King, B.C. 1949. The Napak area of Karamoya, Uganda. *Geol. Surv. Uganda Mem.*, No. 5.

King, B.C. 1965. Petrogenesis of the alkaline igneous rock suites of the volcanic and intrusive centers of Eastern Uganda. *J. Petrol.*, 6.

King, B.C. and D.S. Sutherland. 1960a. Alkaline rocks of Eastern and Southern Africa. Part I. Distribution, ages, and structures. *Sci. Progr.*, 48.

King, B.C. and D.S. Sutherland. 1960b. Alkaline rocks of Eastern and Southern Africa. Part II. Petrology. *Sci. Progr.*, 48.

King, B.C. and D.S. Sutherland. 1960c. Alkaline rocks of Eastern and Southern Africa. Part III. Petrogenesis. *Sci. Progr.*, 48.

Kirillov, A.S. and T.A. Burova. 1967. Lueshit iz karbonatitov Kolskogo poluostrova (Lueshite from carbonatites of the Kola Peninsula). In the book: *Mineralogiya i Geokhimiya*, vol. 2, LGU publication.

Kirillov, A.S. and V.S. Rylov. 1963. Ob istochnikakh magniya v karbonatitov (On the source of magnesium in carbonatites). *Zap. Vses. Miner. Obva*, part 92, No. 2.

Knop, A. 1892. Der Kaiserstühl im Breisgau. Eine naturwissenschaftliche Studie. Leipzig.

Kolotukhina, S.E., Pervukhina, A.E. and A.V. Rozhanets. 1964. Geologiya Mestorozhdenii Redkikh Elementov Afriki i Ikh Ekonomicheskoe Znachenie (Geology of rare-earth elements of Africa and their economic importance). "Nauka" publishers.

Kolotukhina, S.E., I.E. Pervukhina, K.V. Potemkin and A.V. Rozhanets. 1968. Geologiya mestorozhdenii redkikh elementov yuzhnoi ameriki (Geology of Rare Earth Elements of South America). Izd-vo "Nauka".

Konev, A.A. 1960. Ob intruzii perovskitsoderzhashchikh piroksenitov v Vostochnom Sayane (Intrusive perovskitic pyroxenites of Eastern Sayan). *Dokl. AN SSSR*, 133, No. 8.

Kononova, V.A. 1957. Urtit-iiolitovye intruzii Tuvy i rol metasomaticheskikh protsessov prikh formirovanii (The urtite-ijolite intrusives of Tuva and the role of the metasomatic processes in their formation). *Izv. AN SSSR, ser. geol.* No. 5.

Kononova, V.A. and A.N. Tarashchan. 1968. O termolyuminestsentsii karbonatov iz karbonatitov (Thermoluminescence of carbonates from carbonatites). *Geol. Rudn. M-nii*, 10, No. 3.

Kortusov, M.P. 1960. O nefelinsoderzhashchikh porodakh severo-zapadnoi chasti Kuznetskogo Alatau (Nepheline-containing rocks from the northwestern part of Kuznetskii Alatau). In the book: *Magmatizm v Svyazi s*

Nim Poleznykh Iskopaemykh. Gosgeoltekhizdat publishers.

Kostyleva, E.E. 1937. Evdialit i evkolit (Eudialyte and eukolite). In the book: Mineraly Khibinskikh i Lovozerskikh Tundr. Izd-vo AN SSSR, Moscow-Leningrad.

Korzhinskii, D.S. 1947. Bimetasomaticheskie flogopitovye i lazyritovye mestorozhdeniya arkheya Pribaikalya (Bimetasomatic phlogopitic and lazuritic Archean deposits of Prebaikal). *Trudy In-ta Geol. Nauk AN SSSR, ser. Petrograf.*, vol. 29, No. 10.

Korzhinskii, D.S. 1953. Ocherk metasomaticheskikh protsessov (Nature of the metasomatic processes). In the book: *Osnovnye Problemy v Uchenii o Magmatogennykh Rudnykh Mestorozhdenii.* Izd-vo AN SSSR.

Kovalskii V.V. 1963. Kimberlitovye Porody Yakutii (Kimberlitic rocks of Yakutia). Izd-vo AN SSSR.

Kovalskii, V.V. and O.S. Egorov. 1966. Kimberlitovye i karbonatitovye brekchii vostochnogo sklona Anabarskoi anteklizy (Kimberlitic and carbonatic breccias of the eastern flank of the Anabar anticline). *Tezisy Dokladov Soveshchaniya po Geologii Almaznykh mestorozhdenii.* Perm.

Kovalskii, V.V., K.N. Nikishov and O.S. Egorov. 1969. Kimberlitovye i karbonatitovye obrazovaniy a vostochnogo i yugo-vostochnogo skolonov Anabarskoi anteklizy (Kimberlitic and carbonatic formations of the eastern and southeastern flanks of the Anabar anticline). "Nauka" publishers.

Kozyreva, L.V. and G.A. Ilinskii. 1959. K mineralogii dolomito-kaltsitovykh karbonatitov massiva Vuoriyarvi (On the mineralogy of dolomite-calcitic carbonatites of the Vuoriyarvi massifs). In the book: *Mat-ly po Mineralogii Kolskogo p-va.* Pt. 1. Kirovsk.

Kranck, E.H. 1928. On turjaite and the ijolite stem of Turja. *Fennia*, 51 (5).

Krasilnikov, B.N. 1966. Doorogennoe Razvitie Struktury Sayano-Altaiskoi Oblosti i Soprovozhdavushchie Ego Glubinnye Protsessy (Preorogenic development of structures in the Sayan-Altai region and associated deeper processes). "Nauka" publishers.

Krasnova, N.I., N.F. Kartenko, O.M. Rimskaya-Korsakova and V.V. Firyulina. 1967. Torianit iz flogopitonosnykh porod Kovdorskogo massiva (Thorianite from phlogopitic rocks of the Kovdor massif). In the book: *Mineralogiya i Geokhimiya*, vol. 2, LGU publication.

Krasnovskii, G.M. 1948. Enskoe zhelezorudnoe mestorozhdenie (Iron ore deposits of Yenisei). *Sov. Geologiya*, No. 33.

Kravchenko, S.M. and E.V. Vlasova. 1962. Shchelochnye Porody Tsentralnogo Aldana (Alkaline rocks of Central Aldan). Izd-vo AN SSSR.

Krutoyarskii, M.A., B.G. Lopatin, G.A. Bystrova and others. 1959. Kimberlity basseinov rek Omonos i Ukukit (Kimberlites from Omonos and Ukukit river basins). *Trudy NIIGA*, 65, No. 13.

Kukharenko, A.A. 1958. Paleozoiskii kompleks ultraosnovnykh i shchelochnykh porod Kolskogo poluostrova i svyazannye s nim redko-metalnye mestorozhdeniya (The paleozoic complex of ultrabasic and alkaline rocks of the Kola Peninsula and rare-metallic deposits associated with it). *Zap. Miner. Ob-va*, part 87, No. 3.

Kukharenko, A.A. 1962. Osnovnye problemy geologii platformennykh kompleksov shchelochno-ultraosnovnykh porod (The principal problems of the geology of platform-like complexes of alkaline-ultrabasic rocks). *Uch. Zap. LGU, ser. geol. nauk.* No. 312, vol. 13.

Kukharenko, A.A. 1966. K probleme proiskhozhdeniya karbonatitov (On the problem of the origin of carbonatites). In the book: *Mat-ly 2-i Konferentsii po Okolorudnomu Metasomatizmu.* VSEGEI pub., Leningrad.

Kukharenko, A.A. 1967. Shchelochnoi magmatizm vostochnoi chasti Baltiiskogo shchita (Alkali magmatism in the eastern part of the Baltic Shield). *Zap. Vses. Miner. Ob-va*, part 96, No. 5.

Kukharenko, A.A. and E.A. Bagdasarov. 1961. Perovskity ultraosnovnykh shchelochnykh porod Kolskogo poluostrova (Perovskites from alkaline ultrabasic rocks of the Kola Peninsula). *Mat-ly VSEGEI, nov. seriya*, No. 15.

Kukharenko, A.A. and E.A. Bagdasarov. 1962. Paragenezis i kristallo-khimicheskie osobennosti titanovykh granatov iz shchelochno-ultraosnovnykh porod Kolskogo poluostrova (Paragenesis and crystal-chemical characteristics of titanium garnets from alkaline-ultrabasic rocks of the Kola Peninsula). *Uch. Zap. LGU, ser. geol. nauk*, 312, No. 13.

Kukharenko, A.A. and E.I. Dontsova. 1962. K probleme genezisa karbonatitov (On the origin of carbonatites). *Geol. Rudn. M-nii*, No. 2.

Kukharenko, A.A. and M.P. Orlova. 1960. Nekotorye voprosy petrologii nizhne i srednepaleozoiskogo kompleksa ultraosnovnykh i shchelochnykh massivov Kolskogo poluostrova (Some problems in the petrology of the lower middle-paleozoic complex of alkaline ultrabasic massifs of the Kola Peninsula). In the book: *Magmatizm i Svyaz s Nim Peleznykh Iskopaemykh.* Izd-vo AN SSSR.

Kukharenko, A.A., A.G. Bulakh and K.A. Balkanova. 1961. Sulfat-monatsit iz karbonatitov Kolskogo poluostrova (Sulfate-monazite from carbonatites of the Kola Peninsula). *Zap. Vses. Miner. Ob-va*, part 90, No. 4.

Kukharenko, A.A., M.P. Orlova, A.G. Bulakh, E.A. Bagdasarov, O.M. Rimskaya-Korsakova, E.I. Nefedov, G.A. Ilinskii, A.S. Sergeev and N.B. Abakumova. 1965. Kaledonskii Kompleks Ultraosnovnykh, Shchelochnykh Porod i Karbonatitov Kolskogo Poluostrova i Severnoi Karelii (Caledonian complex of alkaline ultrabasic rocks and carbonatites of the Kola Peninsula and North Karelia). "Nedra" publishers.

Kun, De N. 1961. Die Niobkarbonatite von Afrika. *Neues Jahrb. Mineral. Monat.* 1961 (6).

Kupletskii, B.M. 1938. Piroksenitovaya intruziya v stantsii Afrikanda na

Kolskom p-ove (Pyroxenitic intrusive of Afrikanda in the Kola Peninsula). *Trudy Petrograf. In-ta AN SSSR*, No. 12.

Kupletskii, B.M. 1948. Melilitovye porody v shchelochnom komplekse Enskogo raiona Kolskogo p-ova (Melilitic rocks in the alkaline complex in the Ensii region of the Kola Peninsula). *Izv. AN SSSR, ser. geol.*, No. 3.

Kuzmenko, V.I. 1946. Petrovsko-Gnutovskoe mestorozhdenie parazita (Ukr. SSR) [Parisite deposits of Petrovskii and Gnutovskii (Ukrainian SSR)]. *Sov. Geologiya*, No. 12.

Kuzmenko, M.V. and M.E. Kazakova. 1955. Nenadkevichitnovyi mineral (Nenadkevichite—a new mineral). *Dokl. AN SSSR*, 100, No. 6.

Kuznetsov, E.A. 1956. Petrografiya Magmaticheskikh i Metamorficheskikh Gornykh Porod (Petrography of magmatic and metamorphic rocks). MGU pub.

Kuznetsov, Yu.A. 1962. Usloviya obrazovaniya glavneishikh tipov magmaticheskikh formatsii podvizhnykh zon (Conditions of formation of principal types of magmatic deposits in the mobile zones). *Geologiya i Geofizika* No. 10.

Kuznetsov, Yu.A. 1963. Magmaticheskie formatsii i nekotorye obshchie voprosy geologii (Magmatic deposits and some general problems of geology). *Geologiya i Geofizika*, No. 5.

Kuznetsov, Yu.A. 1964. Glavnye Tipy Magmaticheskikh Formatsii (Principal types of magmatic deposits). "Nedra" publishers.

Landa, E.A. 1966. O kharaktere zameshcheniya karbonatitani vmeshchayushchikh porod na primere Maimecha-Kotuiskoi provintskii (On the nature of replacement of mixed rocks by carbonatites, principally from Maimecha-Kotui Province). In the book: *Mat-ly 2-i Konferentsii po Okolorudromu Metasomatizmu.* VSEGEI pub., Leningrad.

Landa, E.A. 1967. O genezise ultrabazitov v intruzivnykh shchelochno-ultraosnovnykh massivakh Maimecha-Kotuiskoi provintsii (On the origin of ultrabasites in intrusive alkaline-ultrabasic massifs of Maimecha-Kotui Province). *Zap. Vses. Miner. Ob-va*, part 96, No. 4.

Landes, K.K. 1931. A paragenetic classification of the Magnet Cove minerals. *Amer. Mineralogist*, 16.

Landes, K.K., B. Parks and V.E. Scheid. 1932. Magnet Cove, Arkansas. Internat. Geol. Congr. 16th Sess., Guidebook 2, Excurs. α-2.

Lapin, A.V. 1960. K voprosu o genezise melilitovykh porod Kovdorskogo massiva (On the problem of the origin of melilitic rocks of the Kovdor massif). *Tezisy Dokladov 2-i Konf. Molodykh Nauchn. Sotr.* IMGRE, Moscow.

Lapin, A.V. 1962. O protsesse melilitizatsii v Kovdorskom massive ultraosnovnykh shchelochnykh porod (On the process of melilitization in alkaline-ultrabasic rocks of the Kovdor massif). In the book: *Redkie Elementy v Massivakh Shchelochnykh Porod. Trudy IMGRE*, vol. 9, USSR Academy of Sciences pub.

Lapin, A.V. 1963. Nefelinizatsiya piroksenitov i zhilnye iiolity v Kovdorskom massive ultraosnovnykh shchelochnykh porod (Nephelinitization of pyroxenites and ijolites in alkaline-ultrabasic rocks of the Kovdor massif). *Izv. AN SSSR, ser. geol.*, No. 5.

Lapin, A.V. and A.G. Zhabin. 1966. Nodulyarnye tekstury khromita v dunite kak rezultata neravnovesnoi evtekticheskoi kristallizatsii (Nodular textures of chromite in dunites due to non-uniform eutectic crystallization). *Dokl. AN SSSR*, 163, No. 5.

Lapin, A.V. and M.E. Kazakova. 1966. O titanovom lueshite iz Kovdorskogo massiva i izomorfizme v gruppe perovksita (Titanium-rich lueshite from the Kovdor massif and isomorphism in the perovskite group). *Dokl. AN SSSR*, 171, No. 4.

Larsen, E.S. 1942. Alkalic rocks of Iron Hill, Gunnison County, Colorado. U.S. Geol. Surv. Profess. Paper, 197-A.

Larsen, E.S. and R.A. Goranson. 1932. The deuteric and later alteration of the uncompahgrite of Iron Hill, Colorado. *Amer. Mineralogist*, 17.

Larsen, E.S. and J.T. Pardee. 1929. The stock of alkaline rocks near Libby, Montana. *J. Geol.*, 37.

Lavrenev, Yu.B. 1960. Nekotorye cherty ultraosnovnoi shchelochnoi formatsii Vostochnoi Sibiri (A few characters of alkaline ultrabasic deposits of Eastern Siberia). *Min. Syre*, No. 1.

Lavrenev, Yu.B. and L.K. Pozharitskaya. 1958. Novyi tip shchelochnykh intruzii v Vostochnom Sayane (New type of alkaline intrusives in East Sayan). In the book: *Mat-ly 2-go Vses. Petrograf. Soveshchaniya*. Uzbek Acad. of Sciences pub., Tashkent.

Leonardos, O.H. 1956a. Carbonatitos com apatita e pirocloro. Brasil. Div. Fomento. Prod. Mineral. Avulso 80.

Leonardos, O.H. 1956b. Recursos minerais do Triangulo. *Mineiro. Engenharia, miner. metalurgia*, 24 (142).

Letnikov, F.A. and Z.V. Zagumennova. 1962. O nakhodke karbonatitov v Severnom Kazakhstane (Occurrence of carbonatite in Northern Kazakhstan). *Trudy Kaz. In-ta Miner. Syrya*, No. 7.

Letnikov, F.A. and N.P. Pankratova. 1966. Obrazovanie karbonatitov i soputstvuyushchego orudeneniya v ultraosnovnykh shchelochnykh porodakh Kokchetavskoi glyby (Formation of carbonatites and associated ore-deposition in alkaline ultrabasic rocks of the Kokchetavskaya block). In the book: *Mat-ly 2-i Konferentsii po Okolorudnomu Metasomatizu*. VSEGEI pub.

Lukanina, M.I. 1959. Svanbergit v boksitakh Kamenskogo raiona na Srednem Urale (Svanbergite in bauxite of the Kamenskii region in Central Ural). *Zap. Vses. Miner. Ob-va*, part 88, No. 5.

Marshintsev, V.K., S.G. Shchelchkova, G.V. Zolnikov and B.B. Voskresenskaya. 1966. Novye dannye o mussanite iz kimberlitov Yakutii (New information about moissanite from kimberlite of Yakutia). *Geologiya i Giofizika* No.10.

Maurice, O.D. 1949. Transport and deposition of the non-sulfide vein minerals. V. Zirconium minerals. *Econ. Geol.*, 44, No. 8.

Maurice, O.D. 1956. Geology of Oka Hills. *Canad. Mining J.* 1956.

Maurice, O.D. 1957. Preliminary report on Oka area, electoral district of Deux-Montagnes. Quebec Dept. Mines and Mineral Dept. Bull. Progr. Rept., 351.

McCall, G.J.H. 1958. Geology of the Gwasi area. Kenya Geol. Surv. Rept., 45.

McCall, G.J.H. 1959. Alkaline and carbonatite ring complexes in the Kavirondo rift valley, Kenya. Internat. Geol. Congr. 20 Sess. Assoc. Serv. Geol. Africanos.

McCall, G.J.H. 1963. A reconsideration of certain aspects of the Rangwa and Ruri carbonatite complexes in Western Kenya. *Geol. Mag.*, 100.

McConnell, D. and J. Gruner. 1940. Carbonate apatite from Magnet Cove, Arkansas. *Amer. Mineralogist*, 25, No. 3.

McKie, D. 1962. Goyazite and florencite from two African carbonatites. *Mineral. Mag.*, 33.

Melcher, G.C. 1954. Nota sobre o distrito alcalino de Jacupiranga, São Paulo. Div. Geol. Miner, Notas Prelim., No. 84.

Meyer, A. and P. de Bethune. 1958. La carbonatite Lueshe (Kivu). *Congo Belge Serv. Geol. Bull.*, 8 (5).

Meyer, A. and P. de Bethune. 1960. The Lueshe carbonatite (Kivu, Belgian Congo). Internat. Geol. Congr. 21 Sess. Rept., Pt. 13

Mikheenko, V.I. 1967. Karbonatity na vostoke Tungusskoi sineklizy (Carbonatites in the Eastern Tunguskaya Syncline). *Geologiya i Geofizika*, No. 5.

Mikheev, V.I. 1957. Rentgenometricheskii Opredelitel Mineralov (X-ray analysis of minerals). Gosgeoltekh pub.

Milashev, V.A., M.A. Krutoyarskii, M.I. Rabkin and E.N. Erlikh. 1963. Kimberlitovye porody i pikritovye profiry Severo-Vostochnoi chasti Sibirskoi platformy (Kimberlitic rocks and picrite porphyrites in the northeastern part of the Siberian platform). *Trudy NIIGA*, 126.

Milton, C., M.E. Mrose, J.J. Fahey and E.C.T. Chao. Labuntsovite from the Trona Mine, Sweetwater County, Wyoming. *Bull. Geol. Soc. America*, 69, No. 12.

Milton, C., M.E. Mrose, J.J. Fahey and E.C.T. Chao. 1959. Norsethite, $BaMg(CO_3)_2$, a new mineral from the Green River Formation, Wyoming. *Bull. Geol. Soc. America*, 70, No. 12.

Milton, C., B.L. Ingram and L.V. Blade. 1961. Kimzeyite, a zirconium garnet from Magnet Cove, Arkansas. *Amer. Mineralogist*, 46.

Moor, G.G. 1940. O shchelochnoi provintsii na severe Sibirskoi platformy

(The alkaline province in the north of the Siberian platform). *Dokl. AN SSSR*, 29, No. 3.

Moor, G.G. 1957a. Differentsirovannye shchelochnye intruzi severnoi okrainy Sibirskoi platformy (Differentiated alkaline intrusives in the northern part of the Siberian platform). *Izv. AN SSSR, ser. geol.*, No. 8.

Moor, G.G. 1957b. Zhilnye shchelochnye bazaltoidy iz severnoi okrainy Sibirskoi platformy (Alkaline basaltoid veins from the northern part of the Siberian platform). *Dokl. AN SSSR*, 116, No. 3.

Moor, G.G. 1958. O vozraste ultraosnovnykh i shchelochnykh porod severa Sibirskoi platformy (On the age of alkaline ultrabasic rocks of the Northern Siberian platform). *Inform Byull. NIIGA*, No. 8.

Motychko, V.F. 1957. K voprosu o genezise melilitovykh porod massiva Odikhincha (Origin of melilitic rocks of the Odikhincha massif). *Inform. Byull. NIIGA*, No. 4.

Motychko, V.F. 1958. Olivinity i slyudity massiva Odikhinca (Olivinites and micas of the Odikhincha massif). *Inform. Byull. NIIGA*, No. 10.

Motychko, V.F. 1959. Karbonatity massiva Odikhinchai ikh genezis (Carbonatite massifs of Odikhincha and their origin). *Trudy NIIGA*, 107, No. 12.

Nalivkin, D.V. and others. 1956. Geologicheskaya Karta SSSR Mashtaba 1 : 2500000 (Geological map of the USSR. Scale 1 : 2500000). VSEGEI pub., Leningrad.

Nickel, E.H. 1956. Niocalite, a new calcium-niobium silicate mineral. *Amer. Mineralogist*, 41.

Nickel, E.H. 1964. Latrappite—a proposed new name for the perovskite-type calcium niobate mineral from the Oka area of Quebec. *Canad. Dept. Mines Techn. Surv. Mines Mem. Miner.*, 8.

Odman, O. 1952. The Jacupiranga phosphate deposit, São Paulo, *Brasil. Engenhuria Miner. metalurgia*, 21, No. 124.

Olson, J.C. and S.R. Wallace. 1956. Thorium and rare-earth minerals in Powderhorn district, Gunnison County, Colorado. *U.S. Geol. Surv. Bull.*, 1027–O.

Olson, J.C., D.R. Schawe, L.C. Pray and W.N. Sharp. 1954. Rare-earth mineral deposits of the Mountain Pass District, San Bernardino County, California. U.S. Geol. Surv. Profess. Paper, 261.

Orlova, M.P. 1963. Nekotorye voprosy petrokhimii i petrologii kaledonskogo kompleksa shchelochno-ultraosnovnykh porod Kolskogo poluostrova (Some problems of petrochemistry and petrology of the Caledonian alkaline-ultrabasic complex of the Kola Peninsula). *Trudy VSEGEI, nov. ser.*, 96.

Orlova, M.P. 1959. O genezise turyaitov Salmagorskogo massiva na Kolskom poluostrove (Origin of turjites of the Salmagorskii massif in the Kola Peninsula). *Mat-ly VSEGEI, nov. ser.*, No. 26.

Orlova, M.P. and A.A. Kukharenko. 1962. Melility iz shchelochno-ultraosnovnykh massivov Kolskogo poluostrova (Melilites from alkaline-ultrabasic massifs of the Kola Peninsula). *Uch. Zap. LGU, ser. geol. nauk.* vol. 312, No. 13.

Orlova, M.P., Yu.P. Rozhdestvenskii and E.N. Baranova. 1963. K mineralogii redkometalnykh karbonatitov Sallanlatvinskogo massiva (Sev. Karelia) [Mineralogy of rare-metallic carbonatites of the Sallanlatva massif (North Karelia)]. *Trudy VSEGEI, nov.* ser., 96.

Parker, R.L., J.W. Adams and F.A. Hildebrand. 1962. A rare sodium niobate mineral from Colorado. U.S. Geol. Surv. Profess. Paper, 450-C.

Parson, G.E. 1957. Nemegosenda Lake columbium area. *Canad. Mining J.*, 78.

Parsons, G.E. 1961. Niobium-bearing complexes east of Lake Superior. Ontario Dept. Mines and Geol. Rept., 3.

Pecora, W.T. 1956. Carbonatites. *Bull. Geol. Soc. America*, 67, No. 11.

Pecora, W.T. 1962. Carbonatite problem in the Bearpaw Mountains, Montana. Geol. Soc. America, Buddington vol.

Pecora, W.T. and J.H. Kerr. 1953. Burbankite and calkinsite, two new carbonate minerals from Montana. *Amer. Mineralogist*, 38.

Perrault, G. 1959. Determination de la composition chimique de pyrochlore d'Oka par spectrofluorescence des rayons X. *Ingénieur, éte*, 1959.

Phillips, K.A. 1955. Some notes on the carbonatite at Nkumbwa Hill, Isoka District. Northern Rhodesia. Geol. Surv. Rec. for 1953.

Polkin, Ya.I. 1958. Trubki vzryva shchelochnykh bazaltoidov severozapdnoi chasti Sibirskoi platformy (Volcanic pipes of alkaline basaltoids in the northwestern part of the Siberian platform). *Inform. Byull. NIIGA*, No. 10.

Popova, V.A. 1964. Novye vykhody karbonatitov v Yuzhno-Kolskoi zone tsentralnykh intruzii (New outlets of carbonatites in the South Kola zone of the central intrusives). *Geokhimiya*, No. 4.

Portnov, A.M. and E.A. Nechaeva. 1967. Nefelinizatsiya v prikoStaktovykh zonakh shchelochnogo massiva Burpala (Severnoe Pribaikale) [Nephelinization in the contact zones of alkaline massif of Burpal (North Baikal region)]. *Izv. AN SSSR, ser. geol.*, No. 5.

Pozharitskaya, L.K. 1960. Karbonatity ultraosnovnogo shchelochnogo kompleksa Vostochnoi Sibiri (Alkaline ultrabasic carbonatite complex of East Siberia). In the book: *Mineralnoe Syre*, vol. 1, Gosgeoltekhizdat pub.

Pozharitskaya, L.K. 1966. O genezise karbonatitov (Origin of carbonatites). In the book: *Osobennosti Petrologii, Mineralogii i Geokhimii Karbonatitov Vostohnoi Sibiri.* "Nauka" publishers.

Pozharitskaya, L.K. and E.A. Razvozzhaeva. 1966. O sodepzhanii redkikh elementov v magnetitakh i slyudakh iz karbonatitov Vostochnoi Sibiri (Presence of rare-earth elements in magnetite and micas in carbonatites of

Eastern Siberia). In the book: *Osobennosti Petrologii, Mineralogii i Geokhimii Karbonatitov Vostochnoi Sibiri.* "Nauka" publishers.

Pozharitskaya, L.K. and E.M. Epshtein. 1963. K voprosu o genezise karbonatitov (Origin of carbonatites). In the book: *Geokhimiya Redkikh Elementov v Izverzhennykh Gornykh Porodakh.* "Nauka" publishers.

Pozharitskaya, L.K. and E.M. Epshtein. 1964. Petrokhimicheskie osobennosti protsessa obrazovaniya karbonatitov (Petrochemical characteristics of the process of carbonatite formation). In the book: *Proiskhozhdenie shchelochnykh Porod.* "Nauka" publishers.

Pozharitskaya, L.K., G.V. Pavlinskii, E.A. Razvozzhaeva and V.S. Samoilov. 1966. O tsirkelite odnogo iz karbonatitovykh massivov (On zirkelite from one of the carbonatite massifs). In the book: *Osobennosti Petrologii, Mineralogii i Geokhimii Karbonatitov Vostochnoi Sibiri.* "Nauka" publishers.

Pozharitskaya, L.K., V.S. Samoilov, G.S. Gormasheva and others. 1966. Statiinost', fatsii i zonalnost karbonatitov Vostochnoi Sibiri (Stages, facies and zoning in carbonatites of Eastern Siberia). In the book: *Mat-ly 2-i Konferentsii po Okolorudnomy Metasomatizmu.* VSEGEI pub., Leningrad.

Pray, L.C. and W.N. Sharp. 1951. Bastnaesite discoveries near Mountain Pass, California (abstr). *Bull. Geol. Soc. America*, 62.

Prider, R.T. 1939. The new mineral wadeite from Australia. *Mineral. Mag.*, 25, No. 166.

Pyatenko, Yu.A. and Z.V. Pudovkina. 1951. O kristallicheskoi strukture kaltsirtita—novoi proizvodnoi strukturnogo tipa CaF_2-CeO_2 (Crystalline structure of calzirtite—new derivative of CaF_2-CeO_2 structural type). *Kristallografia*, 6, No. 2.

Pyatenko, Yu.A. and Z.V. Pudovkina. 1964. Rentgenograficheskoe issledovanie tsirkonolita i ego sinteticheskogo analoga (X-ray analysis of zirconolite and its synthetic analogue). In the book: *Rentgenografiya Miner. Syrya.* No. 4. "Nedra" publishers.

Rabkin, M.I. 1960. Kimberlity severnoi chasti Sibirskoi platformy (bassein r. Olenek) i voprosy ikh genezisa [Kimberlites of the northern part of the Siberian platform (basin of the river Olenik) and problems of their origin]. In the book: *Magmatism i Svyaz s Nim Poleznykh Iskopaemykh.* Gosgeoltekhizdat pub.

Reeve, W.H. and T. Deans. 1954. An occurrence of carbonatite in the Isoka District of Northern Rhodesia. *Colon. Geol. and Mineral Resources*, 4.

Reverdatto, V.V. and A.K. Salko. 1966. O temperature magmy ultraosnovnogo massiva Bor-Uryakh (On the temperature of magma of the Bor-Uryakh ultrabasic massif). *Geologiya i Geofizika*, No. 12.

Rimskaya-Korsakova, O.M. 1947. Mineralogiya Enskogo zhelezorundnogo mestorozhdeniya (Mineralogy of the Enskii iron-ore deposits). In the book: *Problemy Severo-zapadnoi Metallurgii,* SOPS AN SSSR pub., Leningrad.

Rimskaya-Korsakova, O.M. 1950. K voprosu o zakonomernykh srastaniyakh shpineli s magnetitom (The problem of regular concrescence of spinel with magnetite). *Zap. Vses. Miner. Ob-va,* part 79, No. 3.

Rimskaya-Korsakova, O.M. 1959. Kristallograficheskoe izuchenie forsterita iz karbonatitov i magnetitovyky rud Kovdorskogo massiva (Kolskiip-ov) [Crystallographic study of forsterite from carbonatite and magnetite ores of the Kovdor massif (Kola Peninsula)]. In the book: *Mat-ly po Mineralogii Kolskogo p-ova,* vol. 1, Kirovsk.

Rimskaya-Korsakova, O.M. 1963. K voprosu o genezise Kovdorskogo zhelezorudnogo mestorozhdeniya (On the origin of the Kovdor iron-ore deposit). In the book: *Voprosy Magmatizma i Metamorfizma,* vol. 1, LGU pub.

Rimskaya-Korsakova, O.M., T.A. Burova and V.A. Frank-Kamenetskii. 1963. Lueshit iz karbonatitov Kovdorskogo massiva (Kolskii p-ov) [Lueshite from carbonatites of the Kovdor massif (Kola Peninsula)]. *Zap. Vses. Miner. Ob-va,* part 92, No. 3.

Rimskaya-Korsakova, O.M. and E.P. Sokolova. 1964. O zhelezisto-magnezialnykh slyudakh s obratnoi skhemoi absorbtsii (On ferromagnesian micas with reverse scheme of absorption). *Zap. Vses. Miner. Ob-va,* part 93, No. 4.

Rimskaya-Korsakova, O.M. and I.G. Dinaburg. 1964. Baddeleit v massivakh ultraosnovnykh-shchelochnykh porod Kolskogo poluostrova (Baddeleyite in the massifs of the ultrabasic alkaline rocks of the Kola Peninsula). In the book: *Mineralogiya i Geokhimiya,* vol. 1, LGU pub.

Ronenson, B.M. 1966. Proiskhozhdenie miaskitov i svyaz s nimi redkometalnogo orudeneniya (Origin of miaskites and their association with rare-metallic rocks). *Geol. M-nii Redkikh Elementov,* No. 31.

Rose, H.J., L.V. Blade and M. Ross. 1958. Earthy monazite at Magnet Cove, Arkansas. *Amer. Mineralogist,* 43.

Rowe, R.B. 1958. Niobium (columbium) deposits of Canada. *Geol. Surv. Econ. Geol., Ser.* 18.

Rub, M.G. and B.L. Zalishchak. 1964. Shchelochnye intruzivnye porody Primorskogo kraya (Alkaline intrusive rocks of the Primorskii territory). *Izv. AN SSSR, ser. geol.,* No. 10.

Russel, H.D., S.A. Hiemstra and D. Groeneveld. 1954. The mineralogy and petrology of the carbonatite at Loolekop, Eastern Transvaal. *Trans. and Proc. Geol. Soc. South Africa,* 57.

Rust, G.W. 1937. Preliminary notes on explosive volcanism in southeastern Missouri. *J. Geol.,* 45.

Ruzhitskii, V.O. 1963. O trubkakh vzryva na Russkoi platforme (On the volcanic pipes of the Russian platform). *Dokl. AN SSSR,* 152, No. 2.

Saether, E. 1948. The genesis of peralkaline rock provinces. Internat. Geol.

Congr. 18 Sess., Pt. II.

Saether, E. 1958. The alkaline rock province of the Fen area in Southern Norway. *Kgl. Norske vidselskab. skr.*, 1957, No. 1.

Safiannikoff, A. 1959. Un nouveau mineral de niobium. *Bull. Seances roy. Acad., outre-mer.*, 5.

Sahinen, U.M. 1957. Mines and mineral deposits of Missoula and Ravalli Counties, Montana. *Montana Bur. Mines Geol. Bull.*, 8.

Saltyakova, V.S. 1959. Analizy mineralov, soderzhashchekh redkie elementy, vypolnennye khimicheskoi laboratoriei IMGRE (Analysis of minerals containing rare elements conducted by the IMGRE laboratory). *Trudy IMGRE*, No. 2.

Samoilov, V.S. and G.S. Gormasheva. 1966. O fiziko-khimicheskikh usloviyakh shchelochno-karbonatnogo metasomatoza (On physical and chemical conditions of the alkaline carbonatite metasomatism). In the book: *Osobennosti Petrologii, Mineralogii i Geokhimii Karbonatitov Vostochnoi Sibiri.* "Nauka" publishers.

Sampson, D.N. 1956. The volcanic Hills at Igwisi. Tang. Geol. Surv. Rec., 3.

Schneiderhon, H. 1941. Lehrbuch der Erzlagerstattenkunde. B.I. Die Lagerstatten der magmatischen Abfolge. Jena, Verlag G. Fischer.

Searle, D.L. 1952. Geology of the area northwest Kitale Township (Trans Nzioa, Elgon and West Suk). Kenya Geol. Surv. Rept., 19.

Semenov, E.I. 1959a. Izomorfnyi ryad labuntsovit-nenadkevichit (Isomorphic series labuntsovite-nenadkevichite). *Trudy IMGRE*, No. 2.

Semenov, E.I. 1959b. K mineralogii shchelochnykh pegmatitov Khibinskikh i Lovozerskikh tundr (Mineralogy of alkaline pegmatites of the Khibinskaya and Lovozerskaya tundra). In the book: *Mat-ly po Mineralogii Kolskogo P-ova.* vol. 1, Kirovsk.

Semenov, E.I. 1963. Mineralogiya Redkikh Zemel (Rare-earth mineralogy). "Nauka" publishers.

Semenov, E.I. 1965. Vinogradovit-shiroki rasprostranennyi titanovyi mineral (Vinogradovite—a widely found titanium mineral). In the book: *Problemy Geokhimii.* "Nauka" publishers.

Semenov, E.I. and T.A. Burova. 1955. O novom minerale labuntsovite i o tak nazyvaemom titanoelpidite (On the new mineral labuntsovite and so-called titanoelpidite). *Dokl. AN SSSR*, 101, No. 6.

Semenov, E.I. and M.E. Kazakova. 1959. Ankilit v shchelochnykh pegmatitakh Kolskogo poluostrova (Ancylite in the alkaline pegmatites of the Kola Peninsula). *Trudy Miner. Muzeya AN SSSR*, No. 11.

Semenov, E.I., A.P. Khomyakov and A.V. Bykova. 1960. Gipergennyi bastnezit v kore vyvetrivaniya shchelochnogo massiva (Hypergenic bastnaesite in the weathering crust of the alkaline massif). *Trudy Miner. Muzeya AN SSSR*, No. 11.

Semenov, E.I., M.E. Kazakova and V.I. Simonov. 1958. Novyi mineral seidozerit i drugie mineraly gruppy velerita v shchelochnykh pegmatitakh (New mineral seidozerite and other minerals of wöhlerite group in the alkaline pegmatites). *Zap. Vses. Miner. Ob-va*, part 87, No. 5.

Semenov, E.I., E.M. Bonshtedt, V.A. Moleva and N.N. Sludskaya. 1956. Vinogradovit-novyi mineral (Vinogradovite—a new mineral). *Dokl. AN SSSR*, 109, No. 3.

Serba, B.I. 1962. Sallanlatvinskii massiv shchelochnyky porod i karbonatitov (Sallanlatvian massif of alkaline rocks and carbonatites). In the book: *Magmaticheskie Obrazovaniya Kol's-kogo n-ova.* Izd-vo AN SSSR.

Sergeev, A.S. 1959. Fenity i protsessy fenitizatsii v kontaktovom oreole shchelochnykh i ultraosnovnykh intruzii khabozerskoi gruppy (Koskii poluostrov) [Fenites and the process of fenitization at the contact of aureoles of alkaline and ultrabasic intrusives of the Khabozerskii group (Kola Peninsula)]. *Zap. Vses. Miner. Ob-va*, part 88, No. 4.

Sergeev, A.S. 1961. Oksonievyi pirokhlor iz fenitov Kolskogo poluostrova (Accessory pyrochlore from fenites of the Kola Peninsula). *Zap. Vses. Miner. Ob-va*, part 90, No. 4.

Sergeev, A.S. 1962. Fenitizirovannye porody Kovdorskogo massiva (Fenitized rocks of the Kovdor massif). *Uch. Zap. LGU, ser. geol. nauk*, No. 312, vol. 13.

Sergeev, A.S. 1963. Fenity v paleozoiskom komplekse ultraosnovnykh shchelochnykh porod Kolskogo poluostrova (Fenites in the Paleozoic complex of alkaline ultrabasic rocks of the Kola Peninsula). *Trudy Leningr. Ob-va Estestvoispyt.*, 73, No. 1.

Sergeev, A.S. 1967. Fenity Kompleksa Ultraosnovnykh i Shchelochnykh Porod (Fenites from the complex of ultrabasic and alkaline rocks). LGU pub.

Shand, S.J. 1921. The igneous complex of Leeuwfontein, Pretoria district. *Trans. and Proc. Geol. Soc. South Africa*, 24.

Shand, S.J. 1928. The geology of Pilansberg (Pilan's Berg) in the Western Transvaal: a study of alkaline rocks and ring-intrusions. *Trans. and Proc. Geol. Soc. South Africa*, 31.

Shand, S.J. 1931. The granite-syenite-limestone complex of Palabora, Eastern Transvaal, and its associated apatite deposits. *Trans. and Proc. Geol. Soc. South Africa*, 34.

Shand, S.J. 1947. Eruptive rocks. N.Y.

Shanin, L.L., V.A. Kononova and I.B. Ivanov. 1967. O primenenii nefelina v K-Ar geokhronometrii (Application of nepheline in K-Ar geochronology). *Izv. AN SSSR, ser. geol.*, No. 5.

Sheinmann, Yu.M. 1946. Nekotorye cherty geologii severa Sibirskoi platformy (A few geological characteristics of the northern part of the Siberian platform). *Izv. AN SSSR, ser. geol.*, No. 3.

Sheinmann. Yu.M. 1947. O novoi petrograficheskoi provintsii na severe Sibirskoi platformy (A new petrographic province in the north of the Siberian platform). *Izv. AN SSSR, ser. geol.*, No. 1.

Sheinmann, Yu.M. 1955. Nekotorye geologicheskie osobennosti ultraosnovnykh i ultrashchelochnykh magmaticheskikh obrazovanii na platformakh (Some geological characteristics of ultrabasic and ultra-alkaline magmatic deposits in the platforms). *Zap. Vses. Miner. Ob-va*, part 84, No. 2.

Sheinmann, Yu.M. 1956. Nekotorye zakonomernosti rasprostraneniya vulkanicheskikh yavlenii na platformakh (Some rules governing the presence of volcanic activity in platforms). *Trudy. Vses. Aerogeol. Tresta*, No. 2.

Sheinmann, Yu.M. 1957. O polozhenii i vozraste shchelochnykh ultraosnovnykh porod Sibirskoi platformy (On the occurrence and age of alkaline ultrabasic rocks of the Siberian Platform). *Razvedka i Okhrana Nedr*, No. 1.

Sheinmann, Yu.M. 1960a. O prirode iiolit-melteigitov (On the nature of ijolite-melteigites). *Izv. AN SSSR, ser. geol.*, No. 12.

Sheinmann, Yu.M. 1960b. O svyazi shchelochnykh magmaticheskikh formatsii s krupneishimi strukturami materikov (Association of alkaline magmatic formations with large structures). In the book: *Magmatizm i Svyaz' s Nim Poleznykh Iskopaemykh*. Gosgeoltekhizdat pub.

Sheinmann, Yu.M. 1969. Ocherky Glubinnoi Geologii (Nature of deep-seated geology). "Nauka" publishers.

Sheinmann, Yu.M., F.R. Apeltsin and E.A. Nechaeva. 1961. Shchelochnye Intruzii, Ikh Razmeshchenie i Svyazannaya s Nimi Mineralizatsiya (Alkaline intrusives, their distribution and association with other mineralization). Gosgeoltekhizdat pub.

Shikhorina, K.M. 1959. Effuzivnye porody, vmeshchaytoshchie Gulinskuyu intruziyu (Effusive rocks associated with Gulinskii intrusion). *Trudy NIIGA*, 102.

Shurkin, K.A. 1960. O "konglomeratakh" Kandalakshskikh ostrovov i Turego mysa (On the conglomerates of the Kandalakshskie islands and Turi Mis). *Trudy Labor. Geol. Dokembriya*, No. 9.

Singewald, J.T. Jr. and C. Milton. 1930. An alnöite pipe, its contact phenomena, and ore deposition near Avon, Missouri. *J. Geol.*, 38.

Smirnov, A.D., I.B. Nedumov and V.V. Buldakov. 1963. Rifieskie Struktury Vostochnogo Sayana i Polozhenie v Nikh Pegmatitovykh Polei (Rift structures of East Sayan and their occurrence in the pegmatitic zones). Izd-vo AN SSSR.

Smith, W.C. 1953. Carbonatites of the Chilwa Series of southern Nyasaland. *Brit. Mus.* (*Natur. Hist.*) Min., 1, No. 4.

Smith, W.C. 1956. A review of some problems of African carbonatites. *Quart. J. Geol. Soc.* London, 112, No. 446.

Sobolev, N.D. 1947a. Petrografiya raiona Enskogo zhelezorudnogo mestorozhdeniya (Petrography of the region of the Enskii iron-ore deposits).

In the book: *Problemy Severo-zapadnoi Metallurgii*. SOPS AN SSSR pub., Leningrad.

Sobolev, N.D. 1947b. Khimicheskii sostav i opticheskie svoistva mineralov gruppy olivina raiona Enskogo mestorozhdeniya (Chemical composition and optical properties of the olivine group of minerals from the Yenisei deposits). *Dokl. AN SSSR*, 57, No. 6.

Sobolev, N.D. 1951. Egirin-diopsidy shchelochno-osnovnykh gornykh porod (Aegirine-diopside-rich alkaline and basic rocks). In the book: *Megnezialnye Gornye Porody*. Gosgeoltekhizdat pub.

Sobolev, V.S. 1949. Vvedenie v Mineralogiyu Siliakatov (Introduction of silicate mineralogy). Lvov.

Sobolev, V.S. 1960. Usloviya obrazovaniya mestorozhdenii almazov (Conditions of diamond formation). *Geologiya i Geofizika*, No. 1.

Somina, R.Ya. 1966. Trigonalnyi molibdenit iz karbonatitov Vostochnoi Sibiri (Trigonal molybdenite from carbonatites of East Siberia). *Dokl. AN SSSR*, 167, No. 4.

Somina, R.Ya. and A.G. Bulakh. 1966. Florensit iz karbonatitov Vostochnogo Sayana i nekotorye voprosy khimicheskoi konstitutsii gruppy krandallita (Florencite from carbonatites of East Sayan and some problems in the chemical composition of the crandallite group of minerals). *Zap. Vses. Miner. Ob-va*, part 95, No. 5.

Sörum, H. 1955. Contributions to the mineralogy of the Söve deposit I-II. *Kgl. Norske Vid. forhandl.*, 28.

Stille, H. 1942. Die tektonische Entwicklung Americas als der Ostumrahmung des Pazifik. Geotekton. Forsch., No. 2.

Stoyalov, S.P. 1961. Arbarastakhskii massiv ultraosnovnykh i shchelochnykh porod (Arbarastakhskii massif of ultrabasic and alkaline rocks). *Trudy Vses. Aerogeol. Tresta*, No. 7.

Strauss, E.A. and F.C. Truter. 1951a. The alkali complex at Spitzkop, Sekukuniland, Eastern Transvaal. *Trans. and Proc. Geol. Soc. South Africa*, 53.

Strauss, E.A. and F.G. Truter. 1951b. Post-Bushveld ultrabasic, alkalic and carbonatitic eruptives at Magnet Heights, Sekukuniland, Eastern Transvaal. *Trans. and Proc. Geol. Soc. South Africa*, 53.

Strüver, G. 1887. Contribution alia mineralogia del vulcani sabatini. *N. Jahrb. Mineral., Geol., Paleontol.*, 2.

Sudovikov, N.G. 1946. Petrologiya Kovdozerskogo kompleksa shchelochnykh porod (Petrology of the Kovdozerskii complex of alkaline rocks). *Uch. Zap. LGU. ser. geol. pochv. geogr. nauk*, 23, No. 14.

Sukheswala, R.N. and G.R. Udas. 1963. Note on the carbonatite of Amba Dongar (Gujarat State) and its economic potentialities. *Sci. and Culture*, 29, No. 11.

Sutherland, D.S. 1965. Potash-trachytes and ultrapotassic rocks associated with the carbonatite complex of the Toror. Hills, Uganda. *Mineral. Mag.*, 35.

Taylor, R. 1955. The magnetite-vermiculite occurrences of Bukusu, Mbale District. Uganda Geol. Surv. Rec. for 1953.

Temple, A.K. 1959. Petrology of the Nemegosenda alkaline complex, Ontario (abstr.). *Bull. Geol. Soc. America*, 70.

Temple, A.K. and R.M. Grogan. 1965. Carbonatite and related alkalic rocks at Powderhorn, Colorado. *Econ. Geol.*, 60.

Terner, F. and J. Ferkhugen. 1961. Petrologiya Izverzhennykh i Metamorficheskikh Porod (Petrology of igneous and metamorphic rocks). IL.

Ternovoi, V.I. 1960. Kovdorskoe mestrorozhdenie vermikulita (Kolskii p-ov) [Vermiculite deposits of Kovdor (Kola Peninsula]. *Razvedka i Okhrana Nedr*, No. 5.

Tikhonenkov, I.P., M.V. Kukharchik and Yu.A. Pyatenko. 1960. O vadeite iz khibinskogo massiva i usloviya ego obrazovaniya (Occurrence of wadeite from the Khibinskii massif and conditions of its formation). *Dokl. AN SSSR*, 134, No. 4.

Tikhonenkov, I.P. and M.E. Kazakova. 1957. Nioboroparitnovyi mineral iz gruppy perovskita (Nioboloparite, a new mineral of the perovskite group of minerals). *Zap. Vses. Miner. Ob-va*, part 86, No. 6.

Tikhonenkova, R.P. 1962. Genezis kontaktnykh porod Lovozerskogo massiva (Origin of contact rocks of the Lovozerskii massif). *Byull. MOIP, otdel geol.*, 35, No. 4.

Tikhonenkova, R.P. and M.E. Kazakova. 1964. Pervaya nakhodka berbankita v massive nefelinovykh sienitov (First occurrence of burbankite in nepheline-syenite massifs). In the book: *Mineralogiya i Geneticheskie Osobennosti Shchelochnykh Massivov*. "Nauka" publishers.

Thoreau, J., B. Aderca and L. van Wambeke. 1958. Le gisement de terres rares de la Karonge (Urundi). *Bull. Acad. roy. sci. colon. Cl. sci. natur. et med.*, 4, No. 3.

Tokmakov, P.P. 1961. Kovdorskoe mestorozhdenie vermikulita i usloviya ego obrazovaniya (Kovdor deposits of vermiculite and conditions of its formation). *Trudy IGEM AN SSSR*, No. 48.

Tsvetkov, A.I. 1951. Izomorfnye zameshcheniya v gruppe besshchelochnykh piroksenov (Isomorphous replacement in the non-alkaline pyroxene group of minerals). *Trudy In-ta Geol. Nauk AN SSSR*, 13, No. 4.

Tsyrulnikova, R.Ya., E.K. Chechel, L.E. Shustova and R.S. Sokol. 1967. Glubinnoe stroenie vostochnoi chasti Baltiiskogo shchita (Deeper structure of the eastern part of the Baltic Shield). In the book: *Geologiya i Glubinnoe Stroenie Vostochnoi Chasti Baltiiskogo Shchita*. "Nedra" publishers.

Tuchkova, M.I. 1959. Ilmenorutil iz karbonatitov Severnoi chasti Sibirskoi platformy (Ilmenorutile from carbonatites of the northern part of the

Siberian platform). *Inform. Byull. NIIGA*, No. 14.

Tuttle, O.F. and P.J. Wyllie. 1958. Calcite-water join in the system CaO-CO_2-H_2O (abstr.). *Bull. Geol. Soc. America*, 69.

Tuttle, O.F. and J. Gittins et al., 1967. Carbonatites. New York, London, Sydney.

Upton, B.G.J. 1961. The alkaline igneous complex of Kungnat Field, South Greenland. *Medd. Gronland*, 123, No. 6.

Valachi, L.Z. and O.C. Kopp. 1965. Petrographic study of the Norris peridotite, Union County. Tennessee (abstr.). *Geol. Soc.* America, Spec. Paper, 82.

Van der Veen, A.H. 1963. A study of pyrochlore. Verhandel Koninkl. nederl. geol. mijnbouw. Gen., Geol. Ser., 22.

Van der Veen, A.H. 1965a. Calzirtite and associated minerals from Tapira, Brasil. *Mineral. Mag.*, 35.

Van der Veen, A.H. 1965b. Calcite-dolomite intergrowths in high temperature carbonate rocks. *Amer. Mineralogist*, 50.

Vardanyani, L.A. 1961. Trubka vzryva v tsentralnoi chasti Russkoi platformy (Volcanic pipes of the central part of the Russian platform). *Izv. AN Arm. SSR*, 14, No. 2.

Velde Danielle. 1967. Sur le caractere alcalin des basaltes tertialres et quaternaires de France. *C.r. Acad. sci.*, D, 264, No. 9.

Vlasov, K.A., M.V. Kuzmenko and E.M. Eskova. 1959. Lovozerskii Shchelochnoi Massiv (Alkaline massifs of Lovozerskii). USSR Academy of Sciences publication.

Volotovskaya, N.A. 1957. Shchelochnoi kompleks Malogo massiva (Alkaline complex of the Malyi massif). *Mat-ly VSEGEI, nov. ser.*, No. 21.

Volotovskaya, N.A. 1958. Magmaticheskii kompleks ultraosnovnykh shchelochnykh i karbonatitovykh porod massiva Vuoriyarvi (Magmatic complex of ultrabasic, alkaline and carbonatitic rocks of the Vuoriyarvi massif). *Zap. Vses. Miner. Ob-va*, ser. 2, part 87, No. 3.

Volotovskaya, N.A. 1959. Kovdorskii massiv (Kovdor massif). In the book: *Geologiya SSSR, vol. 27. Murmanskaya obl.* part 1. Gosgeoltekhizdat publishers.

Volotovskaya, N.A. 1960. Karelo-Kolskaya petrograficheskaya provintsiya ultraosnovnykh, shchelochnykh, i karbonatnykh porod (Petrographical province of ultrabasic, alkaline and carbonatite rocks of the Karelo-Kola region). In the book: *Petrograficheskie Provintsii, Izverzhennye Metamorficheskie Gornye Porody*. Izd-vo AN SSSR.

Volotovskaya, N.A. and A.A. Kukharenko. 1959. O tipakh karbonatitovykh mestorozhdenii i ikh svyazi s massivami ultraosnovnykh shchelochnykh porod (On the types of carbonatitic deposits and their relation with ultrabasic alkaline rocks). *Izv. AN SSSR, ser. geol.*, No. 3.

Volotovskaya, N.A. and V.V. Fizhenko. 1960. Massiv Vuoriyarvi (Vuoriyarvi massif). In the book: *Geologiya SSSR*, vol. 37, *Karelskaya SSR*, Gosgeoltekhizdat publishers.

Volotovskaya, N.A., B.V. Gubachev and N.A. Eliseev. 1958. Ultraosnovnye i shchelochnye platformennye obrazovaniya kaledonskogo vozrusta (Formation of ultrabasic and alkaline platforms of Caledonian age). In the book: *Geologiya SSSR, vol. 27. Murmanskaya obl.* Gosgeoltekhizdat publishers.

Vorobeva, O.A. 1960. Shchelochnye porody SSSR (Alkaline rocks of the USSR). In the book: *Petrogr. Provintsii, Izverzhennye i Metamorficheskie Gornye Porody.* Izd-vo AN SSSR.

Vorobeva, O.A. 1962. Gabbro-pirkosenito-dunitovyi poyas Srednego Urala (Gabbro-pyroxe-dunitic belt of the Central Ural). USSR Academy of Sciences pub.

Vorobeva, O.A. 1963. Problemy shchelochnogo magnatizma (Problems of alkaline magmatism). In the book: *Problemy Magmy i Genezisa Izverzhennykh Gornykh Porod.* Izd-vo AN SSSR.

Voronkov, A.A. and Yu.A. Pyatenko. 1966. Ob atomnoi strukture minerala carbonatsernaita (Atomic structure of carbocernaite). *Zhurn. Strukt. Khimii*, 7, No. 3.

Voronkov, A.A., N.A. Shumyatskaya and Yu.A. Pyatenko. 1967. O kristallicheskoi structure berbankita (Crystal structure of burbankite). *Kristallografiya*, No. 3:

Wambeke, van. L. 1965. A study of some niobium-bearing minerals of the Lueshe carbonatite deposit. EURATOM Publ., EUR, 2110, e.

Williams, C.E. 1952. Carbonatite structure: Tororo Hills, Eastern Uganda. *Geol. Mag.*, 89.

Wimmenauer, W. von. 1959. Karbonatite im Kaiserstühl. *Fortschr. Mineral.*, 37.

Wimmenauer, W. von. 1963. Beitrage sur Petrographie des Kaiserstühls. Teil VI and VII. *Neues Jahrab. Mineral. Abhandl.*, 99.

Wyllie, P.J. and Jr. Haas. 1966. The system CaO-SiO_2-CO_2-H_2O. II. The petrogenetic model. *Geochim. et cosmochim. acta*, 30, No. 5.

Wyllie, P.J. and O.F. Tuttle. 1960. Experimental verification for the magmatic origin of carbonatites. J. Petrol., 1, Internat. Geol. Congr., 21st Sess., Pt. 13.

Worckman, R. 1911. Calcite as a primary constituent of igneous rocks. *Geol. Mag.*, 5.

Yashina, R.M. 1962. Kharlinskii kontsentricheski-zonalnyi shchelochnoi massiv i usloviya ego obrazovaniya (Concentric-zonal alkaline rocks of the Kharlinskii massif and conditions of its formation). *Trudy IGEM AN SSSR*, No. 76.

Yashina, R.M. and I.V. Bortssevich. 1966. Absolyutnyi vozrast shchelochnykh porod Yugo-Vostochnoi Tuvy (Absolute age of the alkaline rocks of Southeastern Tuva). In the book: *Absolyutnaya Datirovka Tektonomagmaticheskikh Tsiklov i Etapov Orudeneniya po Dannym 1965g*). "Nauka" publishers.

Yoder, H.S. and C.E. Tilley. 1965. Proiskhozhdenie Bazaltovykh Magm (Origin of basaltic magma). "Mir" publishers.

Zambonini, F. 1935. Mineralogia Vesuviana. Napoli.

Zavaritskii, A.N. 1956. *Izverzhennye Gornye Porody* (Igneous rocks). USSR Academy of Sciences pub.

Zdorik, T.B. 1966. Berbankit i produkty ego izmeneniya (Burbankite and products of its change). *Trudy Miner. Muzeya AN SSSR*, No. 17.

Zdorik, T.B. and B.E. Runov. 1961. Novyi massiv shchelochnykh porod i karbonatitov na vostoke Aldanskogo shchita (Occurrence of new massif of alkaline rocks and carbonatites east of the Aldan Shield). *Trudy Vses. Aerogeol. Tresta*, No. 7.

Zdorik, T.B., I.I. Kupriyanova and N.M. Kumskova. 1966. Kristallicheskii ortit iz nekotorykh metasomaticheskikh obrazovanii Sibiri (Crystalline orthite from several metasomatic deposits of Siberia). *Trudy Miner. Muzeya AN SSSR*, No. 15.

Zdorik, T.B., G.A. Sidorenko and A.V. Bykova. 1961. Novyi titanotsirkonat kaltsiya-kaltsirtit (New titanozirconate of calcium-calzirtite). *Dokl. AN SSSR*, 137, No. 3.

Zhabin, A.G. 1959. O novom tipe karbonatitovykh proyavlenii v svyazi s shchelochnym kompleksom Vishnevykh-Ilmenskikh gor na Urale (New type of carbonatites in association with alkaline complex of Vishnevye-Ilmenskie Hills in the Ural). *Dokl. AN SSSR*, 128, No. 5.

Zhabin, A.G. 1965. O stroenii i posledovatelnosti formirovaniya Gulinskogo kompleksa dunitov, ultraosnovnykh i ultraosnovnykh shchelochnykh lav, shchelochnykh porod i karbonatitov (Structure and formation of the succession of dunites, ultrabasic and alkaline ultrabasic lavas, alkaline rocks and carbonatites in the Gulinskii complex). In the book: *Petrologiya i Geokhimicheskie Osobennosti Kompleksa Ultrabazitov, Shchelochnykh Porod i Karbonatitov*. "Nauka" publishers.

Zhabin, A.G. 1967. Kaltsit magmaticheskogo genezisa (Calcite of magmatic origin). *Zap. Vses. Miner. Ob-va*, part 96, No. 3.

Zhabin, A.G. and V.S. Gaidukova. 1961. O vzaimootnosheniyakh pirokhlora, fersmita i kolumbita iz shchelochnykh sienitovykh i karbonatitovykh kompleksov (Interrelated pyrochlore, fersmite and columbite from alkaline syenites and carbonatite complexes). *Geol. Rudn. M-nii*, No. 4.

Zhabin, A.G., V.B. Aleksandrov and M.E. Kazakova. 1961. Eshinit gidrotermalnogo genezisa iz Vishnevykh gor (Hydrothermal aechynite from Vishnevye mountains). *Trudy IMGRE*, No. 7.

Zhabin, A.G., Z.V. Pudovkina and A.V. Bykova. 1961. Katapleit iz Vishnevykh gor (Catapleite from Vishnevye Mountains). *Trudy IMGRE*, No. 7.

Zhabin, A.G., Z.V. Pudovkina and A.V. Bykova. 1962. Kaltsirtit iz karbonatitov Gulinskoi intruzii ultraosnovnykh shchelochnykh porod v Polyarnoi Sibiri (Calzirtite from carbonatites of alkaline ultrabasic intrusions of Gulinskii at the Polar Siberia). *Dokl. AN SSSR*, 146, No. 6.

Zlatkind, Ts.G. 1945. Olivinovye turyaity (Kovdority)—novye glubinnye melilitovye porody Kolskogo poluostrova [Olivinitic turjites (Kovdorites)—new deeper melilitic rocks of the Kola Peninsula]. *Sov. Geologiya*, No. 7.

Zlatkind, Ts.G. and A.I. Shalimov. 1946. Eno-Kovdorozerskii pluton shchelochnykh i ultraosnovnykh porod (Kolskii p-ov) [Alkaline and ultrabasic stocks of Eno-Kovodor (Kola Peninsula)]. *Sov. Geologiya*, No. 12.